Theology After Darwin

Theology After Darwin

Edited by Michael S. Northcott
and R. J. Berry

Paternoster:
thinking faith

MILTON KEYNES ● COLORADO SPRINGS ● HYDERABAD

First published 2009 by Paternoster
Paternoster is an imprint of Authentic Media
9 Holdom Avenue, Bletchley, Milton Keynes, Bucks, MK1 1QR, UK
1820 Jet Stream Drive, Colorado Springs, CO 80921, USA
OM Authentic Media, Medchal Road, Jeedimetla Village,
Secunderabad 500 055, A.P., India
www.loveauthentic.com

*Authentic Media is a division of Biblica UK, previously IBS-STL UK.
Biblica UK is limited by guarantee, with its registered office at Kingstown
Broadway, Carlisle, Cumbria, CA3 0HA. Registered in England & Wales No.
1216232. Registered charity in England & Wales No. 270162 and Scotland
No. SCO40064.*

British Library Cataloguing in Publication Data

A catalogue record for this book is available from the
British Library

ISBN-13: 978-1-84227-646-4

Cover Design by James Kessell for Scratch the Sky Ltd.
(www.scratchthesky.com)
Print Management by Adare
Printed and bound in Great Britain by J.F. Print Ltd.,
Sparkford, Somerset

Contents

Acknowledgements

Our thanks are due to all those involved in the production of this volume in the 200th anniversary year of Charles Darwin's birth and the 150th anniversary year of the publication of *The Origin of Species*. Robin Parry, publishing editor of Paternoster, first suggested the idea for this book to us after reading articles by us in the journal *Science and Christian Belief* in which we were responding to Simon Conway Morris' 2005 Boyle Lecture, based on his important book *Life's Solution: Inevitable Humans in a Lonely Universe*. We are grateful to those who joined us in the project so enthusiastically and for delivering their chapters in a timely fashion. Some of us met in Trinity, Edinburgh in January 2009 for a writers' workshop to peer review every chapter in the book. We are grateful to Professor David Fergusson for providing a subvention from a Science and Religion project fund to assist with the costs of the weekend, and to Robin Parry and Paternoster for their advance on the royalties which helped meet the remaining costs. At that workshop Byron Smith provided superb research assistance, taking notes on all suggested changes and forwarding them to the authors at the end of the workshop. Byron subsequently prepared the composite bibliography and index and we are very grateful for his assistance. Many thanks finally to Kate Kirkpatrick who has been a generous and effective copy-editor.

About the Contributors

Denis Alexander is a Fellow of St Edmund's College, Cambridge, and Director of the Faraday Institute for Science and Religion. His first book on science and faith was *Beyond Science* (1972). More recently he has written the critically acclaimed *Rebuilding the Matrix* (2001) and co-authored *Beyond Belief* (2004). His latest book is *Creation or Evolution: Do We Have to Choose?* (2008). Dr Alexander is Editor of the journal *Science & Christian Belief*.

Francisco J. Ayala is President and Chairman of the Board of the American Association for the Advancement of Science. A biologist and philosopher, he holds several appointments at the University of California, Irvine, and has published over 950 articles and books. Internationally known for his work on population and evolutionary genetics, his latest books have focused on evolution, Darwin, intelligent design, and creationism.

R. J. (Sam) Berry was Professor of Genetics at University College London 1974–2000. He is a former President of the Linnean Society, the British Ecological Society and the European Ecological Federation. He is the author of *Neo-Darwinism* (1982), *God and Evolution* (1988), *God and the Biologist* (1996), *God's Book of Works* (2003 – Gifford Lectures delivered at the University of Glasgow), and *Islands* (2009). He has edited (jointly, with Tom Noble) *Darwin, Creation and the Fall* (2009).

John Bimson teaches Old Testament studies at Trinity College, Bristol. His special interests include the historical and archaeological background to the Old Testament, environmental issues, and developing a biblical perspective on creation care.

Ellen F. Davis is the Amos Ragan Kearns Professor of Bible and Practical Theology at Duke Divinity School. The author of many books and articles, her research interests focus on how biblical interpretation bears on the life of faith communities and their response to urgent public issues. She is a member of the Archbishop of Canterbury's Building Bridges seminar, an international group of Muslim and Christian theologians. Her most recent book is *Scripture, Culture, and Agriculture: An Agrarian Reading of the Bible* (Cambridge University Press, 2009).

Denis Edwards is a senior lecturer in systematic theology in the School of Theology of Flinders University and a priest of the Catholic Archdiocese of Adelaide. Publications include: *Ecology at the Heart of Faith* (2006) *Breath of Life: A Theology of the Creator Spirit* (2004); *The God of Evolution: a Trinitarian Theology* (1999); *Jesus the Wisdom of God: An Ecological Theology*; *Jesus and the Cosmos* (1991).

David Fergusson is Professor of Divinity at the University of Edinburgh and Principal of New College. His most recent book *Faith and Its Critics: A Conversation* **(2009)** is based on his 2008 Gifford Lectures. He is a Fellow of the Royal Society of Edinburgh.

David Grumett is Research Fellow in Theology in the University of Exeter, UK. He is author of *De Lubac: A Guide for the Perplexed* (2007) and *Teilhard de Chardin: Theology, Humanity and Cosmos* (2005).

Amy Laura Hall is an Associate Professor at Duke University. She is the author of articles and chapters on bioethics, biblical ethics, disability and theology, and Christian conceptions of love. Her two books are *Kierkegaard and the Treachery of Love* and *Conceiving Parenthood: American Protestantism and the Spirit of Reproduction*. In addition to her work on muscular Christianity and Christian Darwinism, she is researching stories of Methodist women missionaries as potential models for collaborative, feminist work in areas of global health.

Neil Messer is a theological ethicist who also has a research training in molecular biology, and is a minister of the United Reformed Church. He is currently Senior Lecturer in Christian Theology at the University of Wales, Lampeter. His research interests are focused on bioethics and related areas. Recent publications include *Selfish Genes and Christian Ethics: Theological and Ethical Reflections on Evolutionary Biology* (2007).

Michael S. Northcott is Professor of Ethics in the School of Divinity in the University of Edinburgh. He has been visiting professor at Dartmouth College, Claremont School of Theology, Duke University, the University of Malaya, and Flinders University. He is an ordained Anglican Priest and author of a number of books including *The Environment and Christian Ethics* (1996), *Life After Debt: Christianity and Global Justice* (1999), *An Angel Directs the Storm: Apocalyptic Religion and American Empire* (2007) and *A Moral Climate: The Ethics of Global Warming* (2007).

Introduction

Charles Darwin was born in 1809 on the same day as Abraham Lincoln. They entered a world in a period of political and social turmoil. The American colonies had become independent in 1783; six years later the Bastille fell. The Chartists revolted in 1839 just as Darwin was writing down his evolutionary ideas. *The Origin of Species* was published in 1859; the American Civil War exploded in 1861. Throughout this time industrialization was sucking large numbers into burgeoning cities, disrupting long-established social cohesion. Discoveries of 'deep space' and 'deep time' by astronomers and the newly minted geologists were shattering the finite cocoon of traditional world-views. In his poem 'Dover Beach', Matthew Arnold lamented 'the long withdrawing roar of the Sea of Faith'. The poem was published in 1867. It is conventionally attributed to a pessimism stirred by Darwin's ideas, but it was probably written 15 years earlier and reflects widespread and chronic uncertainty in educated and uneducated alike.

Underpinning all this was a pervasive but somewhat rickety Enlightenment rationality. In theology, the deism of Archdeacon Paley was effectively a manifestation of this. The third US President, Thomas Jefferson, revered Jesus for his benevolence and ethical teaching but rejected miracles and mysteries (such as the Trinity) as incompatible with nature and reason. In 1820 he compiled his own edition of the gospels, the so-called Jefferson Bible, which left out all the miracles. The Bridgewater Treatises published between 1833 and 1840 were intended to declare 'the

Power, Wisdom and Goodness of God as manifested in the Creation',
but they were already out of date. The Scottish anatomist Robert Knox,
client of Burke and Hare, called them the Bilgewater Treatises. At the
time they were appearing, debates were raging about uniformitarianism
versus diluvialism or catastrophism (Lynch, 2002). The static world of
earlier times was being swallowed up by technological progress and
social change. In 1844, Robert Chambers sought to replace natural
theology with verifiable natural laws (Secord, 2000). By the middle of the
nineteenth century, few educated people still believed in a literal six days
of creation (Roberts, 1998). But God still had to be invoked and believed
in as the First Cause. In 1859 *The Origin of Species* burst on the world and
apparently removed this restraint (Holmes, 2008).

But the *Origin* produced a new set of challenges, most acutely about
the nature of humankind. As Peter Bowler has written (2007:7):

> If Christians accepted that humanity was the product of evolution – even
> assuming that the process could be seen as the expression of the Creator's will
> – then the whole idea of Original Sin would have to be reinterpreted. Far from
> falling from an original state of grace in the Garden of Eden, we have risen
> gradually from our animal origins. And if there was no Sin from which we
> needed salvation, what was the purpose of Christ's agony on the cross? Christ
> became merely the perfect man who showed us what we could all hope to
> become when evolution finished its upward course. Small wonder that many
> conservative Christians – and not just the American fundamentalists – argued
> that such a transformation had destroyed the very foundations of their faith.

The reaction to Darwin's ideas was by no means universally hostile. But
we are not concerned here with the immediate impact of Darwin's ideas
in good Queen Victoria's days. This has been described and analysed
by many (e.g. Moore, 1979; Kohn, 1985; Numbers and Stenhouse, 1999;
Desmond and Moore, 2009). We inherit a century and a half of debate.
Rather, the following pages are an exploration of more considered reactions
over the last 150 years to *The Origin of Species* and its complementary
work, *The Descent of Man* (1871), in particular the need to re-think our
theological anthropology and our attitude to the non-human creation.
We cannot ignore past debates; some of them are unresolved. More
importantly we cannot ignore the processes and ideas that have brought
us to the present.

We are only too aware that our enterprise is complicated by passionate
advocates of particular points of view – atheistic and deistic, literalist
and progressive, Barthian and Teilhardian. We do not claim to have risen
above these debates nor that the essays in this book present definitive
theological conclusions, but we do believe that the contributors herein
describe possible ways of viewing creation which are faithful to scripture
and consistent with scientific understanding. Herein is the underlying

challenge of Darwinism. Howard Marshall has suggested how such an endeavour should be approached. He writes,

> we affirm the ongoing supreme authority of Scripture, but we recognize that Scripture needs interpretation and fresh application . . . We do our theology in light of the gospel as the essential core of biblical teaching and by the use of minds that are continually nourished by the gospel and renewed by the Spirit . . . The factors that control our thinking must always be the gospel and the Christian mind that is shaped by it. Since we may be led to conclude that some teachings of Scripture need to be understood and applied differently from in the first century, it follows that such reconsideration is a task that involves considerable risk, but also great is the risk of misleading the church by dwelling in the first century and refusing to go beyond the letter of Scripture (Marshall, 2004: 78).

This is the dilemma of presenting a robust 'theology after Darwin'. We believe that the essays in this collection show us some ways to resolve this dilemma and forward our thinking as post-Darwinian Christians.

1

Biology After Darwin*

R. J. Berry

The Origin of Species was published on 24 November 1859, priced 15 shillings (£0.75). Twelve hundred copies were printed and a reprint was needed immediately. Darwin intended it as merely an 'abstract' of an intended Big Book on evolution, which he had begun writing three years earlier and for which he had drafted a 35-page 'sketch' as long ago as 1842. These plans had been thrown awry in June 1858 when he received a letter from Alfred Russel Wallace – at the time recovering from a fever on the island of Ternate in the Moluccas (or Malukus) – asking him to comment on a manuscript setting out a possible mechanism for evolutionary change. Wallace's proposals were almost identical with Darwin's own. Darwin felt he was morally obliged to pass on Wallace's paper for publication, but he was persuaded by his friends Charles Lyell (the leading geologist of the time) and Joseph Hooker (soon to follow his father as Director of the Royal Botanic Gardens at Kew) to allow

---

*This chapter is concerned with evolutionary biology, but it is not a systematic account of the topic. For such an account, see standard texts on the subject, such as those by Philip Darlington (*Evolution for Naturalists*. Wiley, 1980); Francisco Ayala and James Valentine (*Evolving*. Benjamin-Cummings, 1979); Monroe Strickberger (*Evolution*. Jones and Bartlett, 1990); Mark Ridley (*Evolution*. Blackwell Scientific, 1993); Peter Skelton (*Evolution*. Addison-Wesley, 1993); Ernst Mayr (*What Evolution Is*. BasicBooks, 2001); Stephen Jay Gould (*The Structure of Evolutionary Theory*. Harvard University Press, 2002); Douglas Futuyma (*Evolution*. Sinauer, 2005); Franz Wuketits and Francisco Ayala (*Handbook of Evolution*. Wiley, 2005); Nicholas Barton, Derek Briggs, Jonathan Eisen, David Goldstein and Nipam Patel (*Evolution*. Cold Spring Harbor Press, 2007).

parts of a revised version of his 1842 'sketch' to be read at a meeting of the Linnean Society at the same time as Wallace's communication. This took place on 1 July 1858. Three weeks later, Darwin began writing his 'abstract' and after 'thirteen months and ten days of hard labour' (Darwin's description of it), the *Origin* was published.

The Linnean Society meeting attracted little attention. In reviewing the year, the Linnean President noted, 'The year that has passed has not been marked by any of those striking discoveries which revolutionize the department of science on which they bear'. How gloriously wrong he was only became apparent following the appearance of the *Origin* seventeen months later. Emotions flared, although not all were antagonistic. One of the first responses came in a letter to Darwin from Charles Kingsley, Rector of Eversley in Hampshire and soon to become Regius Professor of Modern History at Cambridge. Kingsley wrote, 'I find it just as noble a conception of Deity to believe that He created primal forms capable of self development . . . as to believe that He required a fresh act of intervention to supply the *lacunas* which He himself had made'.

Darwin's arguments were quickly accepted, contrary to repeated assertions that they remain speculative and 'only a theory'. Details of the reception of the *Origin* are not pertinent here. They have been thoroughly documented, both in specialist works (Hull, 1973; Moore, 1979; Mayr, 1991; Numbers, 1998; Numbers and Stenhouse, 1999; Ruse, 1999) and in biographies of Darwin (Clark, 1984; Desmond and Moore, 1991; Browne, 2002). Ironically Darwin's ideas were assimilated more readily by conservative theologians than by liberals, apparently because of the stronger doctrine of providence of the former (Livingstone, 1987). Many of the authors of the 'Fundamentals', a series of booklets produced between 1910 and 1915 to expound the 'fundamental beliefs' of Protestant theology as defined by the General Assembly of the American Presbyterian Church were sympathetic to evolution. Princeton theologian B. B. Warfield, a passionate advocate of the inerrancy of the Bible, argued that evolution could provide a tenable 'theory of the method of divine providence in the creation of mankind'. The infamous debate between the Bishop of Oxford and Thomas Huxley at the 1860 meeting of the British Association for the Advancement of Science was not really about evolution *versus* creation or even science *versus* religion. On the Bishop's side it was about the danger of legitimizing change in an age when he believed it was having deleterious social and theological effects; Huxley was aiming for the secularization of society, hoping to establish the legitimacy of science against what he regarded as the improper influence of church leaders. It was reported that Wilberforce went away happy that he had given Huxley a bloody nose, while Joseph Hooker (who spoke after Huxley) told Darwin that Huxley had been largely inaudible; as far as the audience was concerned, many scored it as an entertaining draw (Brooke, 2001). The tragedy has been a legacy of inevitable conflict between science and faith, encouraged by Huxley himself and fuelled by two much-read manifestos by Draper (1875) and White (1886).

Darwin's (and Wallace's) ideas were very simple, based on three facts and two inferences. They were concerned with a possible *mechanism* for evolutionary change, not with the actual existence of change. Both Darwin and Wallace were basically naturalists and their proposals were based on observation rather than complicated theory. The mechanism (which is often called 'Darwinism') is patently open to test and therefore possible disproof, contrary to the claim often made by modern anti-evolutionists that it is dogma rather than science. The widely-quoted criticism (later retracted) by Karl Popper that 'Darwinism is not a testable scientific theory but a metaphysical research programme' was based on his rejection of all 'historical' sciences (because they were non-falsifiable), plus a misunderstanding of the Darwinian mechanism.

The two observations at the base of the 'Darwinian mechanism' are that virtually all species have a large potential for increase in number (think of the number of acorns produced by every oak tree or the masses of frog spawn laid by every female frog) whilst numbers remain roughly constant. The inference from this is that there must be a *struggle for existence*, with only a small proportion of young surviving. The existence of such a struggle is essentially an ecological deduction and one well understood in Darwin's time. It forced itself on Darwin's awareness when he read 'for amusement', Thomas Malthus's *Essay on the Principles of Population*, which set out the spectre of the human population outstripping its food supply with the weak and improvident succumbing in the resulting struggle for resources. Darwin's genius was in linking the fact of heritable variation to the ever-prevalent struggle for existence. If only a small proportion of a population survived the struggle, the likelihood would be that it would include those with a trait which gave them some sort of advantage. Over the generations, those carrying the trait would increase at the expense of those lacking the trait. There would be a genetic change in the population, amounting to *natural selection* for the trait in question.

Darwin used the way that human selection had changed domesticated breeds of animals as a model for the processes happening in nature. His contemporary, Herbert Spencer, a railway engineer turned philosopher, coined the phrase 'survival of the fittest' to describe the process. This has been a source of much confusion and repeated accusations that natural selection is tautologous. This is wrong: 'fitness' in its biological sense refers to reproductive success, not health or physical prowess. The 'fittest' are those who raise most offspring – which properly describes natural selection.

1. The *Origin* in Historical Context

Although Charles Darwin can properly be said to have introduced a revolution in thought and understanding, it would be improper to assume that the idea of evolution emerged suddenly in 1858. Darwin himself acknowledged a swarm of scholars who had preceded him in believing that species were subject to change into new species (*transformation* in the language of the time): Marchant (1719), Montesquieu (1721), Buffon (1749), Diderot (1764), Erasmus Darwin (Charles's grandfather) (1794), St Hilaire (1795), Goethe (1795), Lamarck (1809), and Moritzi (1842). Even Darwin's particular contribution of natural selection had been anticipated by Wells in a paper read to the Royal Society of London in 1813 and by Matthew in a book on *Naval Timber and Arboriculture* published in 1831, although neither seemed to have recognized the significance of the idea.

Probably the best known antecedent of Darwin is Jean-Baptiste Lamarck, a Frenchman who worked in the Natural History Museum in Paris from 1788 until his death in 1829. Lamarck believed that there was a progressive increase in perfection from the simplest organisms to its peak in humankind; he argued that over a long period of time, one species would become transformed into another 'higher' one. This got over the problem of species extinction which seemed to contradict the notion of a perfect world created by God and which was becoming increasingly contentious in the late eighteenth century as it became clear that organisms found as fossils were not surviving in a still unexplored El Dorado. During the same period, geologists were massively stretching the history of the Earth from the assumption derived from the biblical genealogies that creation took place around six thousand years ago (Lewis and Knell, 2001). In 1788 James Hutton, the 'father of modern geology' claimed in his *Theory of the Earth* that the world was almost infinitely old.

This realization of a long Earth history allowed time for the procession of change assumed by Lamarck, but it was the Achilles heel of traditional natural theology. A creator could presumably design an organism perfectly adapted to a particular environment, but this perfection would disappear if the environment was not constant. Adaptation to changes in climate, to the physical structure of the Earth's surface, or to predators and competitors is possible only if organisms change. All this produced considerable theological ferment in the first half of the nineteenth century (Gillispie, 1951; Moore, 1986) which is not relevant in this chapter. Suffice it to say that by Darwin's time, the majority of Bible expositors accepted a non-literal interpretation of the early chapters of Genesis (Roberts, 1997).

Lamarck's evolutionary ideas were not widely accepted outside Germany and his native France, although in Britain they were welcomed by intellectual radicals as a justification for attacking the social *status quo* (Desmond, 1989). Fifty years after Lamarck's *Philosophie zoologique*, Darwin wrote that it was 'veritable rubbish . . . I got not a single fact or idea from it'. Notwithstanding Lamarck prepared the way for Darwin by pointing to evidence that evolutionary change must have occurred.

The evolution debate exploded in 1844 with the publication of the *Vestiges of the Natural History of Creation* by Robert Chambers. It was effectively a tract against the deism of William Paley's version of natural theology (Secord, 2000). Chambers wrote that when there is a choice between special creation and the operation of general laws instituted by the creator, 'I would say that the latter is generally preferable as it implies a far grander view of the divine power than the other'. Since there was nothing in the inorganic world 'which may not be accounted for by the agency of the ordinary forces of nature', why not consider 'the possibility of plants and animals having likewise been produced in a natural way'? The *Vestiges* was an immediate bestseller. In the ten years following its publication, it sold more copies that did the *Origin* fifteen years later. But it was full of errors. For Darwin, 'the prose was perfect, but the geology strikes me as bad and his zoology far worse'. Its importance is the debate it stirred. Darwin welcomed it on the grounds that 'it has done excellent service in calling in this country attention to the subject and in removing prejudices'.

2. Objections Made to the *Origin*

Darwin was well aware that his ideas would be criticized, and two chapters in the *Origin* were devoted to 'difficulties' and 'objections' to his theory. His main points concern the nature of species and questions about the effectiveness of selection. In a later chapter he discussed the imperfections of the fossil record.

Species transitions

If one species evolves into another, why are not forms found linking the two species? R. A. Fisher (1954) has argued that the reason Darwin had to discuss this was a hangover from Lamarckian speculation at the time he was writing. Lamarck had suggested that evolutionary change results from the use or disuse of organs and traits, so that transformation arises from variable responses in an existing group. This would mean that there are no firm limits to any species, nor is a 'natural' classification realistically possible.

Darwin rejected this idea of species and assumed a definition close to the modern one, that a species is an effectively isolated population or group of populations and will have arisen at a particular site. He recognized that closely related forms are likely to compete for the same resources, leading to the less-favoured one(s) going extinct. In a large area, different species replace each other geographically. In most cases these species seem to have evolved in isolation and then expanded their ranges to come into contact. An excellent example of this is the *Geospiza* group of finches on the Galapagos Islands, studied in detail by Peter and Rosemary Grant (2008). Geological changes (separating or recombining tracts of land) may play a part in isolating populations.

The effectiveness of natural selection

The most persistent criticism of Darwinism has been that natural selection is merely a negative influence, removing inefficiency but incapable of producing novelty or the seemingly perfect adaptation of the eye of a mammal or the pattern of a butterfly's wing.

Darwin recognized three problems:

1. An organ (such as the wing of a bat) may be so specialized for its function as to bear little resemblance to the prototype (the forelimb of an insectivore) from which it must be presumed to have arisen. The difficulty is envisaging a series of intermediate grades connecting such widely separated extremes.
2. An organ of extreme perfection (such as the eye of higher vertebrates) may stagger the imagination as to how it might arise through an undirected process of trial and error.
3. Some organs of apparently trifling importance (such as the 'fly-whisk' tail of the giraffe) are clearly adapted to their function but it is difficult to understand how they have been a matter of life or death for their carriers for them to have evolved through natural selection.

The first of these applies to all evolution, while the second and third are difficulties of imagination rather than reason. Fisher (1954: 89) commented that 'the cogency and wealth of illustrations with which Darwin was able to deal with these cases was, perhaps the largest factor in persuading biologists of the truth of his views'.

Here we can only note that function as well as structure evolves. In the *Origin*, Darwin quoted Agassiz's work on echinoderms, showing how modified spines may lead to the development of an apparently new and important trait, tube feet. Many such examples of changed use are known; they are open to investigation and test. For example, there are organisms which have no image-forming eyes, but light-sensitive cells.

Any inherited variants which allow detection of the direction of light, its intensity, movement, etc., could give advantage to a possessor, and hence be subject to natural selection. Nilsson and Pelger (1994) have calculated that around 1800 steps are probably needed to produce a mammalian eye from such a beginning, some of these steps being subjected to fairly intense selection. They argue that there would be ample time for this development in the millions of years between the appearance of mammals and their earliest ancestors.

The credibility of such a process has grown enormously since genome mapping became a reality, revealing a remarkable and previously unsuspected developmental flexibility. It is now possible to identify near identical genes (i.e. stretches of coding DNA) through long lineages, often changing their effects in different organisms. Conway Morris (2003) calls this process the 'Principle of Inherency' (or more informally, 'cobbling and co-option'), whereby many of the building blocks of complex structures are available long before they are recruited to new and sophisticated tasks. For example the crystalline proteins which make up the eye lens have been repeatedly and independently 'redeployed' since their origin as stress-related proteins in micro-organisms. Conway Morris identifies '20 or even more independent lines of differentiation [towards eye perfection], including at least 15 cases of independent attainments of photoreceptors with a distinct lens'. Many genes are duplicated in putative lineages, allowing new functions to develop because of the flexibility produced by the introduction of such 'spare' genes. The power of natural selection to produce adaptation could only be illustrated by anecdote until quantitative methods of estimating fitness differences, rates and conditions of gene frequency change, and similar variables became available. Such technologies were developed by R. A. Fisher, J. B. S. Haldane and Sewall Wright in the 1920s, and showed the ability of selection differentials of less than 1 per cent to bring about significant change. The force of these theoretical arguments has been greatly strengthened with the discovery that selection pressures in nature commonly reach 10 per cent or more. Answers given by Darwin to his critics in successive editions of the *Origin* have been repeatedly proved right by subsequent research (Jones, 1999).

A more general criticism of natural selection is that it is driven by chance, dependent on randomly occurring mutation. This is a common assumption of 'creationists', but extends much wider than the beliefs of anti-evolutionists. It was the basis of Jacques Monod's nihilistic *Chance and Necessity* (1971; see reply by Thorpe, 1978). However it is misplaced. The confusion arises because the origin of inherited variation is random, depending on mutation or, much more significantly in sexual organisms, on the phenotypic expression of new variants through recombination. Selection experiments on organisms where mutants have been induced by ionising radiation show that recombination produces variation much more commonly than fresh mutation (Mather, 1973: 86). The Darwinian process does not depend on chance: adaptation results from the selection of advantageous variants and is a deterministic process. While it is true that adaptation relates to survival and the possibility of gene transmission rather than long-term purpose, it is wrong to claim that 'Darwinian evolution' is an entirely fortuitous process. Indeed Simon Conway Morris (2003) has shown that the range of viable options for any trait is so limited that it may lead to the appearance of progress (Berry, 2006). Natural selection is the only mechanism (apart from divine intervention) which fits organisms to their environment. Darwin described this process of adaptation in his 'Essay' of 1844 (a revision of his 'sketch' of 1842) and repeated in his 1858 Linnean Society paper:

> Nature can be compared to a surface on which rest ten thousand sharp wedges touching each other and driven inwards by incessant blows . . . But let the external conditions of a country alter . . . can it be doubted from the struggle each individual has to obtain subsistence, that any minute variation in structure, habits or instincts, adapting that individual better to the new conditions, would tell upon its vigour and health? In the struggle it would have a better *chance* of surviving, and those of its offspring which inherited the variation would have a better *chance* to survive . . . Let this work of selection, on the one hand, and death on the other, go on for a thousand generations; who would pretend to affirm that it would produce no effect.

3. Periods of Debate

Biometricians, Mendelians and Vitalists

Darwin's general thesis was quickly and widely accepted. Frederick Temple, Bishop of Exeter and soon to become Archbishop of Canterbury gave it an *imprimatur* in his Bampton Lectures published in 1885, '[God] did not make the things, we may say; but He made them make themselves'. Four years later, Oxford theologian Aubrey Moore (1889: 99) wrote that Darwin had done the work of a friend under the guise of a foe by making it impossible to accept the image of an occasionally interfering absentee landlord. For Moore, Darwin had made belief about God all or nothing: either God was an active participant, immanent in the world, or he was completely absent. By 1880, special creationists in the US could only identify two working naturalists who were not evolutionists (Numbers, 1992: 10).

But there was a big problem with Darwin's theory: he did not know how variation was maintained. Offspring of any cross seemed to be intermediate between the parents, which meant that advantageous traits would be less marked in the progeny than in the previous generation; their effect would be continually diluted.

This problem was solved by the discovery of particulate inheritance – the recognition that inherited elements (genes) are transmitted unchanged between generations. The appearance of blending is because the expression of these genes is modified by other genes. This was the essence of Gregor Mendel's work, published in 1865 but only realized as significant in 1900 when it was 're-discovered'. But in solving one problem, it raised another for the Darwinians: the genes studied by the early geneticists (or Mendelians, as they were called) were almost all deleterious to their carriers, had large effects, and were inherited as recessives – all properties which seemed counter to the gradual progressiveness expected under Darwinism. A rift appeared between the biometricians studying the evidence of evolution in living or fossil populations and the geneticists who were unquestionably uncovering the physical basis of heredity (Provine, 1971).

This rift persisted and widened through the first decades of the twentieth century. There were no real doubts that large-scale evolution had occurred, but it did not seem to have been driven by natural selection. In a book written for the Jubilee of the *Origin* Vernon Kellogg (1907) spoke of 'the death-bed of Darwinism'. He wrote, 'Darwinism as the all-sufficient or even the most important causo-mechanical factor in species-forming and hence as the sufficient explanation of descent, is discredited and cast down' (374). Into this apparent hiatus, a gallimaufry of other evolutionary theories were poured: Berg's *Nomogenesis*, Willis's *Age and Area*, Smut's *Holism*, Driesch's entelechy, Osborn's aristogenesis and orthogenesis. Invention was rife. Their common feature was some form of inner progressionist urge or *élan vital*. Unfortunately three standard and still-read histories of biology (by Nordenskiöld, Rádl and Singer) were written during this time, perpetuating the idea that evolutionary theory is an illogical mess and that Darwinism had been completely eclipsed.

The scientific confusion spread into theology. The idea that evolution was driven by some sort of purpose was influentially espoused by some distinguished scientists – the zoologist Ray Lankester and the physiologist J. S. Haldane, the psychologists Lloyd Morgan, William McDougall and E. S. Russell, physicists like Oliver Lodge, and the cosmologists A. S. Eddington and James Jeans; as well as by popularizers like Arthur Thomson and politicians such as Arthur Balfour. Not surprisingly with such apparently informed authorities, these ideas were seized upon by churchmen, prominent among them being Charles Gore, and somewhat later by W. R. Inge, Hensley Henson, Charles Raven and E. W. Barnes. This cross-over of evolutionary idealism from science to theology has been elegantly chronicled by Peter Bowler (2001). It eventually died through its perceived ineffectiveness rather than conscious rejection – 'The Modernists saw themselves marginalized not by the new science, of which many remained unaware, but by changing values within the churches, which brought back a sense of human sinfulness and alienation from God incompatible with the idea of progress' (417). One can have some sympathy with the theologians. It took the scientists a long time to reach an evolutionary synthesis, but this does not excuse uncritical use of data by anyone.

The Neo-Darwinian synthesis

The irrelevance of the frenzy of evolutionary speculating was exposed by a series of theoretical analyses in the 1920s, beginning with two difficult and widely non-understood papers by R. A. Fisher (1918; 1922). Fisher showed that continuous variation in a trait was usually the cumulative effect of many genes, each with a small effect, and that genetic dominance was not an intrinsic property of a gene, but the result of interaction with modifying genes. He argued that the dominance or recessivity of any character is the consequence of repeated mutation during evolutionary time, with modification of its effect by other genes – towards greater expression if its effects were beneficial to its carrier or lesser if it had deleterious effects, i.e. its expression would be modified towards dominance or recessivity respectively, thus removing the difficulties raised by the early Mendelians.

Fisher's analyses were supplemented by J. B. S. Haldane in Britain and Sewall Wright in the United States, and summarized in a series of major works (Fisher, 1930; Wright, 1931; Haldane, 1932). They were complemented by studies of inherited variation in natural populations by E. B. Ford (1931) in Britain and Theodosius Dobzhansky (1937) in the US. Their conclusions together with results from many other sources were brought together by Julian Huxley in a book *Evolution: the Modern Synthesis* (1942), which provided the eponymous name to the incorporation of Mendelian genetics into the insights of Darwin, and the final reconciliation of the earlier evolutionary debates.

Neutralism versus selectionism

The Mendelian or neo-Darwinian synthesis of the 1940s has proved to be a robust understanding of evolutionary processes as well as a justification of Darwin's original theory (Mayr and Provine, 1980; Berry, 1982). Its most serious challenge came in the 1960s when biochemical techniques of protein analysis were applied to variation in natural populations and unexpectedly large amounts of inherited variation discovered – between one in four and one in twenty genes tend to be represented by slightly different forms (*alleles*) on the chromosomes received by an individual from the two parents. Conventional understanding was that such high levels of variation would lead to an unsupportable 'genetic load' because the less advantageous allele would reduce the reproductive potential of its carrier. The simplest escape from this dilemma was to assume that such biochemical variants had no effect on their bearer, i.e. that they were 'neutral' and thus not subject to selection. This argument seemed to be supported by apparently regular rates of accumulation of new variants (mutations), to the extent that a 'molecular (or protein) clock' could be calibrated on the basis of the number of gene differences between two lineages.

However it soon appeared that the protein clock did not keep good time. Different proteins could change at rates differing by two orders of magnitude while the same protein may change faster (or slower) in different groups. These effects would be expected if the proteins were subject to selection rather than a physically determined mutation rate. The falsifying of extreme neutralist assumptions led to attention being re-focused on environmental (or ecological) factors in evolution. For example, it is improper to speak of *the* selective effect of an inherited character. Selection varies in both time and space. It may be density or frequency dependent or independent. In the well-known example of moths being selectively predated by birds, the chance of being eaten (i.e. the intensity of selection) varies with the amount and history of the atmospheric pollution. Places where black moths had a high survival rate have changed as pollution has declined following Clean Air legislation, and the survival rate of black moths has declined in proportion.

A positive outcome of the neutralism debates has been to rescue evolutionary studies from the danger of over-dependence on theoretical models and lead them back to an observational and experimental basis – which is where Darwin and Wallace began (Berry, 1989; Berry, Crawford and Hewitt, 1992).

4. Contemporary Challenges

There have been four major periods of debate about evolutionary science: in the decades immediately following the publication of the *Origin*; the Mendelian-biometrician disputes around 1900; the subsequent split between geneticists and palaeontologists, effectively resolved by the neo-Darwinian synthesis of the 1930s; and neutralism and selectionism in the 1970s. Are all the problems now solved? The answer to this is emphatically no. Scientific theories are always open to challenge from new data, new testing, or fresh interpretations. But many of the alleged challenges to evolution do not have much substance. The major issues raised include:

Speciation. It is sometimes said that Darwin wrote little about the actual origin of species. A traditional problem of studying the speciation process was that the genetic differences between species could not be investigated by the classical method of crossing species, because, almost by definition, species are not inter-fertile. This has changed with the ability to unravel individual genomes and identify genetic differences, and there are now many descriptions of species differences and the mechanisms which probably produced them (Coyne and Orr, 2004).

Missing links. It is simply not true that no 'missing links' are known. However it is worth noting that transitions from one species to another will almost certainly occur in a small locality and over a fairly restricted time period. The likelihood of any of the comparatively small number of intermediate forms in any one transition being fossilized is small. We should expect the fossil record to be incomplete and 'missing links' found only rarely.

Punctuated equilibria. In 1972, Nils Eldredge and Stephen Gould pointed out that a marked characteristic of the fossil record was not long-continued change of particular forms, but periods of stability (or stasis), followed by the sudden appearance of a new (albeit related) form. In effect, they challenged the orthodoxy that lack of knowledge of the origin of fossil species was due to gaps in the record, and claimed that an unbiassed interpretation of fossil successions implies that evolution proceeds in fits and starts. This means no more than recognizing that evolutionary rates vary considerably, and that the speciation process is relatively rapid. It is false to oppose this to Darwin's 'gradualism'.

Cladism. In a book published in English in 1966, Willi Hennig, a German entomologist, proposed strict axioms for recognizing ancestry in temporal lineages. The ensuing discipline of *cladistics* has been claimed to throw doubt over evolutionary relationships. By recognizing the possibility of different lineages, the cladistic controversy has obscured a fundamental principle that there can be only one historical lineage for any group. The best way to regard cladism is simply as an attempt by systematists to refine their particular technology. It does not help or hinder evolutionary biology.

Macroevolution. Darwinian selection can be observed and measured in natural populations. Speciation processes can be modelled and even repeated under experimental conditions. Differentiation of 'higher' groups (such as monkeys from other mammals or amphibians from fish) (*macroevolution*) cannot be observed or (yet) repeated. There seems little doubt that macroevolution is capable of taking place by the same mechanisms as those operating in living populations but there must remain uncertainty as to whether some other process may sometimes operate. For example, amniotes (reptiles, birds and mammals) have an embryonic development which is like that of the an-amniotes (protochordates and fish) turned inside out. In a situation like this, it is always possible that a genetic change (mutation) produced a 'hopeful monster' which might fortuitously and rarely have survived to break through into a new habitat – manifesting as a uniquely 'macroevolutionary' event.

For the present we have to remain agnostic as to whether there are specifically macroevolution processes. Where we can be reasonably confident is that all the major living groups share a common ancestor, because they all have a virtually identical genetic code and a very high proportion of shared genes. It is commonly noted that humans share 98 per cent of their genes with chimpanzees, 80 per cent with rats, and incredibly 50 per cent with bananas. Notwithstanding we can say very little about the origin of life. There are various hypotheses as to how life originated but they are not relevant to Darwin or Darwinism. As Darwin wrote to Hooker, 'The origin of the first living globule was as irrelevant as the origin of matter is to the laws of chemical attraction'. For him, 'the only question was whether species of a genus have had a common ancestor'.

5. Human Evolution

Anxious to avoid unnecessary controversy, Darwin steered clear of human evolution in the *Origin*. He included only one mention of the subject, 'I see open fields for far more important researches . . . Much light will be thrown on the origin of man and his history'. However, he could not avoid the topic altogether, and returned to it 12 years later with the *Descent of Man* (1871). He wrote therein 'Man in his arrogance thinks himself a great work worthy of the interposition of a deity. More humble and I think truer [is] to consider him created from animals'.

Darwin knew almost nothing about human fossils. Since his time, many putative hominoid and hominid fossils have been discovered, to the extent that it is fair to claim that *Homo* has a better fossil record than almost any other genus. Unfortunately its credibility has been marred in popular understanding by over-imaginative reconstructions – notably the Piltdown debacle but also many fanciful attempts to portray human ancestors as either hulking brutes or mere variants of modern individuals (Bowler, 1986). The image of human fossil history for many is probably the much-reproduced frontispiece of T. H. Huxley's *Man's Place in Nature* (1863), showing a parade of modern skeletons from a gibbon, through a series of stooping apes, to an upright man ('A grim and grotesque procession' as Darwin's critic, the 8th Duke of Argyll, called it). Notwithstanding and recognizing many uncertainties, there is general agreement among specialists that *Homo* originated from an *Australopithecus* stock in Africa, with the first fossils classified in the genus *Homo* occurring between 2.0 and 1.6 million years ago; they are named

Homo habilis. About 1.8 million years ago, a new form of *Homo* appeared in eastern Africa, *H. erectus*. It persisted in Africa for more than a million years, but also spread out of Africa into Asia (Finlayson, 2005). It had a brain size (or more strictly, cranial volume) of 800–900 ml, about a third greater than *H. habilis* and a less projecting face. Four hundred thousand years ago, fossils regarded as an archaic form of *H. sapiens* (brain *c*.1100–1300 ml) occur. 'Modern' *H. sapiens* appeared in Africa and 'Neanderthal man' in Europe *c*.200,000 years ago. The latter is now regarded as at least sub-specifically different from *H. sapiens*, and coexisted with the latter until disappearing 30,000 to 40,000 years ago (Stringer, 2002).

Developments in molecular biology have driven the recognition of our genetic closeness to the other primates. The earlier calculation that humans and chimps share 98.4 per cent of their genes has been refined now that both genomes have been sequenced; nevertheless there is identity between more than 95 per cent of the genes in the two species (Britten, 2002). Our DNA difference from the chimpanzees amounts to around 10,000 nucleotide changes, most of them in so-called 'junk DNA' which regulates the activity of protein coding sequences. We have one less pair of chromosomes than all the other apes (23 pairs instead of 24), but the difference is the simple result of an end-to-end fusion between two separate elements of the ape chromosome set.

There is no evidence that there are many novel genes in the human genome. Around 8 per cent of the human genome apparently consists of retroviral inserts influencing gene regulation in significant ways. There does not seem to be evidence of positive selection for genes concerned with brain development or function as a whole between chimps and humans, but one of the most intriguing results that has so far emerged from comparative molecular genetics is that since the human and chimpanzee lines separated around six million years ago, a third more chimpanzee genes show signs of selection than do human ones. Put another way, this implies that chimpanzees are more specialized than humans; we are generalists, they are adapted to a particular niche. There is no scientific support for the notion that we have been propelled towards a predetermined end by either a Blind or a Divine Watchmaker.

This is a non-intuitive result. However, many of the characteristic human features (brain size, hairlessness, prolonged adolescence) can be attributed to a neotenous change (retention of juvenile characteristics into the adult) in the human line, which could be a genetically simple event – perhaps the result of mutation at a single gene locus. There is no doubt that a key human characteristic is the complexity of language, without denying or denigrating the sophistication and complexity of communication in many non-human groups. The differentiating feature between ape and human is not the ability simply to make sounds, but precisely to control those sounds. 'The missing ingredient [which prevented the chimps developing more complex speech] may have been a tiny change in anatomy of the proto-human vocal tract to give us finer control and permit formation of a much greater variety of sounds' (Diamond, 1991: 47).

Alfred Russel Wallace argued that natural selection had acted in the earlier stages of human differentiation from the apes, but as our intellectual and moral faculties became 'fairly developed', the body ceased to be subject to selection, and subsequently adaptation was solely 'through the action of the mind'. Similar ideas have been developed by Julian Huxley, C. H. Waddington and others. Wallace's starting point was a belief that brain size was a reliable indicator of mental capacities. The difficulty as he saw it was that both fossil humans and 'savages' had skulls (and therefore brains) of similar size to those of civilized people, and consequently all must be presumed to have the same mental capacities. However it seemed to Wallace that such traits as mathematical ability and the ability to carry out complex trains of abstract reasoning would been useless (if not harmful) in the struggle for existence in primitive cultures. As it was both unneeded and unused, the brain could not have evolved by natural selection alone. Consequently, and certainly influenced by his belief in spiritualism, he proposed that a 'Higher Intelligence' had guided human evolution in a 'definite direction and for special ends'.

Darwin disagreed with Wallace's conclusion that 'natural selection could not have done it all', but he was himself unsure how selection might have acted to produce morality. He wrote in the *Descent of Man* (p. 200): 'He who was ready to sacrifice his life, as many a savage has been, rather than betray his colleagues, would often leave no offspring to inherit his noble nature'. A possible answer to this problem is if a group rather than an individual is the target of selection, and there have been repeated proposals for group selection (e.g. Wilson, 2002; Dugatkin, 2006). However, this seems impossible from all that we know about biological fitness and gene transmission. It was left to J. B. S. Haldane (1932) to show a way forward, pointing out that if individual unselfishness (even to the extent of self-sacrifice) had an inherited basis and helped near relatives, then 'altruistic genes' could be selected and therefore spread within families. In this way, there could be situations where cooperation (or unselfishness) is an advantage to a group of individuals, even if particular individuals are disadvantaged. Haldane's argument was formalized in 1964 by W. D. Hamilton as the concept of 'inclusive fitness,' often called nowadays 'kin selection', and popularized by E. O. Wilson (1975) as 'sociobiology'. Sociobiological ideas have been extremely important in biology, and have stimulated an immense amount of research. They have also provoked much dissent, particularly as they apply to mammals (especially humankind) because of their implications about determinism in behavioural choices. These are scientific debates but it is worth noting that the existence of apparently altruistic or self-giving behaviours in non-human primates do not compromise Christian understanding. Frans de Waal (1997: 216) has written:

> Even if animals other than ourselves act in ways tantamount to moral behavior, their behavior does not necessarily rest on deliberations of the kind we engage in. It is hard to believe that animals weigh their own interests against the rights of others, that they develop a vision of the greater good of society, or that they feel lifelong guilt about something they should not have done.

It is important to note the confusions and difficulties that are regularly produced by naïve and illegitimate extrapolations from biology to sociology (Durant, 1985; Midgley, 1985). Particularly damaging in this context has been Herbert Spencer. He argued that human society could be regarded as an organism, and damage to any part affected the whole. His ideas were immensely popular with North American liberals, because they apparently gave a licence for individual freedom and unfettered capitalism. Under their influence, Yale polymath William Graham Sumner wrote, 'The millionaires are a product of natural selection . . . It is because they are thus selected that wealth – both their own and that entrusted to them – aggregates under their hands'. John D. Rockefeller epitomized this attitude, 'The growth of a large business is merely survival of the fittest [including forcing smaller companies out of business] . . . it is not an evil tendency in business. It is merely the out-working of a law of nature and a law of God'.

Our ancestry has certainly been shaped by selection. However, this does not mean that we will fully understand human nature even if we successfully bring together the disciplines which contribute to evolutionary understanding – embryology, anatomy, genetics, ecology and behavioural studies. Certainly such a synthesis is a necessary preliminary step, but it would be foolish to expect this to give us all the answers we would like about human nature, even if we could develop a rational synthesis. It is not helpful to go down the 'intelligent design' route and, with Wallace, to postulate a guiding 'Higher Intelligence'. Moreover, we have to reconcile the arch-reductionists who insist that we are nothing but survival machines controlled by selfish genes and those who focus on personal and sexual relationships and group dynamics. E. O. Wilson, prophet of a middle road, argues that there are two sorts of people, empiricists and transcendentalists, and that the robustness of this bi-polarity is testable 'by the continuance of biological studies of complex human behaviour' (Wilson, 1998: 264).

These questions point to where biology shades into theology. Theologians from the most conservative to the most liberal have struggled to explain – or even merely to describe – the special nature of humankind in the face of evolutionary science. Peters and Hewlett (2003) have pointed out that 'theistic evolutionists', those who try to reconcile the Christian faith with evolutionary biology, represent a spectrum of views – ranging from B. B. Warfield, the arch proponent of biblical inerrancy, who held 'a doctrine of providence that saw God working in and with, instead of as a replacement for, the processes of nature . . . This principle he felt the Scriptures offered to enable humans both to approach the world fearlessly and to do so for the greater glory of God' (Noll and Livingstone, 2003) to Teilhard de Chardin, of whom it was said that he submerged the ugly facts of science in an all encompassing enthusiasm for cosmic progress.

6. Fact, Fiction and Fancy

The chief effect of the *Origin of Species* (1859) was to convince the majority of Darwin's contemporaries of the fact that evolution had occurred. Darwin's work provided a framework for biogeography and taxonomy, and an explanation for the existence of 'rudimentary' organs (like the tail of primates or the hind-limbs of snakes and whales: Dawkins, 2004).

Contemporary 'creationism' has no intellectual link with the debates of the nineteenth century and the historical acceptance of Darwinism. Rather it stems from the teaching of the Adventist Ellen White and the writings of her followers, notably George McCready Price whose cry was 'No Adam, no Fall; no Fall, no Atonement; no Atonement, no Savior' (Numbers, 1992; Giberson, 2008). At the same time, Presbyterian Albert Johnson claimed that evolution led to 'sensuality, carnality, Bolshevism and the Red Flag'. The sticking point was – and for many, still is – the idea that humans are only upgraded monkeys and not individuals specially created in God's image. For long, most scientists treated creationist attacks as effectively irrational and ignored them. This has changed, because of the perceived harm to the credibility of science and in recent years there have been a number of authoritative defences of the scientific understanding of evolution – by the US National Academy of Sciences (1998, 1999), by the InterAcademy Panel (2006) (representing 66 National Academies, including the Royal Society of London) and an increasing number of individual scholars writing from both a secular and a religious basis (e.g. Kitcher, 1982, 2007; Godfrey, 1983; Dawkins, 1986, 1996; Russell, Stoeger and Ayala, 1998; K. R. Miller, 1999; Berry, 2001; Pennock, 2001; K. B. Miller, 2003; Shanks, 2004; McGrath, 2005; Ruse, 2005; Ayala, 2006; Giberson, 2008).

Darwin died on 19 April 1882 and was buried in Westminster Abbey. Frederick Bridge, the Abbey organist, composed an anthem for the occasion based on Proverbs 3: 13–17:

> Happy is the man that findeth wisdom and getteth understanding. She is more precious than rubies and all the things that thou canst desire are not

to be compared unto her. Length of days is in her right hand and in her left hand riches and honour. Her ways are ways of pleasantness and all her paths are peace.

Darwin certainly gave wisdom and coherence to fragmented understandings of the natural world. The sadness is that so many have found discord and disharmony in his legacy.

2

After Darwin: Is Intelligent Design Intelligent?

Denis R. Alexander

1. The Historical Background

The term 'intelligent design' is one of those slippery terms that means many different things to different people. This is why polls carried out on the level of 'belief in intelligent design' are rarely meaningful unless the term is first carefully defined.

The historical notion of 'design' has a long history, going back to the ancient Stoic philosophers, popularized by the Roman lawyer Cicero (106–43 BC) in his book *The Nature of the Gods* (45 BC) before being taken up by early Christian thinkers such as Tertullian (160–225 AD) as a way of promoting belief in God to the surrounding pagan world (Emerton 1989, 129). Some pagans even wanted Cicero's book suppressed because it was used so successfully by Christian writers! Speaking for the Stoics, Cicero wrote that:

> When we see a mechanism such as a planetary model or a clock, do we doubt that it is the creation of a conscious intelligence? So how can we doubt that the world is the work of the divine intelligence? We may well believe that the world and everything in it has been created for the gods and for mankind.

The anti-religious objections of the atomists were also reported by Cicero:

The world was made by a natural process, without any need of a creator . . . Atoms come together and are held by mutual attraction. Thus are created all the forms of nature which you imagine can only be created by some divine craftsman.

In some ways the debate about design has not moved much further in the intervening two millennia, and the notion of 'divine intelligence' as an ultimate explanation for the order and complexity of the world, contrasted with the notion of 'natural process, without any need of a creator', have remained the two main competing views ever since.

The idea of design in the world was deployed to great effect by many of the founders of modern science in the seventeenth century, playing a central role in what came to be known as 'natural theology': for some the attempt to derive the existence and even something about the character of God from the properties of the natural world, but for others more a way of appreciating the work in creation of a God already known by revelation. Robert Boyle (1627–91), one of the early founders of the Royal Society, echoed Cicero in his use of the clock as an analogy, writing that the world is 'like a rare clock, such as may be that at Strasbourg, where all things are so skillfully contrived, that the engine being once set a-moving, all things proceed, according to the artificer's first design . . . by virtue of the general and primitive contrivance of the whole engine' (cited in Hall, 1960: 150).

Boyle was highly resistant to the idea that there was any kind of mediator between God and the universe, such as 'Nature'. Reformation theologians encouraged the acceptance of the new mechanical philosophy precisely because of their insistence on the radical sovereignty of God in creation, leading to a denial of any autonomous role for matter in this process (Lindberg and Numbers, 1986, 167). Calvin, for example, commented that:

> concerning inanimate objects, we ought to hold that, although each one has by nature been endowed with its own property, yet it does not exercise its own power except in so far as it is directed by God's ever-present hand. These are, thus, nothing but instruments to which God continually imparts as much effectiveness as he wills, and according to his own purpose bends and turns them to either one action or another.

God's activity in nature, Calvin taught, was continuous and complete. There were no 'gaps' which could be attributed to forces or agents outside of God's immediate control. Nature was not autonomous. The Word or command of God was the only edict required to bring direction or purpose into inanimate matter. So Boyle's clockwork universe needed no adjustments because it was all the outworking of God's perfect design. As Boyle himself wrote:

It more sets off the wisdom of God in the fabric of the universe, that he can make so vast a machine perform all those many things, which he designed it should, by the mere contrivance of brute matter managed by certain laws of local motion and upheld by his ordinary and general concourse, than if from time to time he employed an intelligent overseer, such as nature is fancied to be, to regulate, assist, and control the motions of the parts.

But by the 18th century the deists were dragging the notion of design out of such a robustly theistic context and deploying it as an argument for the existence of God the distant law-giver. God's intelligent design, wrote Voltaire, was demonstrated 'as much in the meanest insect as in the planets . . . The disposition of a fly's wings or of the feelers of a snail is sufficient to confound you', as he carried on an imaginary debate with an atheist in his *Dictionary of Philosophy* (1764). But Voltaire's God was that of the deists, not a God continually interacting with the world, least of all performing miracles, but the distant designer who created a somewhat static Nature, ruled by natural laws. Nature, with a big 'N', became ever more autonomous in the hands of French Enlightenment thinkers and their God more remote from the daily workings of the world.

It was left to British natural theology to maintain the theistic notion of a more hands-on God, one who was involved in designing the detailed contrivances of the biological organisms that featured in the natural history collections of so many early Victorian households, not least those of rural clerics. '[E]very indication of contrivance', wrote Archdeacon William Paley in his best-selling book *Natural Theology* (1802), which had sold at least 80,000 copies by mid-century, 'every manifestation of design, which existed in the watch, exists in the works of nature; with the difference, on the side of nature, of being greater or more, and that in a degree which exceeds all computation.' But as Darwin was to famously write in his autobiography much later in the century: 'The old argument of design in nature, as given by Paley, which formerly seemed to me so conclusive, fails, now that the law of natural selection has been discovered'. The contrivances of Paley became the adaptations of evolutionary biology and it seemed to some that Darwin had dealt the death-blow to arguments from design, at least in biology.

Yet even at the time the language of 'intelligent design' was now deployed by others in the service of Darwinism. The term 'Christian Darwinism' was already in use in the USA by 1867, a mere eight years after publication of Darwin's *Origin of Species*. James McCosh was a committed Christian, an early President of what was to become Princeton University, and one of the many Christian academics at the time who introduced Darwinism to North America. McCosh held strongly to the concept of natural selection, but equally strongly believed that 'the natural origin of species is not inconsistent with *intelligent design* in nature or with the existence of a personal Creator of the world' (my italics). Upon looking back over 20 years as president of Princeton, McCosh remarked that 'I have been defending Evolution but, in so doing, have given the proper account of it as the method of God's procedure, and find that when so understood it is in no way inconsistent with Scripture'. His language is informative. No longer was design in biology being looked to as a central plank in natural theology, but the question was more whether biology, now best described by natural selection, was 'consistent with' the creator God that McCosh believed in based upon biblical revelation.

Not until the later decades of the twentieth century did a robust natural theology really gain its nerve once more, this time given impetus not by biology, but by Big Bang cosmology and the anthropic principle. The emphasis was on the design of the universe as a whole with its finely-tuned constants without which life would be impossible. In making such anthropic arguments, no one had in mind earlier generations of design arguments in which God became the designer of specific components of living organisms. The contrast brings out two distinct meanings of the slippery word 'design'. In one it refers to the overall intentions and purposes in the mind of the designer who, as 'primary cause', brings about a universe with the intelligible material properties that fulfill those intentions, the 'secondary causes'. In the other the notion of 'design' is more like that of the architect who specifies a detailed plan that includes the precise specification of the detailed features of designed objects.

2. The contemporary Intelligent Design Movement

The Intelligent Design (ID) movement represents the second of these two understandings of 'design', and in its modern garb emerged into public view in the early 1990s with the publication of *Darwin on Trial* (1991) written by University of California at Berkeley law professor Phillip E. Johnson. The ID acronym will therefore be used here to refer to this contemporary usage since it identifies a distinctive movement of ideas with a supporting Institute, books and a group of proponents putting forward a similar set of ideas.

Phillip Johnson recounts how he was on sabbatical at University College London in 1987 when he came across Richard Dawkins' book *The Blind Watchmaker*. It was Dawkins' assertions about evolution as a godless process, together with what Johnson perceived as its lack of evidence, that spurred him into his anti-Darwinian crusade. There is therefore a certain irony in the reflection that it was the writings of the enthusiastic atheist Richard Dawkins that proved to be a key trigger in launching the ID movement.

By general consent Prof. Johnson was the leading figure in the early days of ID. With the robust style of a US lawyer, Johnson took on Darwinism in a series of best-selling books, attacking evolution as if he were presenting the case for the prosecution and evolution was in the dock. Other books followed, such as *Testing Darwinism* (1997). These books were published by Christian publishers on both sides of the Atlantic who saw them as playing a role in the defence of the Christian faith. Unfortunately, however, by tackling a biological topic without the necessary background in biology, it soon became apparent that much of the science in Johnson's books was misleading, and some of it simply wrong, contributing to the alienation of the scientific community from the ideas of ID since the inception of the movement.

A central target for Johnson's attacks was the 'naturalism' that he saw pervading science in general and evolution in particular. Impressed by Dawkins, Johnson saw evolution as 'a materialistic process in which God played no part', writing that 'Evolution in the Darwinian sense is by definition mindless and godless' (Johnson, 1997: 10, 16). Theistic evolutionists who saw evolution as a description of the creative process whereby God brings about biological diversity, were given short shrift by Johnson, who described the idea of evolution as a 'God-guided system of gradual creation' as a 'mistake' (Johnson, 1997: 22).

Other influential books written by ID proponents followed on from those of Johnson, albeit coming from rather different perspectives. The biochemist Michael Behe from Lehigh University published *Darwin's Black Box* in 1996 in which he described different well-known biochemical mechanisms and pathways, arguing that these were 'irreducibly complex', in the sense that all their components were necessary for their biological functions, and so they could not have come into being by a gradual Darwinian process. In the same year the Discovery Institute of the Center for the Renewal of Science and Culture was established in Seattle, now the flagship of the ID movement. In the late 1990s the Center established its 'Wedge Strategy', stating that the new Center was seeking 'nothing less than the overthrow of materialism and its damning cultural legacies'. 'Bringing together leading scholars from the natural sciences and those from the humanities and social sciences', the document expounding this strategy continues, 'the Center explores how new developments in biology, physics and cognitive science raise serious doubts about scientific materialism and have re-opened the case for the supernatural'.

One of the Fellows appointed by the new Center was William Dembski, with doctorates in both philosophy and mathematics, who has since emerged as a major ID advocate, publishing a series of works in which he refined the understanding of the term 'design' from the ID perspective. The first of these books, *The Design Inference: Eliminating Chance Through Small Probabilities* (1998) was the most technical, presenting methods for distinguishing design from 'apparent design'. More popular works followed, such as *Intelligent Design – the Bridge Between Science and Theology* (1999a), in many ways the manifesto of the ID movement; It was followed by *The Design Revolution* (2004) in which Dembski addresses the various questions and objections raised by his detractors.

ID proponents vary considerably in their stance towards Darwinian evolution. The Presbyterian Phillip Johnson, for example, has been resolutely opposed to anything except variation within a species, seeing all arguments from natural selection as displaying 'naturalism', whereas the Catholic Michael Behe has no problem with common descent and sees a significant role for natural selection in evolution, drawing a line at the perceived 'irreducibly complex' systems in biology, nevertheless maintaining that 'Dawin's theory accounts for only relatively small biological details . . .' (Behe, 2008: 147). On the other hand, William Dembski, now Research Professor in Philosophy at the Southwestern Baptist Theological Seminary, has adopted a middle position, in places in his publications expressing doubt as to common descent, whereas in other places stating that ID is compatible with the evolution of all living things from a common ancestry.

What does unite all ID proponents is a shared antipathy to Darwinian evolution as an inference to the best explanation for the origins of biological diversity, including the origins of all biological complex systems. Dembski is explicit in stating that the one point that ID proponents share in common with so-called 'scientific creationists' is that 'Mutations and natural selection are insufficient to bring about the development of all living kinds from a single organism' (Dembski, 1999a, 249). As it happens, this represents an incomplete statement anyway for defining the evolutionary process, because we now know that other mechanisms, such as the lateral gene transfer that occurs between bacteria and many other species, is also important.

More positively, Dembski has stated that 'Intelligent Design is three things: a scientific research program that investigates the effects of intelligent causes; an intellectual movement that challenges Darwinism and its naturalistic legacy; and a way of understanding divine action. Intelligent design therefore intersects science and theology' (Dembski, 1999a: 13). Understanding ID involves an appreciation of what these statements mean, and it is important that any critique is based upon the explicit claims made by ID proponents, and not on popular accounts, which are frequently unreliable. For example, the UK press often identifies ID with young earth creationism, whereas ID proponents have been careful to distance themselves from creationism, and are explicit in their claim that their ideas do not depend on the Bible or other religious writings.

3. The Core Ideas of ID

What exactly do ID proponents mean when they say that ID is 'a scientific research programme that investigates the effects of intelligent causes'? The core ideas of ID in this context can be summarized in the words of Dembski: first, 'specified complexity is well-defined and empirically detectable'; second, 'undirected natural causes are incapable of explaining specified complexity'; and third, 'intelligent causation best explains specified complexity' (Dembski, 1999a: 247). With regard to the first point, Dembski writes that:

> Intelligence leaves behind a characteristic trademark or signature – what I call *specified complexity*. An event exhibits specified complexity if it is contingent and therefore not necessary; if it is complex and therefore not readily repeatable by chance; and if it is specified in the sense of exhibiting an independently given pattern (Dembski, 2004: 35).

Specified complexity therefore refers to events that are not imposed upon the data after the event. Someone may shoot an arrow at a wall at random, but drawing a circle round the arrow after the event would not render the event specified. To define events characterized by 'specified complexity', Dembski introduces an explanatory filter that can be used to infer design. The filter has decision nodes through which an event needs to pass if it is to be defined as 'designed'. First, is it a necessary or contingent event, object or system? For example, the structure of an ice crystal is necessary in the sense that its structure is defined by the laws of physics, even though it is a unique structure, therefore not 'designed' in Dembski's terminology. But when the Search for Extraterrestrial Intelligence (SETI) researchers in the film *Contact* detected a signal from outer space of 1126 beats and pauses, where 1s correspond to beats and 0s to pauses, they inferred a sequence representing the prime numbers from 2 to 101, taking this signal as decisive confirmation of the existence of extraterrestrial intelligence (Dembski, 1999a: 128).

The second decision node is to ask whether the object, event or system could arise by chance or is it complex? For example, had the SETI researchers received only 8 beats and pauses, then they could have concluded that this was a chance event, insufficiently complex to infer intelligence. To distinguish between events that are merely improbable and those that are complex, Dembski imposes a 'universally probability bound' value of 10^{150} so that 'any specified event of probability less than 1 in 10^{150} will remain improbable even after all conceivable probabilistic resources from the observable universe have been factored in' (Dembski, 2004: 84–85).

The third decision node addresses the question as to whether the object, event or system is 'specified'. By this Dembski wishes to suggest that being both contingent and complex *per se* are insufficient to infer 'design'; in addition it must be shown that there is an unmistakable pattern that displays intelligence. Dembski pictures the 10 billion possible combinations of the lock for a bank safe; if one of them works first time to open the safe, then this is 'specified' in the sense that in the context the opening of the safe could not (realistically) have happened by chance (Dembski, 2004: 89).

An object, event or system that passes successfully through the three nodes or stages of this 'explanatory filter' is then inferred, in Dembski's scheme, to display 'design' and therefore 'signs of intelligence' rather than coming about via 'natural causes'. Michael Behe's examples of supposedly 'irreducibly complex' systems in biology are then taken as exemplars par excellence of how the explanatory filter works in practice: for ID proponents systems such as bacterial flagella, the blood clotting system, the immune system and so forth all pass successfully through the 'filter' and so display empirical evidence for design. It is important to realize in assessing such claims that by 'empirical' the ID proponents mean the assessment of a system according to these criteria, they are not referring to actual experiments.

The overall goal in these types of argument is made very explicit throughout the publications of the proponents of ID. In the words of Dembski, ID 'argues that God's design is accessible to scientific enquiry'. The 'crucial point' is that 'design is *empirically detectable*' (Dembski, 1999a: 17). 'It was Darwin's expulsion of design from biology that made possible the triumph of naturalism in Western culture. So, too, it will be intelligent design's reinstatement of design within biology that will be the undoing of naturalism in Western culture' (Dembski, 1999a: 14).

4. Is Intelligent Design Science?

Since ID proponents are insistent that ID represents science, and should therefore be taught in science classrooms as an alternative to evolution, it is fair to ask whether their core ideas do in fact display the characteristics of science.

Science is notoriously difficult to define because it covers such a wide range of disciplines, and the meaning of the word even varies between different languages. In English 'science' refers to that modern empirically based activity which is carried out in the university labs down the road, but comparable words in most other languages (e.g. *Wissenschaft* in German; *La Science* in French; *Bilim* in Turkish) have much broader meanings, and can include any systematic body of constructed knowledge. But ID proponents use 'science' in its common English usage to refer to modern science. Furthermore, their core arguments focus on biology, so in the discussion on the methods of science that follows, biology will be particularly in mind.

The purpose of science is to understand how the physical components of the universe function: in the case of biology, the components that comprise all forms of life. There are three key aspects of science. First there should be a plausible hypothesis or model that has real explanatory value, that gives new insights into the origins and functioning of living things. For example, the notion of all living creatures being connected in a great 'chain of being' was a common idea for centuries, but had little explanatory value. It did not explain how all living things were connected. But Darwin's theory gave, for the first time, a coherent account that explains the origins of biological diversity. It now became apparent why there were different species in geographically distant locations, it explained similarities and differences in the anatomy and physiology of different organisms, the role of fossils was explained, and so forth. Common descent by natural selection became the inference to the best explanation of a huge array of scientific data.

To take just one of thousands of examples from the current field of comparative genomics, involving the sequencing and comparison of DNA from extant organisms representing different stages of evolutionary history, we can consider the sequence of *Trichoplax*, a placozoan. Placozoans are arguably the simplest free-living animals, only 1–2 mm across, with four known cell-types (compared to our 200 or more), and we last shared an ancestor with them perhaps around 650 million years ago. Yet the *Trichoplax* genome, with its estimated 11,514 protein encoding genes, contains many genes found in cell-types, such as neurons, that it does not possess (Srivastava, 2008: 955). Many of its genes are used in embryonic development in vertebrates like us. In other words, the genes have been co-opted for all kinds of different functions in later evolutionary history. Furthermore, the order in which large blocks of genes are arranged in the *Trichoplax* DNA is the same as that found in human chromosomes ('synteny'), a remarkable example of preservation during billions of individual DNA replication events. All of these observations are readily incorporated within the Darwinian paradigm of 'descent with modification'.

A second important characteristic of a scientific hypothesis or model is that it be fruitful in terms of leading to testable ideas, a research programme resulting in good peer-reviewed publications in the scientific literature. The theory of evolution leads to such testable ideas: the reproductive success of organisms can be measured in different habitats; fossils can be sought that represent transitional forms; comparative genomics reveals homologies (similarities) between genes from widely different species, and so forth.

The third key characteristic is that the hypothesis be potentially falsifiable. If there are no results that could possibly count against it, then the proposed explanation remains vacuous. In this respect evolution could easily be falsified, or at the least data could be found that would severely shake or modify the theory. For example, if it turned out that the genetic code was different in different organisms, then that would undermine the idea of common descent. In fact, bar some tiny differences, the genetic code is identical in all living things. If rabbit (or other mammalian) fossils were found in the pre-Cambrian era, that would severely shake our current understanding of evolution; likewise if human fossilized footprints were found on the same dried up mud-flats as those of dinosaurs.

Once a hypothesis has become established in science, or is at least in the process of being established, and providing it is sufficiently broad in its explanatory capabilities, encompassing a broad array of different kinds of data, then it tends to be called a 'theory'. But, somewhat confusingly for the non-scientist, the word 'theory' is used in science in a technical sense very different from its daily usage as in 'it's only a theory'. Scientists have no doubt that the 'theory of relativity' or the 'Big Bang theory of cosmology' or the 'theory of evolution' are well established, but the word 'theory' in each case refers to an overarching explanatory set of ideas.

Does ID have explanatory power?

If we now take the core ideas of ID and assess them against the three key characteristics of experimental science, how do they fare? The answer is: not very well. The problems become apparent as soon as we start on the first criterion: does the hypothesis have explanatory power? In practice the ideas of 'specified complexity' and 'explanatory filter' remain simply as thought experiments without explanatory power in the world of biology. The reason is that there is no way in practice of using them to explain the origins of complex biological systems, whereas there are in any case much simpler explanations already in place. For example, Behe gives the idea of blood-clotting in vertebrates as an example of an irreducibly complex system that could not have come into being incrementally because the complete cascade involves more than twenty components that need to operate together to function properly. But the fact is we know a lot about the evolution of those components, many of them having come about by gene duplication, and there are also simpler clotting systems in other organisms that reveal evolutionary stages along the way to the vertebrate system (Alexander, 2008: 300).

One of the problems with having mathematicians or philosophers assessing practical biological questions is their unfamiliarity with the challenges of carrying out a research programme in this field. So it is very easy to carry out thought experiments in the office, using analogies drawn from SETI, archaeology, code-breaking, and the like, but the fact is that biologists simply do not find those ideas useful as explanations when it comes to understanding the origins of biological systems, no doubt explaining the lack of scientific publications arising from the ID movement. It is notable in this respect that the only prominent biologist ID proponent, Michael Behe, does not actually use Dembski's theoretical mathematical ideas when talking about biological systems, preferring to keep to the general idea of systems as 'irreducibly complex', without attempting to use Dembski's 'explanatory filter' in assessing what that really means. As a Fellow of the Discovery Institute, Paul Nelson, has stated: 'Easily the biggest challenge facing the ID community is to develop a full-fledged theory of biological design. We don't have such a theory right now, and that's a problem . . .' (Shermer, 2006: 111).

Another significant problem with the suggestion that ID represents a scientific hypothesis with explanatory power comes from a false conclusion inherent in its argument. Advocates for the explanatory filter basically claim that if something cannot, in principle, be explained by either chance or necessity, then it must be designed. But this is not necessarily the case. A fourth alternative might be simply: 'we don't know at present how this entity came into being'.

There is also the problem as to whether 'design' as a concept really counts as an explanation for a complex biological entity. If someone tells me that the bacterial flagellum is very complex and so must be 'designed', in what *scientific* sense am I better informed than before? If one aim of biology is to illuminate how the physical components of living things interact in the organization of life, then I do not see how my *scientific* knowledge is advanced by being told that something displays 'signs of intelligence'. As a Christian who believes in God as creator, I believe that everything that exists is the outworking of his creative purposes, and the scientific enterprise is only possible by a prior understanding of the created order taken as a whole as intelligible. So picking out just particular bits of that created order as inferring intelligent design does not sound like an explanation for anything.

And what precisely is this source of 'design' that is being presented as an explanation? Since ID proponents are explicit in excluding the supernatural and the miraculous as they invoke 'design' as an explanation, it is fair to ask as to what the 'design' refers. In some ID writings it sounds rather like some mysterious intermediate force interposed between God and the physical creation, very like the 'Nature' that Boyle criticized so astutely in the passage already cited (*v.s.* p. 24). For example, Dembski writes that 'ID, though often understood in supernaturalist terms, can also be understood in terms of teleological organizing principles built into nature' (Dembski, 2008: 161). In previous centuries when electromagnetism and the weak and strong nuclear forces were discovered, they were named as such and added to the catalogue of physical forces. If there were really mysterious forces or 'organizing principles' at work that helped to explain the origins of complex entities in biology, then once discovered they would simply be absorbed into the explanatory framework and become part of the panoply of mainstream science. At other times scientists have proposed explanations for things, such as the *élan vital* in biology, put forward by Henri Bergson in his book *Creative Evolution* (1907), or the aether in cosmology, or the phlogiston supposedly contained within combustible bodies, but these various ideas have been discarded by scientists because they do no useful explanatory work. The ID proposal of 'design' seems to be another kind of vitalism which remains vacuous as a scientific explanation.

Is ID testable?

If ID does not fare well in passing the first scientific hurdle, the challenge to be a hypothesis that explains something, what about the second criterion, that of being fruitful in terms of leading to testable ideas? Here again the idea seems scientifically sterile. Let us imagine that I have a PhD student in my laboratory and I give him the task of understanding the origins of the bacterial flagellum. Where did its 30–40 components come from? What are the possible evolutionary pathways that led to its emergence as a chemically powered little outboard motor that enables many bacteria to swim around? After two years of work the student comes back into my office and says: 'I give up. The flagellum is just too complex to explain in this way. Therefore it must be designed'. So what further experimental programme would this suggestion instigate? The answer is 'nothing' and it is for this reason that ID has often been criticized for being creatively sterile, a potential 'science-stopper'.

Contrast this with the ability of evolutionary explanations to explain the origins of the flagellum and the difference is striking. For example, out of the ensemble of 30–40 proteins, there is a 10-protein sub-module known as the Type III secretory complex that functions independently to inject poisons into other bacteria, a quite different function than swimming. Another sub-module of the flagellum is a chemical pump that functions in many bacteria to convert energy into useful work. So it turns out that the flagellum is not irreducibly complex after all, because the complex system can be broken down into sub-modules that have independent functions, giving important clues about the incremental Darwinian pathways involved in its evolution. Each sub-module has its own selective advantage, independently of the flagellum taken as a whole. In addition, homologues of most of the genes (meaning very similar genes) encoding the proteins comprising the flagellum, have been identified in many other organisms where they carry out a range of tasks. Evolution often works by the co-option of genes already present in an organism to collaborate in carrying out new functions. It is also important to remember that bacterial evolution depends on 'lateral gene transfer', whereby genes are exchanged between different strains of bacteria, greatly speeding up the rate of evolutionary change.

In contrast to the testable nature of evolutionary narratives, ID suffers from the vacuous 'fallacy of large numbers'. A multi-component entity such as the flagellum is suggested to be too complex to come into being fully-formed 'by chance', so is defined as 'irreducibly complex'. Of course the chances of that happening are infinitesimally small. But no one believes that happens anyway: evolution is incremental. The problem for ID proponents is that every living system without exception is multi-component – that is how life works, by thousands of molecular components cooperating together. So there is nothing in biology that is *not* 'irreducibly complex' in the ID sense. A notion that 'explains' everything in science ends up explaining nothing and, like vitalism, is discarded.

ID proponents will often protest that there are peer-reviewed ID papers in the scientific literature showing that the ID hypothesis does lead to testable ideas. But when you look at those papers, and there are only a few, they are really nothing of the kind, claiming only that certain evolutionary pathways are difficult to envisage. Well, sure. But that hardly counts as a novel testable idea. Scientific theories are successful because of what they do explain, not because of what they do not. If a theory leads to a fruitful research programme, as evolutionary theory obviously has, then anomalies will be kept on the back-burner, waiting to be sorted out and incorporated into the theory when their time comes.

For example, Douglas Axe is the lead scientist in the ID Biologic Institute, a laboratory set up in Redmond, Washington, with money from the Discovery Institute. Axe has pointed out in previously published work that functional 'folds' in a certain protein are highly constrained in that only a few sequences of amino acids will provide the structure that will allow the protein to function properly (Axe, 2004: 1295). But there are also other papers in the literature showing how proteins 'navigate' in evolutionary steps to the 'correct' functional protein by highly constrained pathways. A research group from Harvard published a paper in 2006 entitled 'Darwinian evolution can follow only very few mutational paths to fitter proteins' (Weinreich, 2006: 111). It is intriguing to read the final sentence of their abstract: 'We conclude that much protein evolution will be similarly constrained. This implies that the protein tape of life may be largely reproducible and even predictable'. So there is a discussion going on in the scientific literature about the evolution of proteins; indeed hundreds of papers pour off the press every month on protein structure-function. But there is nothing in the Axe paper or any other papers about ID, because it is not a testable hypothesis. Pointing out supposed difficulties in Darwinian explanations does not in itself count as an explanation for anything.

Is ID falsifiable?

The third critical aspect of scientific theories is their potential falsifiability, but before ID proponents jump on this as support for the idea that ID is a scientific theory after all, on the grounds that the notion of 'irreducible complexity' has been falsified in the case of the flagellum (and other cases besides), it is worth remembering that 'one swallow does not make a summer. The potential to be falsified is a necessary but not sufficient ground for something to count as a scientific theory. For example, the theory that the planets exert baleful effects on human destinies is, in principle, falsifiable, but that does not in itself make the theory scientific (in the twenty-first century). Theories are accepted by scientists as being scientific when they have the potential to count as better explanations than other theories (a potential open to further experimental testing). This is why a theory which may have been counted as scientific in the seventeenth century may no longer be counted as a valid theory today – it was long ago tested, found wanting, and then discarded.

A further problem with falsifying 'design' as a purported scientific explanation for anything arises from the way in which 'design' in the ID sense is taken to identify gaps in our current understanding of the evolutionary origins of various types of biological complexity. But falsifying a gap in our current knowledge is not really falsifying anything at all. The existence of phlogiston was never really falsified, it was just rendered unnecessary once oxygen was discovered and the chemical mechanism of oxidative combustion was understood.

The Dover trial

In 2005 ID went on trial in a court case, *Kitzmiller v. Dover*. The trial, which attracted extensive press coverage, arose from a local school board in Dover, Pennsylvania, which mandated that ID be introduced into the biology curriculum in a local high school, and that an ID textbook, *Of Pandas and People*, be made available to students. Litigation continued for a whole year and centred around the issue of whether ID is a scientific or religious idea, of key importance in a nation with strict separation between religion and state. The local school board lost the case on the grounds that ID is indeed not science, and the lengthy 139-page ruling by Judge John E. Jones, himself a church-goer, provides a valuable summary of the key points (Jones, 2005). Michael Behe was a witness in the case and his comments under oath on the question of ID's scientific publications are therefore of interest. As Judge Jones reported, 'On cross-examination, Professor Behe admitted that: "There are no peer reviewed articles by anyone advocating for intelligent design supported by pertinent experiments or calculations which provide detailed rigorous accounts of how intelligent design of any biological system occurred".' After listening to six weeks of testimony, Judge Jones concluded that ID was not science, but religion, and should not therefore be taught in US schools.

5. Intelligent Design, Miracles and Natural Theology

If ID is not science, then is it a revived form of natural theology? It
certainly looks very much like it, though some ID proponents protest that
this is not the case. Dembski states explicitly that 'The intelligent design
movement is linked both conceptually and historically to British natural
theology' (Dembski, 1999a: 16), arguing that 'God's design is accessible
to scientific enquiry'. The crucial point is that 'design is empirically
detectable, that is, we can detect it through observation' (Dembski, 1999a:
17). Dembski follows these comments with a survey of the signs in the
Old and New Testaments that demonstrated God's activity in the world,
such as the plagues in Egypt and the miracles of the New Testament,
most importantly the resurrection of Christ. 'The reformulation of the
premodern logic of signs', writes Dembski, 'is precisely what intelligent
design is all about', looking for inspiration to an earlier generation of
natural theologians, such as Thomas Reid, Charles Hodge and William
Paley (Dembski, 1999a: 47, 70–93).

Nevertheless Dembski still wishes to insist that ID does not invoke
miracles in its explanations, nor is it a revivified form of natural
theology. Yet if a 40-component flagellum appeared fully formed one day
embedded in the cell wall of a bacterium, when it had not been there
the day before, which is what ID seems to be suggesting, then I think
most people would be tempted to call this 'miraculous'. In response,
Dembski suggests that it is 'a logical possibility that the design in the
bacterial flagellum was front-loaded into the universe at the big bang
and subsequently expressed itself in the course of natural history as a
miniature motor-driven propeller on the back of the *E. coli* bacterium'
(Dembski, 2004, 184). But it is truly difficult to find any coherent
meaning for this claim, let alone evidence, and it is difficult to avoid the
impression that ID proponents are suggesting that a series of thousands
of miraculous events occurred to bring about all the complex entities
that characterize living matter. The medieval Church was profligate in its
invocation of miracles, not least those attributed to the saints, holy relics
and the Virgin Mary, and there seems to be a strongly analogous hope
in the ID movement that it might be possible to 'prove from science' an
array of such 'special events' in the natural world.

The rejection of ID as natural theology also fails to convince. After
all, Behe states in the final chapter of *Darwin's Black Box*, entitled
'Science, Philosophy, Religion', 'that while one side of the elephant is
labeled intelligent design, the other side might be labeled God', and the
chapter clearly indicates that for him the designer is the God of Christian
theism (Behe, 1996: 233). Indeed, most of the prominent ID proponents
are Christians, and do not hide their intention to use their ideas as an
apologetic tool to attack 'naturalism' and promote the Christian faith.

As Johnson says 'This isn't really, and never has been, a debate about science . . . It's about religion and philosophy' (Shermer, 2006: 109). Dembski sees examples of design in biology as 'signs' of intelligence, pointing to a designer, stating that 'Intelligent design is just the Logos theology of John's Gospel restated in the idiom of information theory' (Dembski, 1999b: 84).

This desire to demonstrate the existence of the 'signs' pointing to a 'designer' by means of science does sound very like a form of natural theology. Dembski protests that the traditional task of natural theology has been to demonstrate the existence and attributes of God, whereas the aim of ID is to draw attention to design without taking the next step to identify the nature of the designer. Such a strategy seems to be promoted in an attempt to by-pass the strict separation of church and state in the USA, although when speaking or writing in a Christian context, most ID proponents make quite clear, as illustrated above, that for them their work has apologetic intentions.

There are many different species of natural theology and it is reasonable to ask whether ID represents a helpful species. A significant problem is that ID points to present gaps in our scientific understanding of the detailed evolutionary origins of different complex systems. Indeed, fully describing, step by step, the evolutionary assembly of biologically complex systems, is a difficult challenge given that many of these systems emerged billions of years ago. What is remarkable is the way that comparative genomics has shed light on the evolution of such systems in ways that we could never have imagined even a few decades ago. But certainly gaps in our knowledge still remain.

It is for this reason that ID has often been accused of simply reviving the long discredited 'god-of-the-gaps' form of argument, except that in this context it would be more accurate to call it the 'designer-of-the-gaps' argument. A complex biological system is identified, there is as yet no detailed account of its evolutionary history, therefore it must have been 'designed'. But of course science moves ahead very fast. Even some of the examples given in 1996 by Behe in *Darwin's Black Box*, such as blood clotting, have evolutionary histories much better understood now than when that book was written (Alexander, 2008: 300). Locating one's 'designer' in current gaps in our scientific knowledge is a hostage to fortune, because sooner rather than later science will fill those gaps, and then what of the 'designer'?

The standard ID response to this critique is that ID is about what we scientifically do know rather than what we do not know. For example, we know a lot about the structure and assembly of the flagellum. But this point is irrelevant, because the gaps in knowledge often lie not in the molecular characteristics of complex systems, but in our understanding of their detailed evolutionary histories. It is into these historical gaps that ID wishes to interject the notion of 'design'.

Isaac Newton famously maintained that God brought about an occasional 'reformation' in the movement of the planets to correct the irregularities that accrued from the supposed friction occurring as they passed through the 'aether' (an 'aether' which we now know does not exist). Even at the time the German Lutheran philosopher and mathematician Leibniz took Newton to task for invoking occasional miracles in order to remedy the deficiencies in his creation. And by the end of the eighteenth century the French mathematicians Laplace and Lagrange had shown that irregularities induced in planetary orbits could be self-correcting. Apparently there was no need for God's occasional corrections.

Dembski has stated that 'it's only when natural laws are viewed as incomplete, so that without the activity of an intelligent agent it is not possible to bring about a given object of nature, that natural theology can remain a valid enterprise' (Dembski, 1999a: 79). But ID proponents should heed the lessons of history that all forms of natural theology that depend on current gaps in our scientific understanding are fragile and unlikely to survive the rapidly advancing tide of science for very long. More robust forms of natural theology see the whole panoply of God's creative actions, without exception, as pointing to the wisdom and power of the Creator.

6. Intelligent Design and Naturalism

One does not need to read very much in the ID literature before realizing, as already mentioned, that 'naturalism' is the main target of their campaign. But ID proponents often use the language of 'naturalism' and its derivatives such as 'naturalistic' in a way that is different from normal usage, so some care is needed in understanding the claims that are being made.

The Oxford Dictionary definition of 'naturalism' in the context of philosophy is straightforward: the 'view of the world that excludes the supernatural or spiritual'. Clearly there are people who practice science who do hold such a world-view. Equally there are many theists who practice science, who see their scientific descriptions as attempts to describe the works of God. In the USA, home of ID, that percentage is at least 40 per cent if one investigates the beliefs of the scientific community as a whole (Larson and Witham, 1997: 435), although the percentage is lower amongst elite groups of scientists (Ecklund, 2007: 289). Clearly a believer in God who does science cannot carry out their science 'naturalistically' because they believe in the supernatural Creator of all that exists, which is the opposite of naturalism.

Nevertheless, Phillip Johnson offers comments such as the following: 'It is conceivable that God for some reason did all the creating by apparently *naturalistic* processes, perhaps the better to test our faith, but surely this is not the only possibility. My writings, and those of colleagues like Michael Behe, argue that design is detectably present in biology, that *naturalistic* substitutes like the blind watchmaker mechanism are inadequate and contrary to the evidence . . .' (Johnson, 1999: 52; my italics). Johnson further comments that 'theistic evolution can more accurately be described as theistic *naturalism*' (Johnson, 1999: 50; my italics). But 'theistic naturalism' is surely an oxymoron. Christian theism, the kind of theism to which Johnson is referring in this passage, refers to the belief in a creator God who is the origin and sustainer of all that exists. So God cannot possibly create by 'apparently naturalistic processes' for the simple reason that if there is a God who creates, then there are no 'naturalistic processes' because naturalism is false.

The writings of ID proponents suggest that there is a 'two-tier universe', a naturalistic tier involving 'natural laws' with the other tier involving 'design'. Dembski comments that the '. . . design theorist is not committed to every biological structure being designed. *Naturalistic mechanisms* like mutation and selection do operate in natural history to adapt organisms to their environments' (Dembski, 2004: 63; my italics). Again: 'If specified complexity is exhibited in actual biological systems, we are justified in attributing such systems to design. That's not to say that every aspect of such systems is designed. (Some aspects may be due to purely *natural forces*)' (Dembski, 2004: 141; my italics).

Dembski envisages a biological world largely explained by 'naturalistic mechanisms' and 'natural forces', and against this backcloth 'designed systems' may be detected. Indeed, without such a backcloth, the rest of his argument would make little sense, since if the identification of designed entities is to be possible, then a non-designed 'naturalistic' backcloth is essential to facilitate the detection of the 'designed' components.

So the ID literature gives the impression that there is something inherently 'naturalistic' about certain aspects of the created order and not about other aspects, and such thinking appears to stem from a very inadequate doctrine of creation. In biblical creation theology, the natural order is seen as a seamless web of God's creative activity. All scientists can do is to describe the consequences of God's creative activity to the best of their ability. Often their theories will be wrong and will need to be modified or discarded. But within this framework of a robust biblical theism, there is nothing in the created order without exception that is not created and sustained by God. Science is definitely not a naturalistic enterprise for the Christian who is a scientist, but rather a cause for worshipping the God who has brought all things into being, including all the biological complexity of the world.

7. Conclusions

ID should not be confused with the traditional arguments from design. These, in various forms, point to the wonders of the created order and cite them as evidence for the existence of an all-powerful creator. They are arguments based on the intelligibility of the world, the coherence that renders the scientific enterprise feasible. The aim of ID is different, to detect signs of intelligent design within the created order by scientific methods in order to argue for the existence of a designer. But the methods suggested do not themselves display signs of being scientific, but instead look much more like an exemplar of a rather poor natural theology.

The core ideas of ID are subverted by the Christian doctrine of creation, in which the creator God faithfully brings into being and sustains all that exists. Science is not a naturalistic enterprise but an attempt to describe God's activities in the created order. There are some scientists who are naturalistic in their personal ideologies, but unfortunately they are unlikely to shift from such beliefs as a result of the arguments of ID.

3

Charles Kingsley's Christian Darwinism

Amy Laura Hall

In the conversation between theology and science, I am not myself concerned about finding or clearing a religious slip of terrain within the evolutionary sciences, or in finding a way that moral theology may sing in harmony with any particular evolutionary model. These are worthy conversations, but I am interested in another conversation, about what Stephen Jay Gould called 'canonical icons' within popularized, evolutionary science. In his essay 'Ladders and Cones: Constraining Evolution by Canonical Icons', he suggests that evolutionary science requires attention to 'canonical icons' as 'the standard imagery attached to key concepts of our social and intellectual lives.' This standard imagery enjoys a complicated relationship with popular science. The imagery is shaped by scientific projects, according to Gould, and imagery shapes the way science proceeds. Gould's particular concern, as an evolutionary biologist, is that this interaction can hinder inquiry. In the case of evolution, 'the image we see reflects social preferences and psychological hopes, rather than paleontological data or Darwinian theory.' He sums up the matter thus: 'The most serious and pervasive of all misconceptions about evolution equates the concept with some notion of progress, usually inherent and predictable, and leading to a human pinnacle' (Gould, 1995: 43).

My concern, as a moral theologian, is slightly different from Gould's. How does the intertwined imagery of progress, predictability, and pinnacle shape British and North American notions of the social applicability of evolutionary thought? This effort involves historical digging for the sake of interpreting the background stories that are in play even today. In Jenny Reardon's book about the failed Human Genome Diversity Project, *Race to the Finish: Identity and Governance in an Age of Genomics*, she suggests that a crucial but largely hidden feature of genomics is the particular story of progress that continues to shape conversations: 'This modern age witnessed the entanglement of rules that govern what can count as knowledge with rules that determine which human lives can be lived' (Reardon, 2004: 5). I am continually concerned about the interplay of moral theology, variously working Darwinisms, and the rules that determine which human lives can be lived. This volume is dedicated to Darwinian thought in particular, and what people usually name as social Darwinism may have little to do with Darwin's own ideals. The term is usually used for a popularized combination of Herbert Spencer's understanding of hierarchical, social evolution and Thomas Malthus's analysis of population growth, poverty, and the danger or responsibility of 'charity' (see Hofstadter, 1992). Yet, even given this historical caveat, I believe a look back at earlier efforts to process Darwin's writings for, to, and about the masses is worthwhile. Such studies may help both scientists and moral theologians to perceive the echoes of English and North American cultural assumptions at work, even in projects thought to be patently universal or keenly cross-cultural.

Specifically, I here offer an English churchman, Charles Kingsley, as a helpful interlocutor for interpreting the intersection of moral and evolutionary thought in the US and UK. By Darwin's own account, Kingsley is precisely the 'celebrated author and divine' of whom he wrote gratefully in the second and subsequent editions of *On the Origin of Species* (Darwin, 1903: 174). Although still beloved in the UK, Canon Charles Kingsley (1819–1875) is not well known in North America. His treatises on Christian socialism and his novels encouraging what came to be known as 'muscular Christianity' are, in their specifics, lost to most. Nevertheless, he represents a connection of themes at play at kitchen tables, in school board meetings, and in public debates today. Kingsley was able to combine politically serviceable elements of evolutionary thought with other aspects of literary-popular culture to offer a helpful theology for Victorian England.

Kingsley was Darwin's churchman, able to process evolution theologically, making a clarifying struggle toward fitness seem downright providential, and, at the same time, crystallizing English conceptions of race, masculinity and progress for a popular (literate) audience. *The Water-Babies*, his enduring children's whimsy, was at the time part of a serious textual output for a whole generation of young men. This, joined with his homiletic call for a reasonably virile English faith, helped create religious Darwinism for his time. Attention to his voice may help one to note the ways that congregants in the United States and England draw on his version of Christian Darwinism. Such a consideration of the past may encourage careful humility among Kingsley's inheritors. I will close the essay by suggesting that we may read even Kingsley as anticipating collaboration with the very people he narrated as in need of tutelage during an earlier era. If there was hope for even him, even then, perhaps there are creative possibilities for readers today.

1. Manifest Domesticity

Evolution, as a concept, need not require that humans take it upon themselves to plan and produce a fitter future. It is logically possible to read *The Origin of Species* as resituating the human species sufficiently below our prior aspirations as to render grand, social planning silly, at least, and even as potentially detrimental to God's creation. But, as Michael S. Northcott notes in his essay for this volume, some of Darwin's readers used *The Origin of Species* further to make the case for the superiority of humans, as the pinnacle of evolution, and thus for the priority of human progress. This priority was for a particular version of human progress. Part of Gould's point in his 1995 article is that the Darwinian revolution does not necessitate a story of progress along an upward trajectory, with particularly fit heroes as agents of change. One possible reason that the pinnacle story took hold so firmly is that a group of Protestant men in England and the United States deemed themselves as holy husbandmen – as men particularly suited to usher in the next stage of human development through domestic and international efforts. For some of Darwin's readers, his findings gave warrant for directing the progress of peoples who seemed less evolved. Many of Darwin's interpreters took up the call implicit in the book's subtitle: *The Preservation of Favoured Races in the Struggle for Life*. Men within the 'favoured races' were able, with some theological effort, to understand their work on peoples at home and abroad to be now proven scientifically as ordained by God.

The most overt forms of this justification by way of evolutionary superiority came from Christian colonialists and, a few decades later, eugenicists. I first came across Kingsley while sorting through sundry American eugenicist texts and researching the formal eugenics movement that flourished in the United States during the first half of the twentieth century, decades after Kingsley's death. Yet Kingsley was a mentor to young churchmen grappling with how best to apply Darwin socially; he had set a pattern for evaluating, sifting, and culling individuals, regions, and populations. For those American clergy who were eager to be of use during what has been called a progressive era, Kingsley's fiction and his *Natural Theology of the Future* (the title of his 1871 essay) offered guidance for remaining relevant.

In my book *Conceiving Parenthood*, I concentrated on the obviously *domestic* side of 'Manifest Domesticity'. I believe it helpful now also to consider a view from the more 'public' eye. In her 1998 essay 'Manifest Domesticity', written for a special issue of *American Literature*, Amy Kaplan suggests a different way of thinking about gender and the too-often presumed split between home and public life.

> Reconceptualizing domesticity in this way might shift the cognitive geography of nineteenth-century separate spheres. When we contrast the domestic sphere with the market or political realm, men and women inhabit a divided social terrain, but when we oppose the domestic to the foreign, men and women become national allies against the alien, and the determining division is not gender but racial demarcations of otherness. Thus another part of the cultural work of domesticity might be to unite men and women in a national domain and to generate notions of the foreign against which the nation can be imagined as home. The border between the domestic and foreign, however, also deconstructs when we think of domesticity not as a static condition but as the process of domestication, which entails conquering and taming the wild, the natural and the alien. Domestic in this sense is related to the imperial project of civilizing, and the conditions of domesticity often become markers that distinguish civilization from savagery (Kaplan, 1998: 582).

Put simply, those historians who have separated domesticity in the home from the process of husbandry across the empire keep alive a serviceable lie about masculinity and femininity, about politics and the nursery. Kaplan suggests that the work of home and the work of empire overlap. The title of her essay plays on the term 'Manifest Destiny', a term used for the presumably providential work Western expansion in the United States, an understanding of providence and fitness that justified theologically the extermination of real people and the obliteration of cultures. Kaplan links this public and violent story to the supposedly private and safe sphere of home-life in the Eastern states. For example, the nineteenth-century home in Sudbury, Massachusetts, was patterned in such a way as to support and justify Western expansion toward what would become Sioux City, Iowa; child-rearing in the Sudbury home involved a form of civilizing that patterned the supposedly civilizing efforts on the frontier. What children read in the New England drawing room had much to do with taming the land and peoples to the West. To consider this dynamic in Victorian England allows one to note that social class often then trumped (and now trumps) gender when forging relational alliances. Kingsley's work spans the spheres, as he was an author as well known to children as to their parents, beloved by royalty as well as to those who had only newly acquired a separate nursery. Canon Kingsley worked on multiple fronts, keeping within his purview for civilizing not only working class Englishmen, but the Irish, the Scots, and the inhabitants of the West Indies. His perspective on providence, nationhood, and the proper work of proper men may be helpful for discerning the more obviously 'Manifest' side of this overlapping sphere in conversations today.

2. To Turn Men into Beasts

In 1859 Charles Kingsley was appointed the official chaplain to Queen Victoria. He later served as the private tutor to the Prince of Wales, who would become Edward VII. While there are many theologians whose work has aged better, Kingsley's writing represents his age very well. Over his writing life, Kingsley's commitments moved fluidly from the alleviation of suffering due to poverty, to Christian socialism, to worries about the enervation of English manhood, to the promulgation of Christian Darwinism. The fairy tale realism of *The Water-Babies* narrated the proper import of Darwinism in the English home for English mothers responsible for raising properly dutiful and courageous English sons. Larry Uffelman puts the matter simply by explaining the explicit purpose of the book:

> Kingsley placed the nineteenth-century conflict between science and religion in the context of a fantasy designed to reconcile them by showing continuous development to be the creative principle at work in the world. Through the death, moral growth, and eventual rebirth of the central character, Kinsley links the principles of evolution in the physical world to the growth and maturity of the spiritual being . . . (Uffelman, 1979: 70–71).

In a matching, whimsical tone, the London *Times* reviewed the first bound copy of the book as displaying the truth that 'the pleasantest things of life are as a rule unintelligible to us until we have lost them.' Some of Kingsley's contemporaries suspected that the new science would reshape the pleasantries of English life. To use Kingsley's own words, 'the great Fairy' known as science was 'likely to be the queen of all the fairies for many a year to come' (Kingsley, 1864: 80). It would behoove pastors and parents to note her allure and adapt accordingly. For those wondering whether evolutionary science would technically explain away *awe*, a main ingredient for English naturalism, Kingsley came to the rescue. The 'quiet sober people' who, as *The Times* describes them, 'favoured *Macmillan* [magazine],' might have been 'a little scandalized' by the 'pure nonsense' of *The Water-Babies* when it was first published serially in 1862, but, *The Times* editorial declared, it was 'by no means necessary to understand a book to know whether or not it is agreeable.' The spritely work had a serious function. Kingsley saved Darwinism with fancy. The English home could have its evolution and keep its idealized sense of both Mother Nature and the children who were her gift.

One enchanting exchange in 1892, between Thomas Henry Huxley and his grandson Julian, shows how much the book eventually hit its mark. Huxley had come under particular attention in *The Water-Babies*. Kingsley depicted his friend as just the sort of researcher potentially incapable of wonder, as someone to whom a skeptic would send a water baby for dissection to verify its non-existence. After receiving a letter from Julian, asking whether his 'Grandpater' had seen a water baby, Huxley wrote back

My Dear Julian,
I never could make sure about that Water Baby. I have seen Babies in water and Babies in bottles; but the Baby in the water was not in a bottle and the Baby in the bottle was not in water. My friend who wrote the story of the Water Baby, was a very kind man and very clever. Perhaps he thought I could see as much in the water as he did – There are some people who see a great deal and some who see very little in the same things. When you grow up, I dare say you will be one of the great-deal seers and see things more wonderful than Water Babies where other folks can see nothing . . . (Huxley, 1900: 436–439).

The combination of nursery play and the dedicated perception of the hidden is key to the book's role in securing a place for wondering inquiry. It was able to catch up the well-churched and those determined-to-be-not-churched. Although Julian would grow up to defend theologian Teilhard de Chardin (as well as popular eugenics), he and his grandfather were both known as hearty agnostics (at least). With *The Water-Babies*, Kingsley made imaginative room for wonder and astute, scientific vision, intertwined with the English family.

Kingsley's magically poetic prose splinters with academic summary. But a few features are obvious. First, Darwin's science most comes alive when one has the eyes to see the intricate wonders of the natural world. To quote the epigraph at the beginning of the 1864 edition, all 'unbelieving Sadducees' and the 'less-believing Pharisees' with their 'dull conventionalities,' should leave to her work 'a country muse at ease; to play at leap-frog, if she please, with children and realities' (Kingsley, 1864: 6). Second, the interplay of children and realities is best kept safe from brittle minds with the help of a rather stretchy version of God. As Kingsley puts it using William Wordsworth, 'not in entire forgetfulness and not in utter nakedness' do we come into this world, but 'trailing clouds of Glory,' sent from the divine. For the child who knows this truth, 'the great fairy Science' will do him only good and not harm (80). Third, scientists who are asleep to the marvel that is reality are silly: 'The truth is, that folks' fancy that such and such things cannot be, simply because they have not seen them, is worth no more than the savage's fancy that there cannot be such a thing as a locomotive, because he has not seen one running wild in the forest' (70). To dress up a flying dragon in the name *Pterodactyl* does not erase the fact that it is flying dragon, the same beloved beast that supposedly 'learned men' had been denying for years (69). Finally, the natural world is best seen by someone washed clean, literally and figuratively, of all that soils their bodies and souls. At the opening of the story, Tom sees his reflection in a mirror and turns, angrily, to expunge this 'little black ape' from the room of 'the little white lady' who slept there (28). Tom's realization that *he* is the 'ape' sends him, by a circuitous route, on the under-watery journey to become a man, even a 'great man of science' (308). If he had remained soiled, and thus ape-like, Tom would have ended up like the efts, creatures who 'will not learn their lessons and keep themselves clean' and thus devolve, growing not only 'nasty, dirty, lazy', and 'stupid', but also growing tails (309–310).

As Jessica Straley suggests, Kingsley drew on a notion within one form of Darwinism at the time that the child was 'a living vestige of the species' bestial, pre-human past' (Straley, 2007: 583). I would add that Kingsley was able to layer on top of the evolution of the species a commentary on the hierarchy of supposed types within the species. I first came across the illustration below, by J. Noel Paton, while digging through books in the St Deiniol's library in Wales. Two of the young interns were shelving, and I asked them what they thought of the image. 'Goodness,' one said to the other, 'doesn't he look just like the face on the marmalade advertisement?' She explained that the image had been taken off of the advertisement, but that it had looked like the same sort of caricature. The young women's immediate response was that Tom looks African, more specifically like a *caricature* of an African child, known generally in the United States as a picaninny and in the United Kingdom as a golliwogg (after the erstwhile marmalade advertisement and a series of children's books by Florence Kate Upton from the turn of the century).

THE WATER-BABIES:

A FAIRY TALE FOR A LAND-BABY.

———

CHAPTER I.

" I HEARD a thousand blended notes,
　While in a grove I sate reclined ;
　In that sweet mood when pleasant thoughts
　　Bring sad thoughts to the mind.

" To her fair works did Nature link
　The human soul that through me ran ;
　And much it grieved my heart to think,
　What man has made of man."

WORDSWORTH.

 NCE upon a time there was a little chimney-sweep, and his name was Tom. That is a short name, and you have heard it before, so you will not have much trouble in remembering it. He lived in a great town in the North country, where there were plenty of chimneys to sweep, and plenty of money for Tom

This illustration fits well Kingsley's original prose. Tom is not only dirty from soot, but he is soiled in a way that requires submersion and elevation. When the fairy queen who first attracts Tom to the water tells the other fairies about Tom, she explains, 'He is but a savage now, and like the beasts that perish . . .' (Kingsley, 1864: 55). The transformation of Tom the chimney-sweep is a transformation of evolution from sooty to clean, from savage to civilized, from working to middle class, and from more nearly black to obviously white.

It would be perhaps more proper here to put the word 'black' in such a way as to indicate the suppleness with which Kingsley used the imagery of race. To employ Kaplan's 'manifest destiny' heuristic here, Tom's role carries meaning for an individual child's recapitulation toward maturity and the evolution of humanity toward an industrious, perceptive, clean race of humans. The images of 'beast' and 'savage' indicate both the English child maturing in the nursery, toward good English manhood, and those peoples who in various ways function to mark the rungs on the ladder by which a child is to climb. Seen in this way, Kingsley writes in *The Water-Babies* a story of recapitulation that draws on the work of Ernst Haeckel. According to one of Haeckel's formulations, each individual in a species repeats the earlier stages of the evolution of that species. As in this understanding of evolution, Tom goes through a transition from a newt-like creature, a water baby, toward becoming a human being, a 'land baby.' By Kingsley's retelling, a savage human returns to the watery womb to go again through the process, this time the right way, toward individual maturation. But the story also rehearses Herbert Spencer's understanding of the evolution of human kinds. With a light tone, Kingsley employs the heavy narration of human evolution from those who remain more nearly savage toward those who have evolved to become more nearly English.

There is a pithy discussion on these matters between a fairy named Mrs. Bedonebyasyoudid, Tom, and Tom's friend, Ellie. The fairy sums up the shape of savagery toward civilization in a way that draws on both an inherited and an acquired version of evolutionary theory. Groups fail to evolve when they pass on to future generations their stubborn incapacity to adapt. As the fairy puts it: '. . . there are two sides to every question, and a downhill as well as an uphill road; and, if I can turn beasts into men, I can, by the same laws of circumstance, and selection, and competition, turn men into beasts' (222). The capricious prose of *The Water-Babies* belies the serious work of narrating social evolution in a way serviceable to the spiritual, moral, and physical superiority of English men. If Darwin could intimate that beasts became men, so could Kingsley use this insight to turn men into beasts. The conversation explicitly on evolution occurs when the fairy Bedonebyasyoudid shows them the story of a group of devolving people called the Doasyoulikes. She explains that the division between apes and men has little to do with 'whether the creatures had hippopotamus majors in their brains or not' (a reference to the contemporary debate over the hippocampus). Rather, some groups of men could become 'more apish than the apes of all aperies' (221). The relevant passage warrants extended quotation

> Some of them talked of sowing corn, as their ancestors used to do, before they came into the land of Readymade; but they had forgotten how to make ploughs (they had forgotten even how to make Jews' harps by this time), and had eaten all the seed-corn which they brought out of the land of Hardwork years since . . . So they lived miserably on roots and nuts, and all the weakly little children had great stomachs, and then died.' 'Why,' said Tom, 'they are growing no better than savages.' 'And look how ugly they are all getting,' said Ellie.' 'Yes; when people live on poor vegetables instead of roast beef and plum-pudding, their jaws grow large, and their lips grow coarse, like the poor Paddies who eat potatoes.' And she turned over the next five hundred years. And there they were all living up in trees . . . 'But what great, hulking, broad-shouldered chaps they are,' said Tom ; 'they are a rough lot as ever I saw' . . . And she turned over the next five hundred years. And in that they were fewer still, and stronger, and fiercer; but their feet had changed shape very oddly, for they laid hold of the branches with their great toes, as if they had been thumbs, just as a Hindoo tailor uses his toes to thread his needle. The children were very much surprised, and asked the fairy whether that was her doing. 'Yes, and no,' she said, smiling. 'It was only those who could use their feet as well as their hands who could get a good living . . . 'But there is a hairy one among them,' said Ellie. 'Ah,' said the fairy, 'that will be a great man in his time, and chief of all the tribe.' And, when she turned over the next five hundred years, it was true. For this hairy chief had had hairy children, and they hairier children still . . . all the rest coughed and sneezed, and had sore throats, and went into consumptions, before they could grow up to be men and women. Then the fairy turned over the next five hundred years. And they were fewer still.' 'Why, there is one on the ground picking up roots,' said Ellie, 'and he cannot walk upright.' . . . 'Why,' cried Tom, 'I declare they are all apes.' 'Something fearfully like it, poor foolish creatures,' said the fairy. 'They are grown so stupid now, that they can hardly think . . .' And in the next five hundred years they were all dead and gone, by bad food and wild beasts and hunters; all except one tremendous old fellow with jaws like a jack, who stood full seven feet high; and M. Du Chaillu came up to him, and shot him, as he stood roaring and thumping his breast. And he remembered that his ancestors had once been men, and tried to say, 'Am I not a man and a brother?' but had forgotten how to use his tongue and then he had tried to call for a doctor, but he had forgotten the word for one. So all he said was 'Ubboboo!' and died (217–222).

Tom learns that his fate would have been similar to the devolved creatures, the 'efts,' if he 'had not made up [his] mind to go on this journey, and see the world, like an Englishman' (222). To see the world, like an Englishman, is, for Kingsley, to see the ways that poverty is materially substantive. Here we may read traces of the Christian socialism of

Kingsley's earlier years. But Kingsley has by this point replaced socialism with a version of social Darwinism. The sloth of one generation would come to bear on its extinction. It may be that Kingsley here has partly in mind the saving of Irish boys forced by poverty to crawl down deadly chimneys, but there is also a reverse lesson. Those who are suffering in poverty are animal-like, and, unlike the true animals, they are beastly *by choice*. Linking misery with 'coarse' lips, and potatoes with imminent descent, those who 'live on poor vegetables instead of roast beef and plum-pudding' become responsible for their demise. It is hardly Paul Du Chaillu's fault not to have recognized the resulting savage as his kin. Within a few generations, the savage had become more akin to a gorilla, one of those exotic creatures Du Chaillu shot and stuffed for museums. Those marked as savage have, in Kingsley's story, become something other than 'a man and a brother.'

This reading of humanity may be read as Kingsley's defense of God's providential plan to secure the beauty of creation. The review in the *The Times* of London notes that *The Water-Babies* carries with it Kingsley's account of faith and moral aesthetics, what the review calls 'the foundation of the theology of his school' (*The Times*, 1864: 6). The reviewer then goes on to surmise that this method, 'to ground the scheme of Christian faith upon its beauty', seems 'to some simple minds like balancing a pyramid upon its apex, and then sitting at rest upon its inverted base'. Noting that the 'criterion of moral beauty is painfully uncertain', *The Times* then poses the problem of the 'pious cannibal' who, prior to proper instruction on duty and beauty from an English missionary, believes cannibalism to represent a 'touching reverence for human life' and to be 'an exquisite fulfillment of filial obligations'. What then of truth and beauty, the reviewer asks. How may the reader fasten the connection between Kingsley's particular faith and the abiding truth of providential beauty? Kingsley's answer comes not in sophism but by way of his reliable aim at a receptive audience. He need not answer this gentle criticism from his reviewer, because his story is to be read in the English household. There, it may remain beautifully true (now as a Puffin Classic). His is not a clearly logical progression made up of what might be read as culturally transferable, universal fact. The line the review notes to be vital speaks with a particularly English voice for a particular purpose: 'It is so beautiful it must be true', they repeat, and in this they catch the genius of Kingsley's writing.

The Times review makes this point in a style that mimics *The Water-Babies* when they connect Tom and Ellie's story to the mid-nineteenth century English fascination with sea anemones:

> But when Mr. Gosse wrote books to describe the wonders which he saw on the coast of Devonshire and at Tenby, and Mr. Lewes exchanged biography, metaphysics, novels, and plays for sea-side studies, and another popular

author published *Glaucus; or, the Wonders of the Shore*, and Germans wrote fat books on the sea, and insisted that Germany ought to be a naval Power and Kiel a German port, and Frenchmen wrote lively books and built La Gloire, and every young lady had her aquarium, and maiden aunts carried about rare actinia in jam-pots, to the fearful punishment of pilfering pages fond of sweets, Tom and Ellie could no longer remain in obscurity, and their delightful history was accordingly written (*The Times*, 6).

The style here is indicative of Kingsley's poetic intellect. The Crimean War is connected to sea-side studies is related to Romance is linked to every young lady, her maiden aunt, jam-pots and pilfering pages. Kingsley uses a rhetorical microscope to focus in on a bit of a sea creature, moves a step out to place the sea creature within a young lady's home, and then takes up a telescope to gain perspective on the grand, political questions of his day. Sweets and ocean vessels are of a piece, pasted together in as delightful a form as Lewis Carroll's Walrus's promised discussion of shoes and ships and sealing wax and cabbages and kings. Mr Gosse and Mr Lewes and their like, men who aptly 'see a great deal' (to borrow Grandpater Huxley's words to Julian) enter the parlour and the nursery by way of Kingsley's tale. Those little boys who learn properly to shine their shoes may someday 'see the world, as an Englishman'. Kingsley's moral aesthetic is thus essentially English.

3. Painful Facts

This pastiche of the everyday domestic and the broadly global is apparent also in *Macmillan's Magazine*, the same publication featuring *The Water-Babies* serially and that, within a decade, presented Kingsley's seminal essay, 'The Natural Theology of the Future'. It is worth noting the previous issue of the publication, as an indication of the intersection *Macmillan's* represents. In February of 1871, the editors featured an essay on the necessity of fortifying London (complete with diagram and budget); a sonnet encouraging that 'he who soareth singeth all the way'; another installment of 'Patty', a romantic/morality novel by Katherine Macquoid; an encomium to the martyr for science, Giordano Bruno; the second part of a travel diary from France; a nifty historical essay on secret codes; and an essay by Francis Galton on 'Gregariousness in Cattle and in Men'. Galton's essay is itself a collage of matters 'abroad' and familial. Having had the 'fortune' of 'an intimate knowledge of certain classes of gregarious animals' – including 'the urgent need of the camel for the close companionship of his fellows' – Galton seeks to apply his observation of 'wild' oxen in Africa, their being apparently of a different kind altogether than the 'English ox'. (The English oxen are, he explains, 'far less gregarious'.) Galton introduces his article thus:

I propose, in these pages, to discuss a curious and apparently anomalous group of base moral instincts and intellectual deficiencies, to trace their analogies in the world of brutes, and to examine the conditions through which they have been involved. I speak of the slavish aptitudes, from which the leaders of men, and the heroes and the prophets, are exempt, but which are irrepressible elements in the disposition of average men . . . I shall endeavour to prove that the slavish aptitudes, whose expression in man I have faintly but sufficiently traced are the direct consequence of his gregarious nature, which, itself, is a result both of his primaeval barbarism and of his subsequent forms of civilization (Galton, 1871: 353).

The magazine, appearing as it would on the library table of the right sorts of homes, thus conveyed the connections between 'the clannish, fighting habits of our forefathers' and the 'savages' living in the region of Africa inhabited by the gregarious oxen. The 'black population of Africa' suffers in a way formally similar to the apparently brutish oxen, which in turn have a lesson to teach readers in 'the present day' about how 'blind instincts' toward sociality are continually 'destroying the self-reliant, and therefore the nobler, races of men'. As Galton closes with his summons for a proper breeding that would encourage 'vigorous, self-reliant men' in England, the magazine features a new essay, on 'England's Place Among the Nations,' by a 'military contributor'.

The editors began the next issue with 'The Natural Theology of the Future' (Kingsley, 1871). Kingsley first establishes the Anglican Church's place among the religions, showing that the 'three greatest natural theologians' (Berkeley, Butler and Paley) are representative of their Church, a Church that is 'eminently rational as well as scriptural.' Yet, he warns, those inheriting Wesley and Whitfield have gone over to a form of sung theology that verges on the irrational: 'There lingers about them a savour of the old monastic theory, that this earth is the devil's planet, fallen, accursed, goblin haunted, needing to be exorcised at every turn before it is useful or even safe for man' (Kingsley, 1871: 370). With the small 'exception of that first curse,' the 'voice of God expressed in facts' is evident 'according to the laws of Nature' (371). That small exception, the exception of the curse, is sufficiently small to make, as Kingsley reads it, a theology of grace indistinguishable from a theology of nature, for, 'the God of Nature and the God of Grace are one'. A natural theology fit for the new science may see that 'the God who satisfies our conscience ought more or less to satisfy our reason also'. Kingsley warns that Bishop Butler's compromise (as he reads it) is necessarily renewed in every age, for, not to compromise is to risk extinction: 'for if in any age or country the God who seems to be revealed by Nature seems different from the God who is revealed by the then popular religion, then that God, and the religion which tells of that God, will gradually cease to be believed in' (370). Religion must evolve.

Developments with the new science tell us is that 'natural facts' are still trustworthy to guide the work of man, as the 'lord of creation'. This lordship is what allows man to repeal the 'exception' that is the curse. Through godly gardening, man is able to 'root up the thorns and thistles'. Kingsley advises *Macmillan's* readership, 'keep your land clean, then assuredly you will grow fruit-trees and not thorns, wheat and not thistles.' From small to large matters, this fact of nature must guide. While this may sound harsh, Kingsley reminds readers that Scripture 'reveals a God not merely of love, but of sternness'. It is at this point that Kingsley elucidates the natural theology of *The Water-Babies*. If natural theologians are going to keep apace, they must bring these natural and Scriptural facts together to consider 'questions of Embryology and questions of Race' (373). The preponderance of the words 'beget and bring forth' show the importance in Scripture of the scientific study of embryology. Thus, the new theology will need to address questions of ontogeny and phylogeny (that is, Haeckel's questions). But, in order to do so well, theologians will need to risk the disapprobation of some, some who think that the new finding 'endangers the modern notions of democratic equality'.

There are those who fear the new findings, those who fear that 'it may be proved that the negro is not a man and brother'. Yet, Kingsley explains, according to 'Mr. Darwin', 'science has proved that he must be such'. Polygenesis thus disproven, monogenesis now established, how is the natural theologian of the future to think about 'the negro'? For, as Kingsley explains, 'the one fact of the unique distribution of the hair in all races of human beings' is 'full moral proof that they had all had one common ancestor'. Common ancestry does not resolve the question of race. Rather, as Kingsley explains,

Physical science is proving more and more the immense importance of Race; the importance of hereditary powers, hereditary organs, hereditary habits, in all organized beings, from the lowest plant to the highest animal. She is proving more and more the omnipresent action of the differences between races; how the more favored race (she cannot avoid using the epithet) exterminates the less favored, or at least expels it, and forces it, under penalty of death, to adapt to new circumstances; and, in a word, that competition between every race and every individual of that race, and reward according to deserts, is (as far as we can see) a universal law of living things. And she says – for the facts of history prove it – that as it is among the races of plants and animals, so it has been unto this day among the races of men (373).

Instead of arguing for the supremacy of science over revelation, Kingsley argues that, when read through proper spectacles, the 'painful facts' of science are evident at the heart of Scripture itself. In so doing, Kingsley uses the potent rhetoric of Christian supersessionism:

The natural theology of the future must take count of these tremendous and even painful facts: and she may take count of them. For Scripture has taken count of them already. . . . Its sense of the reality and importance of descent is so intense, that it speaks of a whole tribe or whole family by the name of its common ancestor, and the whole nation of the Jews is Israel to the end. And if I be told this is true of the Old Testament, but not of the New, I must answer, What? Does not St. Paul hold the identity of the whole Jewish race with Israel their forefather, as strongly as any prophet of the Old Testament? And what is the central historic fact, save one, of the New Testament, but the conquest of Jerusalem – the dispersion, all but destruction of a race, not by miracle, but by invasion, because found wanting when weighed in the stern balances of natural and social law?

Gentlemen, think of this . . . by the light which our Lord's parables, His analogies between the physical and social constitution of the world afford – and consider whether those awful words, fulfilled then and fulfilled so often since – 'The kingdom of God shall be taken from you, and given to a nation bringing forth the fruits hereof' – may not be the supreme instance, the most complex development, of a law which runs through all created things, down to the moss which struggles for existence on the rock? (374)

Tying together the 'importance of race' and the superiority of Christianity, Kingsley effectively reformulates the tale of Roman dispersion as a tale of natural law. A people incapable of winning the struggle of existence is replaced by a superior. The 'central historic fact' of the 'destruction of a race' is congruent with the 'stern balances of natural and social law' now established by the new science.

There is still hope, 'if not to the virtue of all-embracing charity' (indeed), then for the 'virtues of self-sacrifice and patriotism'. Here Kingsley shapes the question of divine grace into a serviceable endorsement of human progress, wrought through the hard work of a superior people:

Do I say that this is all? That man is merely a part of Nature, the puppet of circumstances and hereditary tendencies? That brute competition is the one law of his life? That he is doomed for ever to be the slave of his own needs, enforced by an internecine struggle for existence? God forbid. I believe not only in Nature, but in Grace. I believe this is man's fate only as long as he sows to the flesh, and of the flesh reaps corruption. I believe that if he will *Strive upward, working out the beast, And let the ape and tiger die*; if he will be even as wise as the social animals . . . then he will rise to a higher sphere; towards that kingdom of God of which it is written, 'He that dwelleth in love, dwelleth in God, and God in him' (374).

There is no need for Kingsley to prove 'marks of design' within the new science. 'If the heavens do not declare to you the glory of God, nor the firmament show you His handy-work,' he explains, 'then our poor arguments about them will not show it.' To many of the magazine's readers, it will seem 'self-evident' that 'wherever there is arrangement, there must be an arranger . . . wherever an organization, there must be an organizer.' There is hardly a need for proving a design, for the natural theology of the future is here designed to justify a particular arrangement, a particular organization, and a particular set of stewards for bringing into the world an ever fitter people. Employing Alfred Lord Tennyson, Kingsley shows the usefulness of Darwinian theology in an age marked for colonial expansion. By climbing above, occupying the newly distributed 'kingdom of God,' those within 'the more favored race' may distinguish themselves not only from moss, ape, and tiger but from those peoples whose failure calls for tutelage and/or dispersion. If only 'we clergy' will 'summon up the courage' to tell this story, the 'unknown x' left in the new science may be effectively replaced by 'The Breath of God; The Spirit who is The Lord and Giver of Life' (378).

4. Lastly, To See the World as an Englishman?

Tom has the courage to go on his journey, and evolve to be able to 'view the world' as an Englishman, the fairy tells him. One of Kingsley's last works is *At Last: A Christmas in the West Indies*, which he dedicated to Sir Arthur Gordon, the former governor of Trinidad who had recently been named governor of Mauritius. The book is illustrated with images such as 'Gulf-Weed', 'Sea-Side Grape', 'The Little Ant-Eater', as well as 'Coolies Cooking' and 'A Coolie Family' (Kingsley, 1887). Kingsley's own journey to see the world involved his attempt to sort through the natural laws of flora, fauna, and people. Predictably, he must see the 'brutality' contrasted with the 'refinement,' the 'savage' compared with the 'gentleman'. The 'brutality' of 'negro' coal barging offends what he names as a belief that 'all God's human children may be somewhen, somewhere, somehow, reformed into His likeness' (Kingsley, 1887: 21). (He is not offended by the treatment of the workers, but by the way that the system 'enables Negros of the lowest class to earn enough in one day to keep them in idleness'.) Troubled by what he perceives to be 'the mere excitability and coarseness of half-civilized creatures', Kingsley declares the workers to be excused from 'deliberate depravity'.

Yet, in his last years, many days of sea voyage away from home, Kingsley also receives what he perceives to be a sort of grace. This had been a dream that he symbolically names as having lasted forty years: 'From childhood I had studied their Natural History, their charts, their Romances, and alas! their Tragedies; and now, at last, I was about to compare books with facts . . .' (Kingsley, 1887: 1). The *facts* are all mixed up, however, as Kingsley meets a 'little brown child' who has been renamed at his Christening for this eager, visiting Englishman (362). A little later, while watching a local spectacle, thinking 'what a strange creature man is,' Kingsley sees an 'old gentleman seemingly absorbed in the very same reflection.' His 'aquiline, high-cheek-boned features' prompt Kingsley to assume him 'an old Scot', but, as the man 'turned his head deliberately round to me', he sees to his 'astonishment' the 'features of a Chinese'. As they look one another 'full in the face', Kingsley 'fancied' that they 'understood' one another about 'many things'. Noting that 'the Chinese visage is unfathomable', Kingsley wonders whether the man is 'an honest man and true', or if he is hiding something. Kingsley decides to take 'the more charitable judgment', being 'weak enough to believe that I should know the man and like him' (368).

By one reading, this fancy is no less quixotic than *The Water-Babies* and no less dangerous in its romantic epistemology than the future's natural theology. But, by another reading, this is a crack in the edifice of the solid, English gentleman. Reading this story through the blessing of new wine, one might interpret Kingsley as barely glimpsing, as in the blink of his eye, what it might mean, eventually, for the dispersed 'savages' to enter and inhabit the manifest world of Great Britain. By this (less than fully virile) reworking of Kingsley, it is 'weakness' that must come to bear on his inheritors if he is to get his wish – a wish that, someday, the 'great and worthy exertions' by which English missionaries have converted 'the Negro and the Heathen,' will be returned home to England. In other words (taking only a bit of liberty) Kingsley wished for his grandchildren that Christians from the previously colonized world might bring a vital, Christian word back to bear on a church that thought itself previously to be providentially fit to spread. Those who had been the objects of English perception and subjection would, he hoped, send their own missionaries back, even to 'convert the London Season itself' (371). (I would add here that they might, perhaps, even return to convert dear Cambridge.)

Here, at the end of a historical sort of essay, I would suggest a full, moral – theological, stop. Kingsley's hope at the end of his life – for receptive collaboration with Christians from mission worlds abroad – begs for difficult reckoning with the implications of his influence as a Christian Darwinist for the British Empire. The possibility Kingsley glimpsed *at last*, in the West Indies, was one of Christian truth over cultural presumption, beckoning toward a kinship that has much less to do with evolutionary biology or a muscular military and more to do with Baptism. This possibility will likely raise more sneers from Britain's cultured despisers. Yet it may still be true. The strangers Kingsley encountered in *At Last* might, as he put it, 'assist [England] to take the beam out of its own eye, in return for having taken the mote out of theirs.' Reader, might it be so?

4

Reading the Bible after Darwin: Creation and a Culture of Restraint

Ellen F. Davis

Till we can become divine we must be content to be human, lest in our hurry for a change we sink to something lower. (Anthony Trollope, *Barchester Towers*)

The outraged incredulity that was the immediate and widespread reaction among churchgoers to the publication of *The Origin of Species* was famously articulated in the pronouncement of Samuel Wilberforce, Bishop of Oxford, that the 'principle of natural selection is incompatible with the Word of God'. In 1864, 11,000 clergy signed the Oxford Declaration, denouncing all who denied that the whole Bible was God's Word, and affirming that the wicked would suffer everlasting punishment (Greenslade, 1963: 260, 263). Similarly, if more colloquially, the American evangelist Billy Sunday stated that any minister who believed in evolution must be 'a stinking skunk, a hypocrite and a liar' (Gould, 1999: 63). In many quarters the fervor yielded to calm acceptance within a couple of generations, although the 'Bible versus biology' question has recently attracted debaters on both sides.

For many biblical scholars such as myself, the incompatibility of evolutionary theory and the biblical account of creation has never arisen as a serious question, probably because we imbibed as intellectual mother's milk the understanding that Genesis is teaching theology, not natural history. It is teaching about the human place in the world and the order that obtains between creatures and their Creator, not about the origin of species in any scientific sense. That Genesis offers a poetic and spiritual account rather than a precise naturalistic one is not a new insight; already in the fourth century, Augustine deemed it 'a disgraceful and dangerous thing for an infidel to hear a Christian, presumably giving the meaning of Holy Scripture, talking nonsense' about natural phenomena, adding that 'we should take all means to prevent such an embarrassing situation, in which people show up vast ignorance in a Christian and laugh it to scorn' (Augustine, 1982: 42–43).

My purpose in this essay is not to add fresh fuel to the Bible-versus-biology debate. Rather, I intend to consider how a Christian sense of the human place in the world may be clarified, and our sense of responsibility deepened, by reading the Bible in the light of modern biology and ecology, as those disciplines are informed by Darwin's thought. I have chosen my words carefully in this last sentence. It will be evident that the biological principles that inform this essay are a degree or two removed from Darwin himself; one might say they have 'evolved' through the generations of evolutionary biology that stem from him. Certainly at the core of Darwin's argument is the exactitude of the fit between an organism and its environment; he speaks repeatedly of the struggle for existence within the limits of that space, of 'competition for food and residence' (Darwin, 1928: 78). However, while Darwin emphasizes competition between related species and especially between members of a single species, generations of scientists and naturalists since Aldo Leopold have spoken also of the biotic pyramid, the 'community' of diverse creatures that share a territory, be it local or up to the scale of the planet. Land is conceived not just as space for competition but as 'a fountain of energy flowing through a circuit of soils, plants, and animals' (Leopold, 1966: 253).

Again, Darwin has taught us that humans share a complex history with other life forms, and that all are subject to the same laws; when species exceed the limits of their environment on a regular basis, they die. When the environment changes drastically, species have a chance – offered in a short window of time – to adapt, to change along with it, or else they become history. But we have very recently come to recognize, and in a way different than Darwin himself could possible recognize it, just how fully all this applies to us humans. As terrestrial ecologist Peter Vitousek has recently observed, now for the first time the human species as a whole must find the will to make a drastic change in our behavior in order that life on our planet may continue to be viable and to some degree lovely (lecture, The Land Institute, June 2003). So what we may yet be able to learn from Darwin concerns the immediate moral urgency to adapt our culture to meet the limits, opportunities, and demands that are built into the world. Reflecting upon Darwin's insights, naturalist Barry Lopez observes that 'a cultural exemption from biological imperatives remains in the realm of science fiction' (Lopez, 2001: 41). A Christian should say, too, that it remains in the realm of bad theology. That is the single best reason for theologians and biblical scholars, along with naturalists and biologists, to see how Darwin's work may shine some light on our own.

Although I write as an amateur to the scientific discussion, central to all my work as a biblical interpreter is the conviction that good readings of Scripture and good readings of material reality are mutually illuminating. If each is sufficiently complex, then it will enhance our appreciation of the other. Evolutionary biologist Kenneth Miller observes that scientists have, ironically, strengthened opposition to evolutionary theory by their own widespread failure to acknowledge that science and religion have different domains, and therefore scientific knowledge does not eclipse religion (Miller, 1999: 165–91). Correspondingly, opposition may have been fueled by the failure of theologians over the last two centuries to offer sufficiently *material* readings of the Bible and the religious traditions that stem from it, the failure to help believers bring their religious imagination into fruitful interaction with the sophisticated geophysical and cosmological readings of the world that scientists have produced in the same period of time. We need fresh and complex readings of biblical texts that take account of our deeper scientific knowledge, as well as of the material facts of modern industrial culture. This would move us some distance toward the goal envisioned by Stephen Jay Gould, of 'a respectful, even loving, concordat between the magisteria of science and religion' (Gould, 1999: 9).

1. The World in Our Hearts

I begin with three points of correlation between the (broadly speaking) Darwinian view of natural history and the biblical view of material reality. There are multiple angles to 'the biblical view of material reality', some of them divergent, but the points I highlight here represent a wide and probably total consensus. Within the canon, they are grounded initially in the creation accounts of Genesis, and developed further by many texts in both Testaments of the Christian Bible.

First, both modern science and the Bible say that *the world is ordered as a complex and internally dynamic system*, or a set of interlocking systems. The earth as we know it came into being by processes of change that are consistent over both geological and historical time. A picture of the world's internal dynamism begins to emerge already in the first chapter of Genesis, when God proclaims: 'Let the earth "grass forth" grass, *tadshe' ha'aretz deshe'*' (1:11). The writer apparently coins a Hebrew neologism in order to capture that unprecedented moment when a creature, the earth, first participates in the life-giving creativity of God. Moving to nearly the opposite end of the canon, we encounter the different though complementary assertion in the letter to the Colossians that Christ is 'the firstborn of all creation', that all things have been created in and for Christ 'and in him all things hold together' (Col. 1:15–17).

These are some of the many strong biblical affirmations that the material processes of this world are meaningful. That does not mean they are (any more than historical processes) either predetermined or transparent to God's purposes. Certainly they are not so on a micro scale. Unpredictability – call it what you will: freedom, mystery, wildness – is built into the material *and* historical processes of the world. This is hardly a new observation. Qohelet, the ascerbic wisdom teacher whose voice we hear throughout the book of Ecclesiastes, cautions that 'time and chance happen to all [creatures]' (9:11). Every human being, no matter how strong or discerning, is in this way no different from the poor animals. 'Like the fish caught in an evil snare, and like the birds caught in the net' (9:12), we are overtaken by circumstances in ways that may be traceable and explicable, but not closely predictable. Deadly risk is fundamental to the enterprise of life for every creature.

Kenneth Miller offers a biologist's perspective on God's design of the material world. 'On the larger scale, he made the averaged behavior of matter sensible and predictable', creating an ordered world. But at the same time God introduced into the fine structure of the universe 'the multiple effects of quantum indeterminacy'. As a result, 'we cannot uncritically extrapolate the details of the present backwards to learn the past' (Miller, 1999: 251). The future is open, contingent; this makes our present choices significant, despite the operation of chance. Indeed, 'we are inextricably locked into the present', into the world as it has been given to us – that is, as it has evolved for us to work in and with.

Qohelet, living in Jerusalem during the third century (BC), saw a created world and a human situation not essentially different from what Miller describes. The very first thing he notes in his book is the earth's repeatable material processes:

> A generation comes and a generation goes,
> but the earth stands forever.
> The sun rises and the sun goes down . . .
> All the streams go to the sea,
> yet the sea is not full.
> To the place that the streams go,
> they just keep going (Eccles. 1:4–5, 7).

Like Miller, Qohelet believes that work is worth doing well – 'All that your hand finds to do, do it with all your strength' (9:10) – even though we have far less assurance of outcomes than we could wish (8:17).

God 'has even put the world (*'olam*) into their hearts—and in such a way that no human can know the work that God has done from beginning to end' (3:11). In a book of enigmatic statements, this is one of the least transparent, yet from a Darwinian perspective, it is also one of the most intriguing. The Hebrew word *'olam* means something indefinitely extended in time or space: 'world', perhaps, but also 'eternity'. Moreover, an identical verbal root means 'hiddenness'. I suspect that Qohelet, a subtle teacher and writer, may have intended all three meanings. God has inscribed within us the vastness of the world, and also its ultimate unknowability – lest with all our striving to know, we be tempted to forget that creation remains a mystery. Ironically, there are probably as many creationists as evolutionists who, having lost sight of the boundless mystery of what God has done, treat the material world as a mere datum in an argument, and a repository of resources to be mined for their convenience.

The greatest biblical exposé and exploration of the unknowability that is built into creation is found in God's speeches to Job from the whirlwind (Job 38 – 41). God shows Job that the world is strangely and beautiful ordered, although from a human perspective it is often dangerous and distressing. Job's long struggle, both emotional and intellectual, and his final acceptance of life on God's terms, even to the extent of consenting to bring more children into this unpredictable world (Job 42:13–15) – these testify to the common and deeply painful experience of encountering a cosmic order that is not conformed to human understanding, and does not center on us. Rather, as Job comes to see, God is the orienting center of the created order.

2. Fitting Our Place

A second point of correlation between modern science and the Bible is their affirmation that *humans occupy a distinct but not separate place* within the created order. Darwin says that all species, human and non-human, have some common (if remote) history; we have emerged by the same processes, broadly speaking. Surprisingly to most modern readers, the two strands of composite creation story (Gen. 1:1–2:4a and Gen. 2:4b–25) make the same point, each in its own way. Genesis 1 recounts that humans alone are created in God's image: we are charged to exercise 'dominion', though a better translation might be 'skillful mastery among' the various non-human creatures (Davis, 2009, 55). Yet despite our unique character and responsibility, the story makes it clear that we are closely linked with the other creatures. On the sixth day of creation, humans receive the famous blessing to be fruitful and multiply (Gen. 1:28) – a blessing nearly identical with that which the creatures of sea and sky received on the fifth day: 'Be fruitful and multiply, and fill the waters in the seas' (v. 22). The coincidence of those blessings should teach us, if not humility, then at least inter-species respect. The fruitfulness of birds and fish precedes and conditions our own; we cannot exercise legitimate mastery in any way that inhibits their thriving – a sobering reflection in this Sixth Great Age of Species Extinction.

Likewise, Genesis 2 affirms that humans are unique among the species. God brings the animals to the *adam* (human) to see what he might call them, but finds among them no *'ezer ke-negdo*, 'strength corresponding to him' (v. 20; for this translation, see Friedman, 2001, 19). From the perspective of the story, humans are radically unique, yet not separate. With the inspiration of divine breath, the human becomes *nefesh h ayah*, 'a living being' (v. 7) – exactly the same term that characterizes all the animals at the end of the first creation account (Gen. 1:30). We share with them a part of our core identity before God.

The fact that humans and non-human life forms cohere in the eyes of God is underscored later in Genesis and in other strands of the biblical witness. The following moments are noteworthy but far from exhaustive:

- God's covenant with Noah's family and 'every living being (*nefesh hayah*) that is with [them] for perpetual generations' (Gen. 9:12).
- The psalmist's striking exclamation: 'Human and animal you save, O LORD!' (Ps. 36:6, Heb. 7) – an important corrective to the assumption, common among Protestant Christians at least, that God is exclusively in the business of saving individual *human* souls.
- Paul's declaration of allegiance to 'the gospel that has been proclaimed to every *creature* (*ktisis*) under heaven' (Col. 1:23). The surprisingly inclusive word *ktisis* continues the strong witness of Israel's Scriptures, affirming that God in Christ is committed to furthering the well-being of every creature.

So both Testaments of the Christian Bible affirm that humans and non-human creatures alike participate in salvation and in covenant relationship, are recipients of divine blessing, and are even addressed by the gospel of Jesus Christ. These are the core realities of creaturely existence *vis-à-vis* God; it is just to infer that the points of commonality between us and the non-human creatures are of greater significance than the points of difference.

Characteristically, the starkest canonical statement of that commonality comes from Qohelet, whose book shows that he had reflected deeply on the first chapters of Genesis. Consistently and resolutely, he bursts bubbles of human pride in our *absolute* uniqueness and presses us to embrace a realistic, earthy faith. This is his summary statement on our material existence:

> So I decided, with respect to humankind, to dissociate them from the divine beings and recognize that they are really animals. For the fate of humans

and of animals is a single fate: as dies one, so dies the other; all have one lifebreath. There is no superiority of the human over the animal, in that all are a fleeting vapor. All go to one place:

> Everything came from the dust,
> and everything is going back to the dust. (Eccles. 3:18–20)

It is hard to imagine that Qohelet would be fazed, were he to be introduced to the modern evidence for evolution.

A third point of correlation between the Bible and the Darwinian perspective is the most surprising: both say or imply that the fit between a creature – *Homo sapiens* included – and its place in the created order has much to do with the act of eating. From a biological perspective, there is truth to William Ralph Inge's observation that 'The whole of nature . . . is a conjugation of the verb to eat, in the active and passive' ('Confessio Fidei', in W. Inge, 1926: 56). Survival depends directly on eating enough and not too much, from one generation to the next. Although it is little noted by most theologians, the first chapters of Genesis in several places take up the matter of how the creatures, human and non-human, are to eat: from what God has provided, and within the limits that God has set.

Immediately after the humans are charged to exercise mastery among the creatures, God adds this specification:

> Here, I have given you [plural] all the seed-bearing plants that are on the face of the whole earth, and all trees that have fruit bearing seed – for you [all] it shall be, for eating. And for every animal of the earth and for every bird of the sky and for every creeping thing upon the earth that has in it living being – all the green plant growth [I have given] for eating. (Gen. 1:29–30).

One might ask: Why does this even need to be said? Animals, including humans, are not likely to omit eating for lack of explicit divine instruction. However, coming as it does right after the creation and blessing of humans as the creature made in the image of God, this notice is the first indication of what God expects from us, namely regard for what we now call food chains. It is an oblique acknowledgement that humans are the only creatures that can recognize the dynamics of the so-called 'natural' order and must consciously keep their place in it, and also observe the place and the wellbeing of the other creatures. We above all other creatures must keep our place, for our capacity to violate it is uniquely destructive of the whole created order – something of which the biblical writers were no less aware than we are now. Surely then, part of our proper mastery or dominion is to honor the food chains and thus preserve the biological integrity of the earth.

It might be noted that the original food chains, as Genesis delineates them, were vegetarian – indeed, vegan. The so-called Priestly tradition that is responsible for the great poem of creation in Genesis 1 seems to envision a Beginning characterized by perfect harmony among all the creatures, in which all ate without bloodshed. Within the Priestly tradition, that situation changed after the flood, when the animals, birds, and fish were given into human hands, with dread for their lives – although notably, still in the context of divine blessing and the charge to 'be fruitful and multiply and fill the earth' (Gen. 9:1–4; cf. Gen. 1:28). The picture of bloodless coexistence among the species emerges clearly only one more time in the Bible, in Isaiah's vision of some future time when 'the earth shall be filled with the knowledge of YHWH, as the waters cover the sea' (Isa. 11:6–9; cf. 65:25).

However, the Bible nowhere represents vegetarianism as a general ideal for contemporary culture, the world as we know it now. The *discriminate* killing of animals is represented as acceptable to God as early as Genesis 4, when Abel presents a sacrifice from his flock (v. 4). The story (probably from the Yahwistic tradition) does not explain why on this occasion God 'looked upon' the meat and not upon Cain's grain offering, with the well-known disastrous consequence. At the least, one could say that farmers are from the outset not idealized, nor presumed to be free of a propensity to violence. Further, no clear distinction can be drawn between meat offered for sacrifice and ordinary meat, in an Israelite context. While Abel may not have lived to eat his offering, most meat sacrifices in Israel were subsequently consumed by both priests and worshippers (e.g. Prov. 7:14). Eating meat was a relative rarity for most Israelites, and so it is from a biblical perspective an occasion of celebration and a reason for thanksgiving, as shown by the Psalmist's very explicit expression of oral gratification:

> As with rich meat ['suet and fat'] you have satisfied me,
> and with jubilant lips my mouth offers praise (Ps. 63:5, v. 6 Heb.).

Nonetheless, the fact that the Bible does not argue for vegetarianism does not mean that it has no challenge or guidance to offer regarding our own society's practices of meat production and consumption, which are widely acknowledged to be a major driver of ecological degradation and biodiversity loss worldwide. They contribute both directly, through the poisonous rivers of effluents produced by Confined Animal Feeding Operations (CAFOs), and indirectly, through the razing of forests to plant soy and maize for livestock feed. The means of meat production are unsustainable, and meanwhile the demand for it has grown steadily around the world, on an average of 37 per cent each decade from 1980 to 2005 (Speth, 2008: 50). In contrast to this picture of industrial-scale slaughter and consumption, the food laws of the Old Testament – which many Christians view as devoid of religious value – show a completely different regard for animal life as the gift of God. Only 'clean' animals, birds, and fish may be eaten (Lev. 11, Deut. 14:3–20), practically restricting consumption to a few species in each category. Eating flesh is further restricted by the fact that in the Priestly tradition, animals must be brought to the sanctuary for slaughter (17:3–7), and both the Priestly and the Deuteronomic traditions forbid the eating of blood, 'for the life of all flesh is its blood' (Lev. 17:14; cf. Deut. 12:16). Thus the Bible consistently affirms that eating the flesh of another creature is a covenantal act, a privilege granted by God that must be exercised with mindfulness and restraint.

3. Nature and Culture: Knowledge within Limits

In light of the prominence of God's provision of food in the first chapter of the Bible, it is likely more than coincidence that the first violation of the divine will in the Garden of Eden (Gen. 3) is a matter of eating beyond the limits God has set. Although most biblical critics would argue that Genesis 3 comes from a different strand of tradition than Genesis 1, they cohere within the present form of the book. The Eden story builds upon the established fact that God has provided food sufficient for all. The humans have multiple sources of food, but nonetheless a limit is set on how they may legitimately meet their need: 'From every tree of the garden you are free to eat, but from the Tree of Knowledge of Good and Evil you may not eat—for on the day that you eat from it, you shall surely die' (Gen. 2:16–17). However, the humans – and both woman and man are fully implicated here – allow themselves to be persuaded that God's instruction is misguided, that the tree is indeed 'good to eat' and even 'desirable for achieving enlightenment', or 'success' (3:6), and so they eat as they please. Thus they declare themselves independent of God's judgment about what is good, imagining that they are smart enough to know and get what is best for themselves.

The results are disastrous, even if the man and woman do not die on that day. The fact that they live on, into the bitter consequences of their actions, is part of the realism with which the Bible characteristically represents the human situation. Eating is the fundamental cultural act for all humans; with that forbidden consumption, humans begin to drive a wedge between themselves and nature: the ground sprouts thorns and briars (Gen. 3:18). There sets in a separation between human culture and the immediate presence of God: from that point on, humans will pursue their existence outside Eden. Further, when the humans eat against the rules, they sow the first seeds of discord between themselves: blame enters the world (3:12–13), followed by asymmetrical power relations between man and woman (3:16) and, in the next generation, by homicidal violence (4:1–16).

The story of Cain the farmer hints at further separation between nature and culture. The first murderer is also the founder of the first city, which he names Hanokh, 'Culture' (Gen. 4:17). Biblical narrative most often uses indirection to help us draw connections. We might legitimately infer that the biblical writers themselves were aware that agriculture, the activity whereby human culture interacts most deeply with natural systems, is not inherently innocent. But it may have been reserved for our own generation to realize the full implications of what Genesis has to say about eating beyond the bounds that God has set. According to the 2005 UN Millennium Ecosystem Assessment, agriculture likely constitutes the 'largest threat to biodiversity and ecosystem function of any single human activity' (Millennium, 2005: 777). The global industrial food system has for a short time – a little over half a century – permitted humans to eat in a way that far exceeds the limits of the planet. However, food prices that are skyrocketing as I write indicate that we are now coming to the bumpy end of the cheap ride that Richard Manning has dubbed 'catastrophic agriculture'. Our ride has been fueled by petroleum and chemicals, by a high cultural tolerance for soil degradation, forest clearance, and unsustainable water consumption, and by a willingness to change the genetic composition of our food without heed for the consequences, which are still mostly unknown. We humans, who according to Genesis are meant to observe and maintain the dynamic integrity of the 'garden' God has planted (Gen. 2:15), have arrived at a place where we must recognize our dominant cultural practices, as represented in our largest and most essential industry, as a threat that the planet will no longer tolerate.

Farmer and evolutionary biologist Wes Jackson founded the Land Institute in Salina, Kansas, in order to pursue Natural Systems Agriculture, which represents an alternative and genuinely new paradigm for agriculture. The aim of NSA is to develop a model of agriculture that works like an ecosystem. Specifically, the model is based on the cultivation of perennial grains grown in polyculture – in contrast to the practice, standard over the ten to twelve millennia of agriculture, of growing annual grains in monoculture. 'Scientists at work in the dominant paradigm either ignore Nature or seek to subdue Nature' (Jackson, 2000: 15). Natural Systems Agriculture, by contrast, 'embrac[es] nature as our standard or measure', as 'the Tree of Life' (16); it assumes that natural systems will work over *the long term* more safely and productively than any industrial innovation. In language that reflects the story in Genesis 3, Jackson observes: 'Life would be easier if the implementation of a technology or practice allowed us to live or drop dead immediately . . . Use methyl bromide on a crop one time and you die . . . Because we don't drop dead, we allow ourselves to draw our boundaries of consideration much narrower than the boundaries of causation' (15).

Jackson finds a basic coherence between the biblical creation story and what he calls a Deep Darwinian worldview, because together they serve to help us extend the 'boundaries of consideration'. That is, they remind us how complex is the interaction between humans and the natural systems in which we are embedded and upon which we purport to exercise mastery. Underlying Jackson's appeal to a Deep Darwinian perspective is the principle that a plant or animal is adapted, in essential yet often hidden ways, to the particular conditions of its place within a natural system (cf. Darwin, 1928: 78–79). He comments:

> Most biologists, including many evolutionary biologists, are not what I would call Deep Darwinians. If they were, they would not stand by when dead sheep are fed to cattle – resulting in Mad Cow disease. Nor would they sit idle as huge cattle, hog and chicken confinement operations are put in place, operations which require heavy doses of antibiotics, which in turn breed resistance by disease-causing organisms. Deep Darwinians would count any human-made chemical with which humans have not evolved as guilty until proven innocent (15).

Together, the Genesis story and Deep Darwinian thinking instruct us that, 'the Tree of Knowledge is inadequate' (16) and indeed dangerous, if as 'consumers' of knowledge we turn away from God and thus become separated from the Tree of Life, that is, from the biological integrity that ensures the future of life on our planet. Jackson's Deep Darwinian view has more in common with the Bible than with the belief, derived from the conviction of Descartes (and Bacon) that 'through science we could (and should) "render ourselves the masters and possessors of nature"' (15). The recognition that the Tree of Knowledge of Good and Evil does not itself lead to life does not mean that we are meant to be ignorant of the world in any absolute sense. Jackson frequently advocates the cultivation of 'knowledge informed by ignorance' (Vitek and Jackson, 2008: 31) – that is, by humble recognition of the limits of what we can ever know. Because the knowledge on which we can afford to act without risking irreparable harm is circumscribed, we must learn from ecosystems that have been in place for time out of mind.

In the context of the biblical creation story, one could well argue that Adam and Eve should have acquired knowledge of their world through walks with God 'in the breezy time of the day' (Gen. 3:8); instead they chose the quick and dirty method. What is certain, however, is that the Bible throughout shows no interest in knowledge that is abstracted from relationship with God and responsible relationship to the world that God has made. As far as we know, Israel did not value 'theoretical knowledge'; if Israelites wrote treatises on math, geometry, or reading entrails (as did their Mesopotamian and Egyptian neighbors), they took no care to preserve them for generations to come. Instead, they were interested in *wisdom*, namely knowledge of the world that is informed by the religious imagination and felt as a moral obligation. The more precise biblical term for this way of knowing the world is *yir'at YHWH*, 'fear of the LORD', and it is 'the best part of knowledge' (Prov. 1:7).

4. Vision Across the Boundaries

Notably, the question on which the debate between creationists and evolutionists largely centers – 'By what mechanism and in what timeframe did the world come into being?' – is exactly the kind of abstract question in which the Bible displays no interest. This question is abstract because its answer – whatever answer we may accept – imposes no obligation for us to act upon the world in just and honorable ways. As the foregoing discussion implies, it is better to ask, while reading the early chapters of Genesis, 'What does it mean for humans to be creatures among other creatures, all of us radically dependent upon God? What actions are incumbent upon us as a consequence of our status as creatures?' Rowan Williams offers an answer fully congruent with the whole biblical account: 'Being creatures is learning humility, not as submission to an alien will, but as the acceptance of limit and death' (Williams, 2000: 78). Consciously being creatures means discovering the trustworthiness of God, and allowing 'a generosity creative of community to be "enacted" in us' (76). However, his further observation appears somewhat too sanguine now, an ecologically disastrous decade after it was written: 'The discovery of solidarity in creatureliness has obvious consequences, *which hardly need spelling out*, for our sense of responsibility in the material world; it puts at once into question the model of unilateral mastery over the world' (76; emphasis added).

In fact, the most urgent theological task for this generation may well be spelling out the material consequences of a sense of self that proceeds from contemplating '"the wise, ordered, gracious and loving mutual correspondence" among creatures' (Williams, 2000: 76, citing St John of the Cross). Surely theologians, professional and lay, will need to do that in conversation with scientists, naturalists, and natural philosophers, including but not exclusively people of biblical faith. The words of philosopher Paul Shepard, a pioneer of Deep Ecology, are a fruitful starting point for conversation. Like Williams, he focuses on the essential relatedness of the self; characterizing the self as 'a center of organization, constantly drawing on and influencing the surroundings, whose skin and behavior are soft zones contacting the world instead of excluding it' (Shepard and McKinley, 1969: 2). Conventional thinking regards each human, plant, or animal as a 'contained self'; ecological thinking, by contrast, 'requires a vision across boundaries. The epidermis of the skin is ecologically like a pond surface or forest soil, not a shell so much as a delicate interpenetration. It reveals the self enabled [sic] and extended rather than threatened as part of the landscape and the ecosystem, because the beauty and complexity of nature are continuous with ourselves.'

Within the Bible, Psalm 104 stands with God's speeches to Job as the most fully articulated examples of such 'a vision across boundaries'. The psalm reads as a poetic meditation on the particular ways in which God provides food for all creatures, as Genesis 1 asserts. It shows a world that is beautifully diversified and integrated, yet not idyllic. Here lions do not lie down with lambs; rather they 'roar for prey, seeking their food from God' (Ps. 104:21). God is the consummate reality that occupies the psalmist; the poem begins and ends with blessing for the God who 'made them all in wisdom' (v. 24). The human place as represented here is not above the other creatures (contrast Psalm 8), but alongside them: God 'causes grass to sprout for beasts, and plants for human cultivation' (v. 14). Sun and moon establish the work shifts, so to speak: the lions prowl until sunrise, and then the humans go out to their own labors (vv. 22–23). 'All of them look to [God] to give their food at the right time' (v. 27), and in due course, all 'return to their dust' (v. 29).

In just one respect do humans have a unique place in this psalmist's vision across boundaries, and that special mention is not to the credit of our species. A single petition concludes the long poem of praise: 'May sinners be finished off from the earth, and the wicked, until there are none' (v. 35). Our distinction among the creatures is the capacity for working evil, through deliberate action or culpable neglect. Biblical scholar Patrick Miller cautions against defining sin too narrowly here:

> The context . . . makes us think of any who violate the creation, who take human life, who interfere with God's good provision for each creature, who tear down the trees in which the birds sing, who destroy Leviathan playing in the ocean, who poke holes in the heavenly tent, who let loose the forces of nature that God has brought under control in the very creation of a world (Miller, 2007: 189–90).

Psalm 104 is a poem in the ancient and still useful concept known in the Western philosophical tradition as the Great Chain of Being (see Lovejoy, 1936). The function of that transcultural tradition of poetic texts, which includes the first chapters of Genesis and numerous other passages in the Bible, is to enable us to 'preserve our union, the possibility of harmony, with the natural world and "higher law"' (Berry, 1983: 186). It belongs to the honesty of the tradition to acknowledge how frequently the possibility of harmony is shattered by human injustice. From a biblical perspective, and contrary to our ordinary way of thinking, human injustice is offensive to God, not only because it skews the social order, but also because it strikes a fundamental blow to the structure of the created order. In our time, it may be the work of Deep Darwinians to help us understand how deeply this is so, and how we may properly respond to God's own work of creating 'in wisdom'.

5. Sabbath and a Culture of Restraint

The search for the social implications of Darwin's insights began almost immediately following publication of *The Origin of Species*. The philosopher Herbert Spencer popularized the phrase 'survival of the fittest', arguing that the biological struggle for existence naturally extends into social and economic life. Although Darwin commented that Spencer's 'deductive manner of treating any subject is wholly opposed to my frame of mind', he in fact took up the phrase in his later work, including subsequent editions of *Origin* (Ayala, 2007: 47). In our own day, many of those who accept evolutionary theory now recognize that 'Social Darwinism' is an illegitimate and damaging doctrine. That does not mean, however, that a Darwinian understanding of the world has no positive potential for shaping culture. Rather, as Wes Jackson's remarks imply, a Deep Darwinian reckoning with the integrity of the created order, one that also takes account of the biblical perception of reality, now confronts us forcibly with the need for restraint as a cardinal virtue that can reshape our scientific and economic practices, and thus our social and personal lives.

The notion that observing material limits is essential to our life with God receives little attention in our culture, at least from mainstream religion. Yet the importance of practicing such restraint is a very common theme throughout the Bible. As we have seen, the Bible from the outset is at odds with our modern view that under ideal conditions ('Eden'), our take from the world should correspond fully with our immediate desire. It is notable that when the Apostle Paul produces a short catechism for the Roman governor Felix, he sums up the whole of biblical faith with just three basic concepts: 'justice, self-restraint, and the coming judgment' (Acts 24:25).

At the base of all the Bible has to teach about the practice of restraint is the manna story in Exodus 16. From the perspective developed here, with its focus on eating, it is especially noteworthy that this is the second and final moment in the Bible when God sets an explicit limit on food consumption, and humans knowingly violate it. The manna account comes at a crucial juncture: this is the first story of the Israelites once they have crossed the Red Sea out of Egypt. It is therefore the moment when Israel begins to establish its own culture, under God's dominion rather than Pharaoh's. God promises to heal these escaped slaves of 'all the sickness' of Egypt (Ex. 15:26) and sustain them with 'bread from heaven' (16:4), provided they observe just two ground-rules. First, every household can collect only what it requires for a single day, except on the sixth day of the week, when they collect double. The second rule is that everyone stays home on the seventh day and eats leftover manna; on Sabbath, every Israelite is to relax in the holy presence of God. The manna story comes from the same Priestly stream of tradition as does Genesis 1, and it expresses the understanding inscribed in the creation account: All food comes from God, and God provides sufficiently for all. Manna is more than emergency rations in the desert; God specifically calls it a test, to determine 'whether they can follow my instruction or not' (16:4).

Some, however, don't get it: They take more than they need, and it rots overnight; they go out to collect on Sabbath. And these seemingly minor infractions enrage Moses and God. Why? Because the manna discipline is how Israel is meant to learn the 'moral economy' of life with God. It is an economy of sufficiency and restraint, one in which the whole community regularly *stops* – something that industrial economies, such as Pharaoh's, and our own, never do – and in that stopping, recognizes that God alone grants the means of subsistence.

Sabbath itself is the central biblical symbol of restraint and justice for every creature; in the Exodus tradition, Sabbath is the great commemoration of God's work in creation, the time to take our hands off the controls and honor God as the one who 'made the heavens and the earth, the sea, and all that is in them' (Ex. 20:11). Thus 'remember[ing] the Sabbath, to keep it holy' is a spiritual habit that bears closely on how we value the material goods and all the creatures that make up our world. Everyone in the Israelite household or township – servant or slave, sojourner, child, master or mistress – is to keep Sabbath as a time of refreshment. Even the ox and the ass take the day off with their human work-partners (Deut. 5:14).

The intertwined symbols of manna and Sabbath point to the biblical understanding that only an economy disciplined by restraint does justice to the God who created heaven and earth, and therefore to all the creatures that God sustains in life. Like Deep Darwinian thinking, the manna economy and Sabbath observance bespeak an understanding that the existence of life remains a mystery, a gift beyond calculation. A living world with sufficiency for all is a trust and responsibility, not simply a resource.

I conclude by highlighting a rare if not unique phenomenon, namely a contemporary political economy that aspires to reform itself, based on the principle of restraint, in order to live out such an understanding of the world. At the time of my writing, the Ecuadorian government has made the pioneering proposal to forgo development of its largest oil reserve and forfeit revenue estimated at $9.2 billion, in partnership with the international community and in exchange for debt cancellation and bilateral aid, as well as direct financial contributions. The incentive for such a proposal is the fact that the Ishpingo Tambococha Tiputini oil bloc lies beneath the most biodiverse area of the entire Amazon basin, Yasuni National Park. Known as 'the cradle of the Amazon', the region of a million hectares (2.4 million acres) has the highest concentration of floral, faunal, and insect diversity of any region of the world. A single hectare contains almost as many tree species as all of North America. The proposal represents an attempt to move toward a post-petroleum economy for Ecuador and to reduce carbon emissions, a large portion of which come from deforestation itself. Lucia Gallardo, deputy environmental advisor in the Ministry of Foreign Relations, comments: 'We want to demonstrate that a small country, with a marginal contribution to the climate change problem, can avoid the releasing of greenhouse gases and at the same time lay the foundation for a more just and equal economy' (Koenig, 2007: 11).

The Ecuadorian proposal is, in biblical terms, a manna vision: an economic vision that begins with recognition of the sufficiency, the abundance of what God provides. Like the manna story, this vision for a new economy emerges from a relatively poor nation, and it presents a challenge and a way forward for the world. It serves to focus the concern that environmentalist James Gustave Speth identifies as *the* fundamental question facing societies today: '[H]ow can the operating instructions for the modern world economy be changed so that economic activity both protects and restores the natural world?' (Speth, 2008: 7). Reading the Bible a century and a half after Darwin, in light of the current profound crisis, we must recognize the need to change our behavior – above all our economic behavior – and change it drastically, so that we humans may fit our place in the world. With imagination and hope, the Ecuadorian proposal offers one viable path toward that goal. Darwinian realism informs us that the stakes are high, and the time for choosing a new path for our species is short. Yet that is not new information; the Israelite psalmist saw it already millennia ago:

> For the LORD knows the way of the righteous,
> but the way of the wicked vanishes (Ps. 1:6).

5

Darwin and Providence

David Fergusson

The Origin of Species is often represented as a watershed in the history of relations between science and religion. With the explanatory mechanism of natural selection, it was argued, much that had previously been attributed to the operation of divine design could now be explained by purely natural causes. Almost overnight, God had become redundant. Although not put about by Darwin himself, this view was encouraged by some of his followers most notably T. H. Huxley, famously dubbed 'Darwin's bulldog'. For Huxley, the teleology favoured by Archdeacon Paley earlier in the nineteenth century could now be given natural explanation. The adaptation of means to ends throughout creation no longer required design. Organs had evolved with greater complexity, species had adapted to the environment, and changes had taken place in life forms under the pressure of natural selection rather than divine design. According to Huxley, what theology called providence, science perceived only as natural order (cited in Livingstone, 1987: 49). This fundamental opposition was affirmed also by voices on the theological side. John Duns, who taught natural science at New College in Edinburgh from 1864, scornfully dismissed the idea that one species could evolve from another. The evidence of geology as well as Genesis, he insisted, pointed to species having existed from the beginning of the world as distinct and separate.[1] Meanwhile, in Princeton, Charles Hodge pronounced Darwinism to be atheism on the ground that it excluded teleological explanation from nature. This he regarded as a defining feature of Darwinism, and the one that rendered it in principle opposed to religious explanation.[2]

We find echoes of this dialectical opposition of scientific and religious explanation in much of today's new atheism. It is admirably captured in Daniel Dennett's metaphor of cranes and sky hooks (Dennett, 1995: 136). As the power of nature's cranes becomes better understood with the march of science, so the need to appeal to a sky hook recedes. Here the assumption is that science and religion occupy common ground in their explanatory accounts of nature. At earlier stages in the history of ideas, large and incomprehensible gaps in our understanding of nature were filled by recourse to a divine skyhook. However, as these gaps diminish so the cranes start to do the heavy lifting with the result that religion becomes ever further marginalized. Richard Dawkins is the most strident exponent of this view today. Once upon a time natural theology had sought to explain the appearance of complex organs such as the eye, as well as the extraordinary adaptation of species to environment. But now a neo-Darwinian account of genetic mutation and natural selection can offer a powerful story of how this all came to be. Darwin's brilliant idea works like a powerful acid upon earlier forms of theological reflection. Instead of a worldview dominated by the hypothesis of intelligent design, we now have a naturalist outlook in which God lacks any substantial explanatory role. However, despite its powerful advocates, this view is neither historically nor philosophically compelling. Soon after the appearance of *Origin of Species*, Christian theologians showed themselves both persuaded by the force of Darwin's science and ready to offer it theological accommodation. Many of their arguments adumbrate positions adopted by scientists and theologians today in relation to evolutionary theory.

It is a tactical error of serious proportions for theologians to assume that Darwinism must be contested by denying the scientific plausibility of evolutionary theory. What Darwin had seen by 1859 was that his theory was a high-level hypothesis that formed a 'consilience of inductions', a notion articulated earlier by the Cambridge scientist, William Whewell. According to Whewell, the most powerful scientific theories are those that are confirmed by a wide range of phenomena and which in turn can provide a single, elegant explanation of the same. Darwin's theory

---

[1] 'The existence of specific character, as something fixed in the creative act, is clearly and most emphatically recognised in the Bible. The Scriptures thus decide the question of the *origin* of species' (Duns, 1866: 205). For a discussion of the reception of Darwin in Scotland see Livingstone, 2004.

[2] Hodge's study is scientifically well-informed and advances detailed criticisms of Darwin that were the strongest available at that time (Hodge, 1874).

functions in this way. It is not a low-level hypothesis that offers an explanation of one type of phenomenon. Instead, it connects with other assumptions about the age of the earth, changes in the earth's surface, the formation of rocks, the appearance of different sets of fossils in different strata, the physiological variations and similarities across species and so on. As a consilience of inductions, *Origin of Species* develops one long, extended argument across a wide range of phenomena, all of which eventually confirm a single unfolding story. Its simplicity and explanatory power quite quickly swayed the vast majority within the scientific community.

Given the ways in which Darwin's theory of evolution built upon a significant body of scientific discovery in the first half of the nineteenth century, we should not be surprised to discover that theologians were already somewhat prepared for the subsequent debate. Charles Lyell's work in geology had persuaded many that the earth must be millions of years older than the traditional dating of 4004 BC proposed by Archbishop Ussher on the basis of the biblical record. Although it is nowadays customary to lampoon Ussher, in terms of the body of evidence available in the early seventeenth century this was quite a good calculation. Yet by the early nineteenth century, geologists could show that through 'uniformitarian' processes the formation of rocks and changes to the earth's surface could be explained by natural causes such as volcanoes, glaciers, sedimentation and erosion by water. These processes, however, required a great deal of time and only a much older universe than the one posited by Ussher would fit the bill. From about 1820, therefore, we find many theological writers denying a young universe that had been decisively shaped by a catastrophic event, i.e. the flood. The capacity to interpret Genesis 1–11 in non-literal ways was already apparent.[3] As always, the intellectual causes for a sudden shift in perspective are complex and multiple. Why then did Darwin's theory seem to cause such an intellectual upheaval for religion? At least four reasons are apparent – each will be explored in what follows, alongside a possible fifth.

1. God as Remote from the Cosmos

The natural theology that had dominated British theology until the early nineteenth century was epitomized by William Paley. Here the evidence of divine design was everywhere manifest, so much so that little credence was given to Hume's scepticism advanced earlier. While the arguments of Philo in Hume's *Dialogues* may have appeared unassailable to later analytic philosophers, for much of the nineteenth century they were

---

[3] Symbolic readings of the Genesis story were commonplace in the early church in any case, as is evident for example in Augustine's *Confessions*.

regarded as overblown and fanciful. The evidence of design was too compelling to sustain such scepticism. Successive contributions to the Bridgewater Treatises, including that of Thomas Chalmers, confirmed this confidence in the design argument (Chalmers, 1833). So much of the natural world was inexplicable without appeal to the God-hypothesis that it was assumed that a greater understanding of its workings would only confirm the intuitive impression of design. But if natural selection could explain what had formerly been assigned to the mechanism of supernatural design then the latter would become redundant. This was undoubtedly a fear in some theological quarters matched by the hopes of Huxley, et al. Yet, this placing of God on the unemployment register was much too hasty. Since at least the time of Newton scientists and theologians, impressed by the explanatory power of scientific law, had seen its rational operation as evidence of the majesty of the creator. Already we see here a conviction about the consistency of belief in a divine Creator with explanation according to scientific law. If the laws of nature could explain the formation of rocks then this merely registered the power of the Creator who had ordained those laws (see Hedley Brooke, 1992). One way of understanding this theological appropriation of natural science is to note how what was formerly attributed to the working of special providence was now assigned to a general providence. God was not required occasionally or frequently to intervene in the cosmic process in order to achieve the intended results. Instead, the manner in which the world had been established under the general working of natural law was itself sufficient to realize those creaturely states and entities desired by God. Not surprisingly, this move was to become a stock response to Darwinian theory. If evolution is how states of greater complexity emerge in the history of the cosmos, then it is open to the theologian to claim that this is how God does it. In his 1884 Bampton Lectures, we find Frederick Temple adopting this strategy. He writes that God 'did not make the things, we may say: no, but He made them make themselves' (1884: 115). This was teleology at one distance removed and it offered a different account of design to Paley. Indeed in an important respect, Temple sees his view as improving upon Paley. Instead of an Artificer who has to interject at regular intervals to bring about the intended effects in the production of life forms, we have a Creator who has from the very beginning endowed the creation with sufficient natural powers to evolve as intended.

This argument was already employed by Principal Robert Rainy (1874) in his inaugural address at New College, Edinburgh in 1874. According to Rainy, the patterns of an evolving world require to be explained by reference to divine design. All that has changed is our conception of a world that is originally endowed with sufficient fruitfulness to yield these emergent patterns. Rainy notes that there may be some loss 'of the argumentative benefit of pleading earlier interpositions as analogical instances' of divine revelation in history. A God who regularly intervenes to direct the course of history might be expected to do the same in the natural world. However, this assumption can be yielded in favour of an evolutionary world-view. While expressing some reservations about Darwinism, he seeks to distinguish the approach of the natural scientist from that of the theologian. These different forms of understanding occupy separate domains allowing a relative independence within each but a complementarity when viewed in conjunction. One upshot of all this is the clearer recognition of the disciplinary boundaries between theology, philosophy and the natural sciences.

It is worth noting that already embedded in this approach is the best response today to creation science and intelligent design theory. An evolving world, as described by the natural sciences, can equally well be viewed as the outcome of divine design. We do not need to seek gaps in scientific explanation in which to interject the agency of God. By allowing these spaces to be filled by subsequent scientific research, we can concede this domain of explanation to the natural sciences. At the same time, the theologian can insist that God has endowed the creation with the capacity to evolve increasingly complex patterns of life forms.[4] To appeal to divine intrusion at the point when the latest scientific explanation falters is to give hostages to fortune. As science progresses so the gap is closed. In any case, such defensive strategies fail to recognize the different and complementary levels at which physical and theological explanation operate.[5]

Of course, this line of response can expose the theologian to the charge of deism. While a role is assigned to divine providential design, it is a singular action that belongs to the creation of the world. The action of God is thus reduced to an originating impulse with no further interaction or ordering required. God is confined to the far end of the cosmos with little subsequent input apparent. The work of God is thus singular, original and complete. Any interest we may have in this is purely speculative and antiquarian. To this charge, several comments might be offered. In the first place, the mere fact that this accommodation of Darwinism happens to be consistent with deism does not in itself commit the theologian to that position. It is probably consistent with many types of theism, of which deism is but one. Secondly, we need to recall that deism comes in many shapes and sizes, some of them much more closely resembling Christian orthodoxy than others. The current trend to use the epithet as a pejorative label obscures the variety of 'deist' positions that were held in the eighteenth century, some of them with strong providentialist, ethical and eschatological overtones.[6] A third type of response will tend to

---

[4] This is the response favoured by Van Til (1998/9).
[5] This is eloquently argued by Collins (2006).
[6] One might see the famous sermons of Hugh Blair in this way (see Broadie, 2001: 146ff.).

counter the accusation by arguing that a theology of general providence is not exhaustive. There will be other forms of divine sustaining, interaction and involvement with the cosmos that are compatible with this claim about God making a world that makes itself. Here we need to avoid accounts of divine agency which suggest that this can only take one form. The trinitarian shape of Christian theology might assist us here in important ways. Those actions such as creation and preservation that are appropriated to the Father do not exclude the assignation of other actions such as incarnation, remaking and indwelling to the Son and the Spirit, described by Irenaeus as the 'two hands of God'.[7]

2. The Role of Chance and the Loss of Providential Control

Much theological anxiety can be detected around the role assigned to 'chance' by Darwinian science. Even amongst writers in search of an alliance with evolutionary theory, we find attempts to replace the function of chance with a more deterministic mechanism. Of course, for Darwinian theory 'chance' does not refer to the inexplicable or the uncaused. Instead, it is the denial of a single deterministic trajectory followed by the evolution of life forms. There seem to be two types of process that are characterized by the language of chance. One of these concerns the minor physiological variations that are evident through the reproduction of species, and the other is in the intersection of unrelated causal systems, e.g. the impact of a sudden change in climate upon the development of species in a hitherto stable ecological niche. The mechanism governing physiological variation was not understood until the later development of genetics, and many informed critics of Darwin in the nineteenth century recognized this lacuna in his theory. It was eventually to be filled by developments in genetics, thus providing the neo-Darwinism synthesis with its twin principles of natural selection and genetic mutation dominate explanatory theories.

Yet it was the random course of evolution, as described by Darwin, that most offended Charles Hodge in Princeton. He regarded this as practically atheistic since there could be no governing purpose or overriding control exercised over the direction of nature. What was under threat here was not so much the doctrine of creation from Darwinian evolution – a transcendent origination of the whole scheme could still be conceived – as the doctrine of providence. Hodge could concede that a process of evolution was consistent with theism. However, the particular account offered by Darwin with its stress on natural selection led him to believe

---

[7] This was a point stressed repeatedly by Colin Gunton (1998).

that it was metaphysically inconsistent with the teleological principle that belonged both to revealed and natural theology. If God were no longer in control of the course of life on earth, then it could not be perceived as proceeding towards an appointed end. For a Reformed theologian such as Hodge, this was tantamount to a practical atheism. Many passages from Darwin were cited to demonstrate that the appearance of design and intentionality in nature was in fact only a veneer. The salient causal processes were basically material – these could be characterized without any reference to divine intention or interposition. Apart from his scruples about the details of Darwinian theory – and Hodge was here very well informed – he seems to have concluded that the creative role assigned to natural causes effectively renders God otiose. 'This banishing God from the world is simply intolerable and, blessed be his name, impossible. An absent God who does nothing is, to us, no God. Christ brings God constantly near to us' (Hodge, 1994: 88). Hodge seems to have assumed that the appearance of organs such as the eye could not be explained by a natural, incremental process. To suggest such was simply incredulous – in raising this possibility, Darwin himself pointed to its impossibility. It is 'the most credulous men in the world (who) are unbelievers. The great Napoleon could not believe in Providence, but he believed in his star and in lucky and unlucky days' (Hodge, 1994: 88).

Nevertheless, within that same tradition others reached different conclusions by placing evolution within a wider context that was perceived to be providentially ordered. Asa Gray, the Harvard botanist, replied to Hodge. His difficulty with Darwin, Gray claimed, arose out of an unduly restricted account of how divine teleology works. The Creator can endow nature and organisms with the powers of evolution into states of greater complexity. Hodge simply begs the question against this type of teleology with its commitment to an older, Paleyian type of strategy. This was also the line take by Robert Flint in his Baird lectures on *Theism* that went through numerous editions during the late nineteenth century. Here his interaction with Darwinism offers a set of responses that have become standard in theological appropriations of evolutionary science. The development from lower to higher organisms can be explained as a mark of design. The tendency towards improvement and progression requires explanation. Evolutionary process can be envisioned as a vast scheme of order and beauty, rather than a grim arena of conflict and waste. This more positive vision of evolutionary complexity would be later developed by writers such as J. Arthur Thomson and Patrick Geddes (1912).

Later in Princeton, Alexander Hodge and B. B. Warfield would make their peace with Darwinism arguing that it was scientifically sound but also consistent with an account of divine providence. What much of this shows is that there was no clear consensus about Darwinism at that time. It was interpreted in a wide variety of ways so that even to talk of Darwinism, as if it meant one thing to everyone, is quite misleading. James Moore, biographer of Darwin, has argued that in the 1860s there were as many as five different types of Darwinism, each contending with one other (Moore, 1991: 353–408).

Princeton theology itself proved capable of simultaneously moving in the opposite direction to that of Hodge. James McCosh felt able to welcome key aspects of Darwinism, especially evolutionary descent, and to accommodate it within a wider teleological system. What it represented was the outworking of a vast orderly and regulated system that betokened divine design. The discernment of laws governing the evolutionary process together with the apparently inevitable rise of increasing complexity suggested for McCosh that Darwinian science and Christian theology could be reconciled. In this respect, McCosh was to be followed by B. B. Warfield, another distinguished Princeton theologian, who regarded Darwinian explanation as unavoidable within the scientific domain but as readily consistent with theological determinism. That Darwinism perceived an order, regularity and lawfulness governing the seemingly haphazard history of life enabled theologians quite quickly to reach an accommodation and to maintain patterns of teleological explanation. This was the apologetic move argued against Huxley and Haeckel by writers such as Flint, Drummond and George Campbell, the Duke of Argyll. Darwin himself, they noted, had used the language of purpose in his descriptions of how natural selection operated. Although this may have been intended metaphorically, it showed how easy the reconciliation of evolution and theism could be. Aubrey Moore, Canon at Christ Church, Oxford, expressed it succinctly in his remark that the 'belief in the universality of law and order is the scientific analogue of the Christian's belief in Providence' (Moore, 1889: 197).

The key differences between Hodge and McCosh may actually reflect a fundamental disagreement that persists amongst evolutionary theorists today. To what extent is the course of life a one in a million shot, a random walk, a sequence of haphazard events strung together? Stephen Jay Gould has argued that, even if replayed many times over, the tape of life would never resemble again the course of natural history on our planet. Against this, we find Simon Conway Morris (2003) arguing for evolutionary constraints and patterns of convergence that ensure that a species like human beings, i.e. mammals with large brains, would emerge given the setting of our planetary system. The physical, biochemical and environmental conditions of evolution on our planets are sufficiently restricted to ensure that particular features, activities and life-forms will inevitably arise.

Other theological responses after the publication of *Origin* offered a more immanent account of divine involvement in the evolutionary process. This suggests a different model of providence and again it is one that continues to attract defenders today. In his essay in *Lux Mundi*, Aubrey Moore also wrote in an oft-quoted passage:

> The one absolutely impossible conception of God, in the present day, is that which represents him as an occasional visitor. Science has pushed the deist's God further and further away, and at that moment when it seemed as if He would be thrust out all together Darwinism appeared, and, under the disguise of a foe, did the work of a friend (1889: 9).

Moore's claim is that Darwinism affords a positive opportunity for Christian theology to re-affirm its commitment to a perpetual involvement of the divine spirit in the natural world. Instead of the more remote and disengaged God of deism, we now have an immanent divine presence that is at work in the creative and open-ended processes of evolutionary history. Rather than posing a threat, therefore, the apparently free movement of natural forms is consonant with a God who is present and active within the creative process, in a manner analogous to God's same involvement with human history. This model of divine engagement resonated with the kenotic theologies that flourished in the late-nineteenth century and it has exercised a particularly strong hold over Anglican thinkers to the present day with their stress on divine possibility. The model here is of God's 'letting the world become itself', not in such a way as to abandon it but in the interests of a patient accompanying that seeks to work within and alongside creative processes. A model of providence is thus suggested that avoids the perceived determinism of much of the Augustinian tradition but also the deism that had persisted from the early modern period.

More than most who sought an accommodation with Darwinism, Moore was able to see clearly some positive theological gains. The occasional interventions of a remote deity could now be replaced by the constant sustaining and creative activity of the divine spirit. This has the significant benefit of correlating the Christian understanding of how God acts in nature and history. The God of the Bible is portrayed as deeply involved in the stories of Israel, Christ and the church, an ongoing personal drama that takes a narrative shape in the successive books of Scripture. By contrast, the model of divine action suggested by deism, at least in one of its standard forms, was that of a transcendent Creator who perfectly ordered the world so that subsequent historical interaction was unnecessary, even undesirable. Given the way in which this mode of divine action contrasted with the standard Scriptural account, it was hardly surprising that deist writers were more or less sceptical of historical revelation. At best, revelation provided a republication of the truths of natural religion (see, for example, Tindal, 1730). While Paley's teleology did not amount to a wholesale commitment to deism, its model of the God-world relationship seemed to lean in that direction with the notion of a perfectly ordered world in little need of repair or further development. After Darwin, however, theologians could see the world of nature as having a history, as being constantly in the process of making. It had a narrative shape that could increasingly be detected by advances in the natural sciences. Like history, therefore, nature was a work in progress, a construction site in which God could be seen as a sustaining, creative, guiding presence. This appearance of the natural world as undergoing significant change across time was of course further confirmed by the emergence of big-bang cosmology in the following century.

The challenge for this view is in specifying the forms that divine involvement in creation takes. Clearly, there is a keen sense of divine sustaining and presence throughout the evolutionary process but does God actually make a difference to what happens? This has been the source of intensive discussion in recent work on science and theology, most notably by Arthur Peacocke and John Polkinghorne. Would the outcomes be any different without this form of divine engagement? Both Peacocke and Polkinghorne answer this in the affirmative but in different ways. For Peacocke, the presence and involvement of God in nature is seen in terms of whole-part causation, instances of which are elsewhere evident in natural systems. This model does not interpose God within the gaps, but sees the divine presence as acting creatively upon the interconnected whole and therefore hidden within natural processes (Peacocke, 1990). His account of divine creativity is part of a strong emergentist thesis in which lower-level types of explanation yield higher-level forms of explanation that are not reducible to the lower and which can exercise a downward causal influence upon these (as discussed in Gregersen, 2006). While sharing some similarities to Peacocke's approach, Polkinghorne has utilized developments in chaos theory to describe the possible ways in which God can act in nature through informational input, yet without violating the integrity of creaturely processes (Polkinghorne, 1989). This yields in his writings an account of providence that avoids the remoteness of deist conceptions of God without drifting towards the perceived determinism of much of the western theological tradition. In divine providential activity there is both a 'letting be' of creation to become itself, but also a divine causal interaction within this process (see Polkinghorne 2001: 90–106). God is neither a cosmic tyrant nor a detached spectator on this model. Polkinghorne's account of divine action seems to me attractive and possibly under-rated within the theological community. At the very least, it offers an account of divine involvement in creation that can make some sense of practices such as petitionary prayer while it offers a low-key but plausible account of what might be meant by the miraculous. One standard criticism is that it is another God-of-the-gaps account. Polkinghorne's response to this is to argue that all rational agency requires an openness in physical processes when viewed in term of lower-level description. The openness is not a function of ignorance so much as an inherent feature of the world as we experience it. And as Keith Ward has often pointed out, we should not rush into wholesale abandonment of theological convictions simply because we lack a fully coherent account of divine action in the world – the same applies to the philosophy of human action, yet this is no reason for giving up our intuitions about freedom and responsibility.

'There is a sense in which all free action, ours or God's, depends upon 'gaps', just as the resultant flexibilities require for their lasting significance that they be exercised within a generally reliable environment. God is the sustainer of the whole of his creation, the God of 'gaps' and regularities alike' (Polkinghorne, 1989).

3. The Intensification of the Problem of Evil

A further recurrent concern in the theological reception of Darwin concerns the problem of evil. Of course, this was hardly a new challenge to confront Christian theology. The Book of Job already reveals a long history of reflection on this in Jewish traditions. And, in any case, the facts of disease, suffering and death were manifestly visible before any theory could explain their contribution to the evolutionary story. But what was striking in Darwin's description of evolution was the extent to which suffering, waste and the competition for survival were the drivers of evolution. These were part of the 'design' that enabled the emergence of species, including human beings. Instead of Paley's notion of creatures living always in a state of equilibrium, their prosperity secured by a single divine blueprint, theologians now faced a bleaker scenario in which earlier species were driven to extinction in a perpetual warfare of life forms. How could this suggest a divine providence?

One type of theodicy that quite confidently took Darwinian explanation on board argued, more or less, that the end justified the means. Since evolution produced fitter and more advanced species, particularly *Homo sapiens*, we could conclude that the laws of evolution were all part of a benevolent divine plan. The production of better adapted forms of life could thus be seen as an outworking of an overall teleology. This was the strategy pursued by the aforementioned Duke of Argyll and Henry Drummond in Scotland, and also Temple in his Bampton Lectures (Livingston, 2006: 69ff.). At the same time, these writers sought to introduce a different set of metaphors to overcome the prevailing sense of waste and random, meaningless suffering. Attention is drawn to the interdependence of species, the unity of the natural world, the long periods of relative equilibrium characterized in large measure by the enjoyment of life, and the beautiful harmony of flowers and insects.

> [T]he doctrine of Evolution binds all existing things on earth into one. Every mineral, every plant, every animal has such properties that it benefits other things beside itself and derives benefit in turn. The insect developes the plant, and the plant the insect; the brute aids in the evolution of the man, and the man in that of the brute. All things are embraced in one great design beginning with the very creation (Temple, 1884).[8]

Others would point to patterns of self-sacrifice in nature that adumbrated later Christian moral ideals. In his study *Christianity and Evolution*, James Iverach noted that the individual often sacrifices itself for the well-being of the species to the extent that something like a virtuous family life emerges naturally (1894: 184). One danger inherent in this kind of teleology is that it works with a principle of the end justifies the means. If nature discards the weak and the unsuccessful, then this is so that fitter and better-adapted species may emerge. The ends of evolution enable us to explain why the system is one in which much is discarded as unfit, superfluous, and disposable. This could tilt in dangerous directions particularly as human evolution came into focus. Should social policies be developed that artificially selected the fittest for reproduction? We are not so very far here from theories of social Darwinism and the eugenic theories and practices that were evident in the early twentieth century, and not just in Nazi Germany.[9]

Nevertheless, by the later nineteenth century, this rather confident style of theodicy was being replaced by more reserved approaches to the problem of suffering. While a divine plan may be in a process of outworking, its meaning and significance are not yet discernible from a human vantage point. We simply cannot speculate on what purpose long aeons of animal suffering may serve. Again, however, a virtue can be made out of a necessity. The theologian has no business reading off the details of divine design from the pages of natural history. The only index to providence is that of faith in Christ – more speculative and comprehensive accounts should be eschewed. At the same time, Darwinism may also helpfully save the theologian from embracing too narrow an anthropocentrism. Given the relatively late emergence of human beings and the extent to which animal life has evolved for much of the time with no reference to ourselves, we cannot assume that God's purposes are solely directed towards our own species. God must have more in mind than the evolution of humankind (Moore, 1889: 108f.).

---

[8] Temple, op. cit., 122.
[9] For further discussion see Paul, 2003: 214–239.

4. The Threat to Human Significance

This last point brings us to another hotly debated topic emerging from Darwinism, namely the significance of human beings in creation (for recent discussion see van Huyssteen, 2006). To a large extent, the fear surrounding evolutionary theory was that it threatened to undermine our most fundamental convictions about the intellectual, moral and spiritual distinctiveness of human being. This was expressed immediately after the publication of *Origin of Species* in 1859 and before the appearance of the *Descent of Man* in 1871. Indeed, this fear continues to infect much of the debate today. If human beings emerged from other mammals over millions of years of evolution, is their uniqueness thereby destroyed? Again a religious accommodation with Darwinism was proposed by successive writers, while also maintaining a traditional commitment to human distinctiveness. Scholars like Rainy and Temple argued again for a complementarity of explanations. It was open to the scientist to point to the ways in which human beings had emerged from other primates while also displaying significant similarities to other species. Yet the theologian could also point to phenomena such as consciousness, our moral capacities, and spiritual discernment that demand different forms of explanation and understanding from those available to the natural sciences.

Much of the late nineteenth- and early twentieth-century literature was dominated by discussion of the faculty of conscience which seemed to require a non-natural transcendent explanation. In this domain, a careful distinction needs to be made between competitive and complementary forms of understanding. It is too tempting for the theologian to seek out a major lacuna in scientific explanation and then immediately to postulate God. If we cannot explain the evolution of consciousness, then God must be invoked. If we cannot discern obvious analogues of conscience in animal life, then there must be a transcendent cause. Yet these types of argument evidently give hostages to fortune. When science advances and starts to fill in the gaps, then religious explanation becomes squeezed to the margins. A better type of argument will insist upon complementarity. Even after science has done all its work, there will be ways of understanding and describing the phenomena that draw upon different conceptual resources. In the aforementioned work, Iverach argues that Huxley's moral commitments cannot be adequately characterized by natural science alone. Here is a strategy reminiscent of that employed by recent apologists against Richard Dawkins. There are questions, commitments and insights that by their nature require description in terms that are not reducible to the methods of the natural sciences. No single discipline has an exhaustive or totalizing role to play. If the engagement with Darwinism has taught theologians one thing it might be this. The sciences must be given their place freely to investigate and hypothesize according to their methods and findings. A clearer delineation of the differences with theology will result in a recognition of complementarity rather than a misplaced anxiety about the directions in which science might lead us. The converse of this is that 'scientific' description will itself need to be challenged when it steps beyond its boundaries by seeking to 'explain away' other types of description.

In one further respect, the emergence of evolutionary theory impacted upon the study of religion more than many of the standard accounts acknowledge. The attempt to see religion itself as developing along evolutionary lines was a hallmark of much historical and social scientific study in the late nineteenth and early twentieth centuries. Pioneer figures such as Robertson Smith, Frazer and Tyler sought to locate all religion in terms of a single evolutionary stream of development that could be discerned from the earliest available historical and anthropological evidence. This was to prove at least as important a development for Christian theology with its claims for divine revelation in history and scriptural authority. Having reached a relatively swift accommodation with Darwinism, Victorian Scotland was shaken by the trials of Robertson Smith. These drew attention to those very claims for historical criticism of the Bible that the Free Church had sought to suppress in disciplining their gifted young Old Testament scholar. The Belfast historian David Livingstone has pointed to the seeming disparity between the swift acceptance of Darwin within the Free Church and its simultaneous resistance to the kind of historical and anthropological work that scholar of religion advocated (Livingstone, 2004).

Smith argued in his article on the Bible in the ninth edition of *Encyclopaedia Britannica* that the writings of the prophets, the Pentateuch and the Gospels must be viewed in light of the historical circumstances from which they emerged and the concerns they registered. This led to some startling though incontrovertible conclusions that made Mosaic authorship of the Pentateuch impossible to defend, and attributed the formative influences to the Old Testament canon to events much later than those narrated in the texts themselves. In the case of the gospels, Smith pointed to the ways in which the reception and presentation of the story of Jesus were embedded in the historical circumstances of first-century Christian communities. If not invoking the Darwinian principle of natural selection, this is clearly an attempt to position Scripture within the evolutionary stream of historical religion.

The theological ramifications of historical study for faith were most searchingly explored not in Scotland but in Germany by Ernst Troeltsch and others. All historical events must be understood relative to the circumstances and context in which these took place and with reference to our understanding of other events and epochs. How then can an absolute and unique significance be attached to any one single portion of history? This was the problem of the 'absoluteness of Christianity' with which Troeltsch wrestled. An evolutionary approach to history, as well as nature, requires us to understand each event with reference to what comes before and what arises after. The meaning of the event then resides in the place it occupies within a total series, rather than in any radically new and decisive character that is intrinsic to it. This problem would set an agenda for twentieth-century theologians, many of whom would draw upon the work of Kierkegaard and others who sought in religious faith a mode of knowledge that transcended and complemented that of historical study. Again the solution is not to deny or check the course of free historical enquiry but to recognize that its claims need not be exclusive of other forms of understanding.

Where then does this leave us with respect to divine providence in natural and historical processes? The engagement with Darwin provides at least three lessons. In the first place, it suggests a greater degree of independence between scientific and theological work than appeared to be the case up until that time. The explanatory descriptions of science and theology work in different ways – we might say at different levels – so that the integrity of each can be recognized by the other. What is impressive in reading writers such as Flint and Hodge was their command of the science of the day, their capacity to understand its recent developments and assess the difficulties attending the formulations. It also reveals the extent to which the academic communities of their time were less fragmented. The much greater degree of disciplinary specialism required today makes this range of competences almost impossible, but it carries also the need for mutual respect and the avoidance of the totalitarian claims of scientific critics of religion such as Richard Dawkins.

A second instructive feature of the encounter with Darwinism was the extent to which it showed the Bible and the Christian tradition capable of providing resources for dealing with a new set of problems, in some cases resources that had been overlooked by earlier generations. The anthropocentric turn of deism might have been challenged by the place assigned to human beings in evolutionary science. But the Bible with its more theocentric vision could suggest a divine concern with creatures and stretches of cosmic history that do not directly involve *Homo sapiens*. Similarly, if the Enlightenment projects of theodicy now found themselves in trouble by the end of the nineteenth century, it was open to Christian scholars to point to the lack of such theodicies in Scripture, to the rejection of easy solutions in the Book of Job, and ways in which much of the response to evil was resistance, protest and redemption through the dying and rising of Christ, rather than metaphysical explanation. If the occasional interpositions of Paley's God were now questionable, the way was opened to stress a continuous creation suffused with the divine presence and open to its agency.

Finally, theology after 1859 showed itself not so much in a state of retreat or denial of what scientists were discovering about the age of the universe and the emergence of life forms on earth. It accommodated itself with surprising swiftness to these claims and showed how its central tenets could consistently co-exist with the best of modern science. In some ways, this encounter may even have promoted accounts of providence that were chastened, more mysterious, more receptive to the idea of a continuous creation, and more dependent upon the particular convictions of faith as opposed to natural theology. Nevertheless, a world that was governed by law and processes of emergence could be seen to possess a stunning beauty and also an intelligibility that continued to evoke wonder. The appearance of human beings could be regarded not as an accident against all the odds, but as constrained by a world that is intrinsically creative and productive of increasing states of complexity. While emerging from earlier kindred species of higher primate, human beings developed language, culture, ethics, art, science and religion. All these were new activities in the long history of the cosmos, so far as we can tell, and all require patterns of description and understanding that have their own integrity and are not reducible to physical and biological explanation alone.

6

Being Human after Darwin

Francisco J. Ayala

Mankind is a biological species that has evolved from other species that were not human. In order to understand human nature, we must know our biological make-up and whence we come, the story of our humble beginnings. For a century after the publication of Darwin's *On the Origin of Species* in 1859, the story of evolution was reconstructed with evidence from paleontology (the study of fossils), biogeography (the study of the geographical distribution of organisms), and from the comparative study of living organisms: their morphology, development, physiology, and the like. Since the mid-twentieth century we have had, in addition, molecular biology – the most informative and precise discipline for reconstructing the ancestral relationships of living species. Molecular biology has shown that our closest relatives are the chimpanzees, who are more related to us, and we to them, than they are to gorillas and much more than to orangutans.

The deciphering of the human and chimpanzee genomes and other molecular biology exploits have shone much light on what it is that makes us humans and how we got here through the evolution of our genetic make-up. But the accelerating rate of discovery of hominid fossils has provided indispensable information for reconstructing the evolution of the human lineage. (Hominids are the members of the human lineage after it separated from the chimpanzee lineage.) Darwin's contemporaries asked: If humans have evolved from non-human ancestors, where is the 'missing link', the intermediate creature between humans and apes? This challenge was not unreasonable since no fossils were known in Darwin's time that would have likely been our hominid ancestors. But the missing link is no longer missing. Not one, but hundreds of fossil remains belonging to hundreds of individual hominids have been discovered since Darwin's time and continue to be discovered at an accelerated rate.

In the pages that follow, I will briefly summarize the paleontological evidence concerning the evolution of the human lineage, since the time when it separated from the lineage of the chimpanzees, our closest relatives. I will then point out that human biology in the twenty-first century faces three great research frontiers: ontogenetic decoding, the brain–mind puzzle, and the ape-to-human transformation. By ontogenetic decoding I refer to the problem of how the unidimensional genetic information encoded in the DNA of a single cell becomes transformed into a four-dimensional being, the individual that develops, grows, matures, and dies. Cancer, disease and aging are epiphenomena of ontogenetic decoding. By the brain–mind puzzle I refer to the interdependent questions of (1) how the physicochemical signals that reach our sense organs become transformed into perceptions, feelings, ideas, critical arguments, aesthetic emotions, and ethical values; and (2) how, out of this diversity of experiences, there emerges a unitary reality, the mind or self. Free will and language, social and political institutions, technology and art are all epiphenomena of the human mind. By the ape-to-human transformation I refer to the mystery of how a particular ape lineage became a hominid lineage, from which emerged, after only a few million years, humans able to think and love, who have developed complex societies and uphold ethical, aesthetic and religious values. The human genome differs little from the chimp genome.

I will refer to these three issues as the egg-to-adult transformation, the brain-to-mind transformation, and the ape-to-human transformation. The egg-to-adult transformation is essentially similar, and similarly mysterious, in humans and other mammals, but it has distinctive human features. The brain-to-mind transformation and the ape-to-human transformation are distinctively human. These three transformations define the *humanum*, that which makes us specifically human. No other issues in human evolution are of greater consequence for understanding ourselves and our place in nature. These three transformations are major concerns for theologians and for people of faith. Are scientists claiming that humans are just another kind of ape, not any more different from chimpanzees than gorillas and other apes are? Does this imply that the religious view of humans, as special creatures of God, is without foundation? The answer to these questions is that in some biological respects we are very similar to apes, but in other *biological* respects we are very different, and these differences provide a valid foundation for a religious view of humans as special creatures of God. We will return later to this issue.

Erect posture and a large brain are two most significant anatomical traits that distinguish us from non-human primates. But humans are also importantly different from chimpanzees and other animals in their behavior, both as individuals and socially. Distinctive human behavioral attributes include tool-making and technology; abstract thinking, categorizing and reasoning; symbolic (creative) language; self-awareness and death-awareness; science, literature and art; legal codes, ethics and religion; complex social organization and political institutions. These traits may all be said to be components of human culture, a distinctively human mode of adaptation to the environment that is far more versatile and successful than the biological mode.

1. Human Origins

As we have already noted, our closest animal relatives are the chimpanzees, who are more closely related to us than they are to the gorillas, and much more than to the orangutans. (The chimpanzees include two species closely related to one another, but both equally related to humans, *Pan troglodytes* or common chimpanzee, and *Pan paniscus* or bonobo.) The hominid lineage diverged from the chimpanzee lineage 7–8 million years ago (Mya) and it evolved exclusively in the African continent until the emergence of *Homo erectus*, somewhat before 1.8 Mya.

The oldest known fossil hominids are 6 to 7 million years old, come from Africa, and are known as *Sahelanthropus* and *Orrorin* (or *Praeanthropus*). These ancestors were predominantly bipedal when on the ground and had very small brains. *Ardipithecus* lived about 4.4 million years ago, also in Africa. Numerous fossil remains from diverse African origins are known of *Australopithecus*, a hominid that appeared between 3 million and 4 million years ago. *Australopithecus* had an upright human stance but a cranial capacity of less than 500 cubic centimeters (500 cc), comparable to that of a gorilla or chimpanzee and about one-third that of modern humans (500 cc are equivalent to 500 grams; one pound is 454 grams). The skull of *Australopithecus* displayed a mixture of ape and human characteristics – a low forehead and a long, apelike face but with teeth proportioned like those of humans. Other early hominids partly contemporaneous with *Australopithecus* include *Kenyanthropus* and *Paranthropus*; both had comparatively small brains, although some species of *Paranthropus* had larger bodies. *Paranthropus* represents a side branch of the hominid lineage that became extinct.

Along with increased cranial capacity, other human characteristics have been found in *Homo habilis*, which lived between about 2 and 1.5 million years ago in Africa and had a cranial capacity of 600–700 cc (about one-and-one-half pounds), and in *Homo erectus*, which evolved in

Africa somewhat before 1.8 million years ago and had a cranial capacity of 800 to 1,100 cc (from nearly two pounds to nearly two-and-one half pounds).

Homo erectus is the first intercontinental wanderer among our hominid ancestors. Shortly after its emergence in Africa, *H. erectus* spread to Europe and Asia, even as far as the Indonesian archipelago and northern China. Fossil remains of *H. erectus* have been found in Africa, Indonesia (Java), China, the Middle East, and Europe. *Homo erectus* fossils from Java have been dated at 1.81 and 1.66 million years ago, and from Georgia (in Europe, near the Asian border) between 1.8 and 1.6 million years ago.

Several species of hominids lived in Africa, Europe, and Asia between 1.8 million and 500,000 years ago. They are known as *Homo ergaster*, *Homo antecessor* and *Homo heidelbergensis*, with brain sizes roughly that of the brain of *Homo erectus*. Some of these species were partly contemporaneous, though they lived in different regions of the Old World. These species are sometimes included under the name *Homo erectus* (*sensu lato*, in a broad sense). The transition from *Homo erectus* to *Homo sapiens* may have started around 400,000 years ago. Some fossils of that time appear to be 'archaic' forms of *H. sapiens*. Yet, *H. erectus* persisted until 250,000 years ago in China and perhaps until 100,000 years ago in Java. (The fossil remains of *Homo floresiensis*, discovered in 2004 on the Indonesian island of Flores, seem related to *H. erectus*, although *H. floresiensis* was much smaller and lived around 12,000–18,000 years ago. These fossil remains are being actively investigated and their precise identification remains controversial.)

The species *Homo neanderthalensis* appeared in Europe more than 200,000 years ago and persisted until 30,000 years ago. The Neandertals have been thought to be ancestral to anatomically modern humans, but now we know that modern humans appeared more than 100,000 years ago, much before the disappearance of Neandertals. It is puzzling that, in caves in the Middle East, fossils of anatomically modern humans precede as well as follow Neandertal fossils. Some modern humans from these caves are dated at 120,000 to 100,000 years ago, whereas Neandertals are dated at 60,000 and 70,000 years, followed by modern humans dated at 40,000 years. It is unclear whether Neandertals and modern humans repeatedly replaced one another by migration from other regions, or whether they coexisted, or indeed whether interbreeding may have occurred. Comparisons of DNA from Neandertal fossils with living humans indicate that no, or very little, interbreeding occurred between Neandertals and their contemporary anatomically modern humans.

2. Co-Lateral Relatives versus Ancestors

Lucy is the whimsical name given to the fossil remains of a hominid ancestor classified as *Australopithecus afarensis*, a species of bipedal hominids, small brained and some three-and-a-half feet tall. Lucy is duly famous because about 40 percent of the whole skeleton of this young woman was found on a single site when it was discovered 30 years ago. Experts generally agree that *A. afarensis*, who lived between 3 million and 3.6 million years ago, is in the line of descent to modern humans.

Australopithecus africanus, which lived more recently than *A. afarensis* and was the first *Australopithecus* species ever discovered, was also short and small-brained. However, *A. africanus* is not our ancestor, but is rather a co-lateral relative, the likely ancestor of *Australopithecus (Paranthropus) robustus* and other co-lateral hominids, who lived for two million years or more after their divergence from our ancestral lineage and, thus, long co-existed in Africa with some of our ancestors (*A. afarensis*, *H. habilis* and *H. erectus*). Some of these co-lateral relatives became somewhat taller and more robust, but their brains remained small, about 500–600 cc at the most.

The discovery of hominid fossils has increased at an accelerated rate over the last two decades. In 1994, *Ardipithecus ramidus* from Ethiopia, a more primitive hominid than *Australopithecus afarensis*, was discovered, soon followed by *Australopithecus anamensis* from Kenya (dated ~3.9 to ~4.2 million years ago), as well as more specimens of *Ardipithecus* (~5.5 to 5.8 million years old) and the already mentioned *Sahelanthropus* (~6–7 million years old, from Chad) and *Orrorin* (~5.7–6.0 million years old, from Kenya). The position of these fossil hominids, whether in the direct ancestry of *Homo* or as co-lateral relatives remains largely a subject of debate. It has been commonly assumed, however, that *A. anamensis* is the ancestral species to *A. afarensis*, whose earliest definitive specimen is ~3.6 million years old.

The analysis and recent publication, on 13 April 2006, of 30 additional hominid specimens – representing a minimum of eight individuals, of *Australopithecus anamensis* from the Afar region of Ethiopia, and dated to ~4.12 million years ago – confirms this interpretation. The new fossils suggest, moreover, that *Ardipithecus* was the most likely ancestor of *A. anamensis* and all later australopithecines. The fossils suggest that a relatively rapid evolution from *Ardipithecus* to *Australopithecus* occurred in this region of Ethiopia.

3. Modern Humans

Some anthropologists have argued that the transition from *H. erectus* to archaic *H. sapiens*, and later to anatomically modern humans, occurred concurrently in various parts of the Old World (Africa, Asia, and perhaps Europe). Most scientists argue instead that modern humans first arose in Africa somewhat earlier than 100,000 years ago and spread from there throughout the world, replacing the pre-existing populations of *H. erectus* and related hominid species, including, later, *H. neanderthalensis.* Some proponents of this African replacement model argue further that the transition from archaic to modern *H. sapiens* was associated with a very narrow bottleneck, and that this bottleneck consisted of a small number of individuals who are the ancestors of all modern humans. Molecular studies of a number of genes indicate, however, that the number of ancestors was never smaller than about ten thousand and, probably, rarely if ever smaller than 100,000.

Analyses of DNA from living humans has confirmed the African origin of modern *H. sapiens*, which is dated by these analyses at about 156,000 years ago in tropical Africa. The DNA estimates of ancestral dates have, however, broad ranges of possible variation (the so-called 95 percent 'confidence interval'). The estimated origin of modern humans based in these DNA investigations is more appropriately given as 100,000–200,000 years ago.

Shortly after their origin in tropical Africa, modern humans spread through Africa and throughout the world. Southeast Asia and the region that is now China were colonized by 60,000 years ago and Australasia at about the same time. Europe was colonized more recently, only about 35,000 years ago, and America even more recently, perhaps only 15,000 years ago. Ethnic differentiation between modern human populations is therefore evolutionarily recent, a result of divergent evolution between geographically separated populations during the last 50,000 to 100,000 years. Why modern humans reached Europe later than they reached China and Australasia, which are geographically much more distant, is not known. Between nearly 200,000 and 35,000 years ago, as pointed out earlier, Neandertals occupied much of Europe. A reasonable conjecture is that their presence may have inhibited, or even impeded, its colonization by modern humans.

4. The Egg-to-Adult Transformation

Biological heredity is based on the transmission of genetic information from parents to offspring, in humans very much the same as in other animals. The DNA of humans is packaged in two sets of 23 chromosomes, one set inherited from each parent. The total number of DNA letters (the four nucleotides represented by A, C, G, T) in each set of chromosomes is about three thousand million. The Human Genome Project has deciphered the sequence of the three thousand million letters in the human genome (that is, in one set of chromosomes; the human genome sequence varies between genomes by about one letter in a thousand).

The two genomes (chromosome sets) of each individual are different from each other, and from the genomes of any other human being (with the trivial exception of identical twins, who share the same two sets of genes, because identical twins develop from one single fertilized human egg). I estimate that the King James Bible contains about three million letters, punctuation marks, and spaces. Writing down the DNA sequence of one human genome demands one thousand volumes of the size of the Bible. The human genome sequence is, of course, not printed in books, but stored in electronic form, in computers where fragments of information can be retrieved by investigators. But if a print-out is wanted, one thousand volumes will be needed just for one human genome. Printing the complete genome information for just one individual would demand two thousand volumes, one thousand for each of the two chromosome sets. Surely, again, there are more economic ways of presenting the information in the second set than listing the complete letter sequence; for example, by indicating the position of each variant letter in the second set relative to the first set. The number of variant letters between one individual's two sets is about three million, or one in one thousand.

The instructions that guide the ontogenetic process, or the egg-to-adult transformation, are carried in the hereditary material. The theory of biological heredity was formulated by the Augustinian monk Gregor Mendel in 1866, but it became generally known by biologists only in 1900: genetic information is contained in discrete factors, or genes, which exist in pairs, one received from each parent. The next step toward understanding the nature of genes was completed during the first quarter of the twentieth century. It was established that genes are parts of the chromosomes, filamentous bodies present in the nucleus of the cell, and that they are linearly arranged along the chromosomes. It took another quarter century to determine the chemical composition of genes – deoxyribonucleic acid (DNA). DNA consists of four kinds of nucleotides organized in long, double-helical structures. The genetic information is contained in the linear sequence of the nucleotides, very much in the same way as the semantic information of an English sentence is conveyed by the particular sequence of the 26 letters of the alphabet.

The first important step toward understanding how the genetic information is decoded came in 1941 when George W. Beadle and Edward L. Tatum demonstrated that genes determine the synthesis of enzymes; enzymes are the catalysts that control all chemical reactions in living beings. Later it became known that amino acids (the components that make up enzymes and other proteins) are encoded each by a set of three consecutive nucleotides. This relationship accounts for the linear correspondence between a particular sequence of coding nucleotides and the sequence of the amino acids that make up the encoded enzyme.

Chemical reactions in organisms must occur in an orderly manner; organisms must have ways of switching genes on and off since different sets of genes are active in different cells. The first control system was discovered in 1961 by François Jacob and Jacques Monod for a gene that encodes an enzyme that digests sugar in the bacterium *Escherichia coli*. The gene is turned on and off by a system of several switches consisting of short DNA sequences adjacent to the coding part of the gene. (The coding sequence of a gene is the part that determines the sequence of amino acids in the encoded enzyme or protein.) The switches acting on a given gene are activated or deactivated by feedback loops that involve molecules synthesized by other genes. A variety of gene control mechanisms were soon discovered, in bacteria and other microorganisms. Two elements are typically present: feedback loops and short DNA sequences acting as switches. The feedback loops ensure that the presence of a substance in the cell induces the synthesis of the enzyme required to digest it, and that an excess of the enzyme in the cell represses its own synthesis. (For example, the gene encoding a sugar-digesting enzyme in *E. coli* is turned on or off by the presence or absence of the sugar to be digested.)

The investigation of gene control mechanisms in mammals (and other complex organisms) became possible in the mid-1970s with the development of recombinant DNA techniques. This technology made it feasible to isolate single genes (and other DNA sequences) and to multiply them, or 'clone' them, in order to obtain the quantities necessary for ascertaining their nucleotide sequence. One unanticipated discovery was that most genes come in pieces: the coding sequence of a gene is divided into several fragments separated one from the next by noncoding DNA segments. In addition to the alternating succession of coding and noncoding segments, mammalian genes contain short control sequences, like those in bacteria but typically more numerous and complex, that act as control switches and signal where the coding sequence begins.

Much remains to be discovered about the control mechanisms of mammalian genes. The daunting speed at which molecular biology is advancing has led to the discovery of some prototypes of mammalian gene control systems, but much remains to be unraveled. Moreover, understanding the control mechanisms of individual genes is but the first major step toward solving the mystery of ontogenetic decoding. The second major step will be the puzzle of differentiation.

A human being consists of one trillion cells of some 300 different kinds, all derived by sequential division from the fertilized egg, a single cell 0.1 millimeters in diameter. The first few cell divisions yield a spherical mass of amorphous cells. Successive divisions are accompanied by the appearance of folds and ridges in the mass of cells and, later on, of the variety of tissues, organs and limbs characteristic of a human individual. The full complement of genes duplicates with each cell division, so that two complete genomes are present in every cell. Yet different sets of genes are active in different cells. This must be so in order for cells to differentiate: a nerve cell, a muscle cell, and a skin cell are vastly different in size, configuration and function. The differential activity of genes must continue after differentiation, because different cells fulfill different functions, which are controlled by different genes. Nevertheless, experiments with other animals (and some with humans) indicate that all the genes in any cell have the potential of becoming activated. (The sheep Dolly was conceived using the genes extracted from a cell in an adult sheep.)

The information that controls cell and organ differentiation is ultimately contained in the DNA sequence, but mostly in very short segments of it. In mammals, insects and other complex organisms there are control circuits that operate at higher levels than the control mechanisms that activate and deactivate individual genes. These higher-level circuits (such as the so-called *homeobox* genes) act on sets rather than individual genes. The details of how these sets are controlled, how many control systems there are, and how they interact, as well as many other related questions, are what needs to be resolved to elucidate the egg-to-adult transformation. The DNA sequence of some controlling elements has been ascertained, but this is a minor effort that is only helped a little by plowing the way through the entire three thousand million nucleotide pairs that constitute the human genome. Experiments with stem cells are likely to provide important knowledge as scientists ascertain how stem cells become brain cells in one case, muscle cells in another, and so on.

The benefits that the elucidation of the egg-to-adult transformation will bring to mankind are enormous. This knowledge will make possible understanding the modes of action of complex genetic diseases, including cancer, and therefore their cure. It will also bring an understanding of the process of aging, the unforgiving disease that kills all those who have won the battle against other infirmities.

Cancer is an anomaly of ontogenetic decoding: cells proliferate although the welfare of the organism demands otherwise. Individual genes (oncogenes) have been identified that are involved in the causation of particular forms of cancer. But whether or not a cell will turn out cancerous depends on the interaction of the oncogenes with other genes and with the internal and external environment of the cell. Ageing is also a failure of the process of ontogenetic decoding: cells fail to carry out the functions imprinted in their genetic codescript or are no longer able to proliferate and replace dead cells.

5. The Brain-to-Mind Transformation

The most complex and most distinctive human organ is the brain. It consists of 30 billion nerve cells, or neurons, each connected to many others through two kinds of cell extensions, known as the axon and the dendrites. From the evolutionary point of view, the animal brain is a powerful biological adaptation; it allows the organism to obtain and process information about environmental conditions and then to adapt to them. This ability has been carried to the limit in humans, in which the extravagant hypertrophy of the brain makes possible abstract thinking, language and technology. By these means, mankind has ushered in a new mode of adaptation far more powerful than the biological mode: adaptation by culture.

The most rudimentary ability to gather and process information about the environment is found in certain single-celled micro-organisms. The protozoan *Paramecium* swims apparently at random, ingesting the bacteria it encounters, but when it meets unsuitable acidity or salinity, it checks its advance and starts in a new direction. The single-celled alga *Euglena* not only avoids unsuitable environments but seeks suitable ones by orienting itself according to the direction of light, which it perceives through a light-sensitive spot in the cell. Plants have not progressed much further. Except for those with tendrils that twist around any solid object and the few carnivorous plants that react to touch, they mostly react only to gradients of light, gravity and moisture.

In animals the ability to secure and process environmental information is mediated by the nervous system. The simplest nervous systems are found in corals and jellyfish; they lack co-ordination between different parts of their bodies, so any one part is able to react only when it is directly stimulated. Sea urchins and starfish possess a nerve ring and radial nerve cords that co-ordinate stimuli coming from different parts; hence, they respond with direct and unified actions of the whole body. They have no brain, however, and seem unable to learn from experience. Planarian flatworms have the most rudimentary brain known; their central nervous system and brain process and co-ordinate information gathered by sensory cells. These animals are capable of simple learning and hence of variable responses to repeatedly encountered stimuli. Insects and their relatives have much more advanced brains; they obtain precise chemical, acoustic, visual and tactile signals from the environment and process them, making complex behaviors possible, particularly the search for food, selection of mates, and social organization.

Vertebrates – animals with backbones – are able to obtain and process much more complicated signals and to respond to the environment more variably than insects or any other invertebrates. The vertebrate brain contains an enormous number of associative neurons arranged in complex patterns. In vertebrates the ability to react to environmental information is correlated with an increase in the relative size of the cerebral hemispheres and of the neopallium, an organ involved in associating and co-ordinating signals from all receptors and brain centers. In mammals, the neopallium has expanded and become the cerebral cortex. Humans have a very large brain relative to their body size, and a cerebral cortex that is disproportionately large and complex even for their brain size. Abstract thinking, symbolic language, complex social organization, values and ethics are manifestations of the wondrous capacity of the human brain to gather information about the external world and to integrate that information and react flexibly to what is perceived.

With the advanced development of the human brain, biological evolution has transcended itself, opening up a new mode of evolution: adaptation by technological manipulation of the environment. Organisms adapt to the environment by means of natural selection, by changing their genetic constitution over the generations to suit the demands of the environment. Humans, and humans alone, have developed the capacity to adapt to hostile environments by modifying the environments according to the needs of their genes. The discovery of fire and the fabrication of clothing and shelter have allowed humans to spread from the warm tropical and subtropical regions of the Old World, to which we are biologically adapted, to almost the whole earth; it was not necessary for wandering humans that they wait until genes would evolve providing anatomical protection against cold temperatures by means of fur or hair. Nor are humans biding their time in expectation of wings or gills; we have conquered the air and seas with artfully designed contrivances, airplanes and ships. It is the human brain (the human mind) that has made mankind the most successful, by most meaningful standards, living species.

There are not enough bits of information in the complete DNA sequence of a human genome to specify the trillions of connections among the 30 billion neurons of the human brain. Accordingly, the genetic instructions must be organized in control circuits operating at different hierarchical levels so that an instruction at one level is carried through many channels at a lower level in the hierarchy of control circuits. The development of the human brain is indeed one particularly intriguing component of the egg-to-adult transformation.

Within the last two decades, neurobiology has developed into one of the most exciting biological disciplines. An increased commitment of financial and human resources has brought an unprecedented rate of discovery. Much has been learned about how light, sound, temperature, resistance, and chemical impressions received in our sense organs trigger the release of chemical transmitters and electric potential differences that carry the signals through the nerves to the brain and elsewhere in the body. Much has also been learned about how neural channels for information transmission become reinforced by use or may be replaced after damage; about which neurons or groups of neurons are committed to processing information derived from a particular organ or environmental location; and about many other matters. But, for all this progress, neurobiology remains an infant discipline, at a stage of theoretical development comparable perhaps to that of genetics at the beginning of the twentieth century. Those things that count most remain shrouded in mystery: how physical phenomena become mental experiences (the feelings and sensations, called 'qualia' by philosophers, that contribute the elements of consciousness), and how out of the diversity of these experiences emerges the mind, a reality with unitary properties, such as free will and the awareness of self, that persist through an individual's life.

I do not believe that the mysteries of the mind are unfathomable; rather, they are puzzles that humans can solve with the methods of science and illuminate with philosophical analysis and reflection. And I will place my bets that, over the next half century or so, many of these puzzles will be solved. We shall then be well on our way toward answering the Socratic injunction: 'Know thyself'.

Theologians, philosophers and people of faith might say that the soul accounts for the human mind. That is a legitimate claim in a religious or philosophical domain, but scientists will nevertheless want to understand the biological (as well as chemical and electrical) correlates that account for mental experiences. It is well known that the philosopher and mathematician René Descartes (1596–1650) proposed that the soul influences the body by acting through the pineal gland of the brain. This fanciful suggestion leaves unresolved the issues that I have raised: What are the physiological correlates of the mental experiences? We know, for example, that memories are stored in the brain. However, our understanding of the brain states that encompass our mental experiences, or vice versa (i.e., understanding how our mental experiences impact our brain states), remains in its infancy. How the soul, a spiritual entity, might interact with the brain and/or modulate the human mind remains a suitable subject for philosophical and/or theological investigation. It would not seem to be a proper subject for scientific investigation, nor are there any scientific grounds why it should be negated by science.

6. The Ape-to-Human Transformation

The Human Genome Project of the United States was initiated in 1989, funded through two agencies, the National Institutes of Health (NIH) and the Department of Energy (DOE). (A private enterprise, Celera Genomics, started in the US somewhat later, but joined the government-sponsored project in achieving, largely independently, similar results.)

The goal was the complete sequence of one human genome in 15 years at an approximate cost of three thousand million dollars, coincidentally about one dollar per DNA letter. A draft of the genome sequence was completed ahead of schedule in 2001. In 2003 the Human Genome Project was finished. The sequence has become known with as much precision as would be desired.

Knowing the human DNA sequence is a first step, but not more than one step, towards understanding the genetic make-up of a human being. Think of the one thousand Bible-sized volumes. We now know the orderly sequence of the three thousand million letters, but this sequence does not provide an understanding of human beings any more than we would understand the contents of one thousand Bible-sized volumes written in an extraterrestrial language, of which we only know the alphabet, just because we would have come to decipher their letter sequence.

Human beings are not gene machines. The expression of genes in mammals takes place in interaction with the environment, in patterns that are complex and all but impossible to predict in the details – and it is in the details that the self resides. In humans, the 'environment' takes a new dimension, and becomes the dominant one. Humans manipulate the natural environment so that it fits the needs of their biological make-up; for example, making clothing and houses to live in cold climates. Moreover, the products of human technology – art, science, political institutions, and the like – are dominant features of human environments.

There are two conspicuous features of human anatomy: erect posture and a large brain. In mammals, brain size is generally proportional to body size. Relative to body mass, humans have the largest (and most complex) brain among all mammals. The chimpanzee's brain weighs less than a pound; a gorilla's slightly more. Our hominid ancestors had, since at least five million years ago, a bipedal gait, but, as pointed out above, their brain was small, little more than a pound in weight, until about two million years ago. Brain size started to increase notably with our *Homo habilis* ancestors, who had a brain of about one pound and a half. They became tool-makers (hence the name *habilis*) and lasted for a few hundred thousand years, starting about two and a half million years ago. Adult *Homo erectus*, their descendants, had brains reaching up to somewhat more than two pounds in weight. An adult of our species, *Homo sapiens*, has a brain of about three pounds in weight, three times as large as that of the early hominids.

Our brain is not only much larger than that of chimpanzees or gorillas, but also much more complex. Our cerebral cortex, where the higher cognitive functions are processed, takes up a disproportionally greater part of our brain than that of the apes.

A draft of the DNA sequence of the chimpanzee genome was published on 1 September 2005. In the genome regions shared by humans and chimpanzees, the two species are 99 percent identical. The differences appear to be very small or quite large, depending on how one chooses to look at them: One percent of the total seems very little, but it amounts to a difference of 30 million DNA letters out of the three billion in each genome. Twenty-nine percent of the enzymes and other proteins encoded by the genes are identical in both species. Out of the one hundred to several hundred amino acids that make up each protein, the 71 percent of non-identical proteins differ between humans and chimps by only two amino acids, on the average. If one takes into account DNA segments found in one species but not the other, the two genomes are about 96 percent identical, rather than nearly 99 percent identical as in the case of DNA sequences shared by both species. That is, a large amount of genetic material, about 3 percent or some 90 million DNA letters, have been inserted or deleted since humans and chimps initiated their separate evolutionary ways, 7 or 8 million years ago. Most of this DNA does not contain gene coding for proteins.

Comparison of the two genomes provides insights into the rate of evolution of particular genes in the two species. One significant finding is that genes active in the brain have changed more in the human lineage than in the chimp lineage. Also significant is that the fastest evolving human genes are those coding for 'transcription factors', that is, 'switch' proteins, which control the expression of other genes. They determine when other genes are turned on and off. On the whole, 585 genes, including genes involved in resistance to malaria and tuberculosis, have been identified as evolving faster in humans than in chimps. (It might be mentioned that malaria is a severe disease for humans but not for chimps.)

Genes located in the Y chromosome, found only in the male, have been much better protected by natural selection in the human than in the chimpanzee lineage, in which several genes have incorporated disabling mutations that make the genes nonfunctional. Also, there are several regions of the human genome that seem to contain beneficial genes that have rapidly evolved within the past 250,000 years. One region contains the *FOXP2* gene, involved in the evolution of speech.

All this knowledge (and much more of the same kind that will be forthcoming) is of great interest, but what we know so far advances but very little our understanding of what genetic changes make us distinctively human. However, we know some basic features that account for human distinctness and therefore can serve as foundations for a religious view of humankind: the large brain and the accelerated rate of evolution of genes, such as those involved in human speech.

Extended comparisons of the human and chimp genomes and experimental exploration of the functions associated with significant genes will surely advance considerably our understanding, over the next decade or two, of what it is that makes us distinctively human. Surely also, full biological understanding will only come if we solve the second conundrum, the brain-to-mind transformation, which I identified earlier. The distinctive features that make us human begin early in development, well before birth, as the linear information encoded in the genome gradually becomes expressed into a four-dimensional individual, an individual who changes in configuration as time goes by. In an important sense, the most distinctive human features are those expressed in the brain, those that account for the human mind and for human identity.

Some Christian believers will say that the fundamental difference between humans and apes is that we have a soul, created by God, which the apes do not have. I noted earlier that this is a religious or theological question. It will be satisfying for many believers, but it is not *scientifically* satisfactory. What I mean is that, soul or no soul, scientists still want to learn how the anatomical and behavioral differences between humans and apes come to emerge from genetic differences between them. Surely, believers in the soul would not, I hope, believe that there are no biological correlates that account for the ape-to-human differences. That is what scientists seek to understand: what are the genetic and other features that distinguish our species from apes and other animals. Consider, by analogy, a human individual. People of faith may believe that it is the soul infused by God that accounts for what each person is. But surely, this does not deny that each individual develops from a fertilized egg in the mother's womb and later by multiple cell divisions. Nor will we want to ignore the genetic and other features that distinguish one person from another.

Theologians and people of faith who believe in the existence of a spiritual soul, directly created by God for each individual, would want to ask when in hominid evolution were ancestors first endowed with a soul. Did our early hominid ancestors of seven million years ago have a soul? Did *H. habilis* or *H. erectus* have a soul? These are theological, not scientific questions. Similar questions arise in the development of each individual. When is the soul infused into the developing embryo? At the time of conception? Or is the soul created and infused only when the developing fetus first acquires human form, as Thomas Aquinas and other theologians would have it? Or is it when the fetus first has a functional nervous system connected to the brain, which may only happen after the twenty-third week of pregnancy?

As biological understanding of the differences between humans and apes advances, there will surely be much left for philosophical reflection, as well as plenty of issues with great theological significance. Biological knowledge does not eliminate religious belief. Rather, scientific knowledge may provide a basis for theological insights.

7. From Biology to Culture

Humans are notably different from other animals not only in anatomy, but also and no less importantly in their behavior, both as individuals and socially. Humans live in groups that are socially organized, and so do other primates. But primate societies do not approach the complexity of human social organization. A distinctive human social trait is culture, which may be understood as the set of non-strictly biological human activities and creations. Culture includes social and political institutions, ways of doing things, religious and ethical traditions, language, common sense and scientific knowledge, art and literature, technology, and in general all the creations of the human mind.

There are in mankind two kinds of heredity – the biological and the cultural; they may be called organic and superorganic. Biological inheritance in humans is very much like that in any other sexually reproducing organism; it is based on the transmission of genetic information encoded in DNA from one generation to the next by means of the sex cells. Cultural inheritance, on the other hand, is based on transmission of information by a teaching-learning process, which is in principle independent of biological parentage. Culture is transmitted by instruction and learning, by example and imitation, through books, newspapers and radio, television and motion pictures, through works of art, and by any other means of communication. Culture is acquired by every person from parents, relatives and neighbors, and from the whole human environment.

Cultural inheritance makes possible for people what no other organism can accomplish – the cumulative transmission of experience from generation to generation. Animals can learn from experience, but they do not transmit their experiences, their 'discoveries' (at least not to any large extent) to the following generations. Animals have individual memory, but they do not have a 'social memory'. Humans, on the other hand, have developed a culture because they can transmit cumulatively their experiences from generation to generation.

Cultural inheritance makes possible cultural evolution, that is, the evolution of knowledge, social structures, ethics, religion, and all other components that make up human culture. Cultural inheritance makes possible a new mode of adaptation to the environment that is not available to nonhuman organisms – adaptation by means of culture.

Cultural adaptation has prevailed in mankind over biological adaptation because it is a more rapid mode of adaptation and because it can be directed. A favorable genetic mutation newly arisen in an individual can be transmitted to a sizeable part of the human species only through innumerable generations. However, a new scientific discovery or technical achievement can be transmitted to the whole of mankind, potentially at least, in less than one generation. Moreover, whenever a need arises, culture can directly pursue the appropriate changes to meet the challenge. On the contrary, biological adaptation depends on the accidental availability of a favorable mutation, or of a combination of several mutations, at the time and place where the need arises.

Erect posture and a large brain are distinctive anatomical features of modern humans. High intelligence, symbolic language, religion, and ethics are some of the behavioral traits that distinguish us from other animals. The account of human origins that I sketched above implies a continuity in the evolutionary process that goes from our non-human ancestors of eight million years ago through primitive hominids to modern humans. A scientific explanation of that evolutionary sequence must account for the emergence of human anatomical and behavioral traits in terms of natural selection together with other distinctive biological causes and processes.

7

Doctrines of the Fall and Sin
After Darwin

John J. Bimson

Introduction

The Darwinian view of human origins is in evident conflict with traditional
views of the Fall. The evolution of *Homo sapiens* from more primitive
hominids is incompatible with the idea that the first human beings fell from
a state of perfection. In addition, in the decades since the 'New Synthesis',
sociobiology has had some apparent success in explaining human nature
without recourse to the Fall and original sin (Williams, 2001; Domning and
Hellwig, 2006; but cf. Polkinghorne, 2005: 44–45).

There has been a wide range of responses to this situation. To mention
only the four positions most commonly encountered (some of which
occur in several variants):

1) At one extreme, some have rejected an evolutionary view of human
   origins altogether, preferring to defend Genesis 1–3 as a (more or less)
   literal account of our beginnings (e.g. MacArthur 2001). This response,
   which relies on naïve hermeneutics and dubious science, has been
   ably answered elsewhere (Collins, 2007; Alexander, 2008) and need
   not detain us here.
2) The opposite extreme has been to treat the early chapters of Genesis
   as primitive aetiologies which are not to be taken seriously by the
   modern believer (Williams, 2001: 64–70, 89–90; Burge, 2005: 95–98).
   However, many biblical scholars and theologians (including this
   writer) think there is rather more to these narratives than this.

3) For some it is simply an error to read Genesis 3 as the story of the Fall; it is an analysis of the universal human situation rather than a description of how it came to be (e.g. Tillich, 1957: 33; Hick, 1966: 181; Brueggemann, 1982: 50–54; Southgate, 2008: 28–9 and 101–02). Arguably it is possible to hold a coherent view of Christ's work of redemption without belief in a historical Fall (e.g. Hick, 1966; Southgate, 2008; see also Williams, 2001; Domning and Hellwig, 2006; Messer, this volume).

4) For others, however, a historical Fall remains an indispensable element of Christian belief, and they have tried to find a place for it within an evolutionary view of human origins (e.g. Ward, 1998: 132–33; Berry, 1999; Polkinghorne, 2005: 139; Schwager, 2006; Alexander, 2008).

Rather than analyze each of these positions, I will begin by considering the nature of Genesis 2–3 and asking what the narrative is saying. That discussion will direct us to position (4), and we will then examine two different attempts to integrate a view of the Fall with evolutionary theory.

Our discussion of Genesis 2–3 will also highlight the need to distinguish between the traditional understanding of the Fall and what the biblical text actually says. In the Western Churches the traditional understanding reflects the overwhelming influence of Augustine of Hippo (AD 354–430). In Augustine's view, Adam and Eve were created physically and morally perfect, enjoying perpetual gladness in the presence of God. But (inexplicably!) they began secretly desiring to live for themselves; thus they became open to the devil's snares and fell through disobedience (*City of God* xiv, 13 and 26). It is also to Augustine that we owe the concept of original sin. Although earlier Christian writers had used this term for an impulse towards evil that has been with us since the Fall, in the Augustinian tradition 'sin is *contingent, radical, communicable* and *universal*' (McFadyen, 2000: 16; italics original). Augustine also gave us the idea that all the descendants of Adam share in his guilt for the first sin (*Enchiridion* 26; *City of God* xiii, 14).

In developing his doctrines of the Fall and original sin Augustine obviously drew on biblical passages such as Genesis 2–3 and Romans 5:12–21. However it is important to notice that his *interpretation* of those texts was influenced by ideas from elsewhere. As Hill explains (2003: 86), Augustine's idea of original sin can be traced partly to Platonism and partly to a theory that every child existed 'in seed form' in its father before being implanted in its mother's womb: 'So Augustine could plausibly believe that the entire human race really did exist "in Adam" at the time of his sin, like a set of Russian dolls.' In other words, Augustine's interpretation of the biblical texts was influenced by the 'genetic theory' of his day. There is no reason to think this influence operated subconsciously. Augustine believed that, to avoid looking foolish in the eyes of non-believers, Christians should equip themselves with the best knowledge available and employ it in their reading of scripture (*The Literal Meaning of Genesis*, 1, xix, 39). It is ironic that in searching for an interpretation of the Bible that makes sense in the light of evolutionary theory we are following Augustine's own recommendation.

After examining how, if at all, the message of Genesis 2–3 may have coherence in an evolutionary context, I will briefly address the question of a 'cosmic fall' before drawing some conclusions.

1. The Nature of the Genesis 2–3 Narrative

The first thing of which we must remind ourselves is that Genesis 2–3 is ancient Hebrew literature. It is easy to forget this because it seems to transcend specifically Israelite concerns, dealing with mankind in general rather than with Israel in particular. Indeed the name Adam means 'mankind' (and first appears as a noun in Gen 1:26). But, whatever its larger themes, Genesis 2–3 also forms part of a prologue to the history of Israel, and has features that are specifically Israelite. When Adam names his wife Eve, and when she names her first son Cain, the names involve wordplays in classical Hebrew (a language the first human beings are unlikely to have spoken!). The description of Eden resonates with Israelite iconography: 'Water, gold, jewels, cherubim and so on link the Garden of Eden with the tabernacle and temples described later' (Wenham, 1990: 318; cf. Walton, 2007: 124–5).

As Israelite literature, Genesis 1–11 also belongs to the wider world of the ancient Near East and it should not surprise us that it shares motifs with other literature from that world. There was a time when it was fashionable to view Genesis 1–11 as a collection of stories borrowed, with appropriate modification, from ancient Mesopotamia at the time of the Babylonian exile. Now it is generally recognized that the relationship between the biblical narrative and earlier myths is subtle and sophisticated (Wenham, 1987: xlvi–l; Middleton, 2005: 93–145). Where elements of Near Eastern myths are recalled in the early chapters of Genesis, they are 'used self-consciously, in such a way that it is plain that Genesis is keeping a deliberate distance from, even taking explicit issue with, the ethos of the myths' (McConville, 1980: 8–9; cf. Wenham, 1987: 52–3). Because of this polemical quality Genesis – 11 could be called 'anti-myth'. However, as McConville points out (1980: 9), this does not mean we can leap to the conclusion that it is not myth but history:

> Indeed there is a sense in which 'anti-myth' must be closely akin to myth . . . When Genesis opposes the myths it is actually fulfilling a very similar function to that which they fulfil. It is answering fundamental questions about existence primarily in a given (Israelite) society. The questions are the same.

The answers are different (the right ones rather than the wrong ones!). But it is important to realize that Genesis . . . takes its character primarily from circumstances and necessities which characterized the ancient world in which it was given.

But if the genre and intent of Genesis 2–3 mean the story is not to be taken literally, do they also mean it makes no reference at all to actual events? Is it paradigmatic (this is the universal human situation), or is it aetiological (here's how we came to be this way)? It has reasonably been argued – and it is the view taken in the present chapter – that it is both, and that we fail to do justice to this subtle narrative if we neglect either aspect (McConville, 1980: 10–15; Wenham, 1990: 318–321; Fretheim, 2005: 71).

In its aetiological aspect, then, the narrative refers to a real event within history. But it does so with great literary freedom in language that is culturally encoded, symbolic and metaphorical (Habel, 1965: 3–9; McConville, 1980: 15). Put simply, it speaks of a real disruption at the start of the human story, but does not require us to believe this involved two people, a piece of fruit and a talking snake.

Three important things follow from all this. Firstly, the narrator has chosen a literary form which conveys deeper truth than is found in straightforward historiography. It provides not history but theological commentary, bringing out the significance of the events to which it refers. Secondly, those actual events remain unrecoverable by the modern historian. The text is not open to the kind of questions a historian would like to put to it. This means that proposals concerning the realities to which the narrative alludes must always be speculative. Thirdly, it is a text addressed to a faith community; it is within a faith community seeking to understand reality and the overarching purposes of God that it can be expected to speak.

2. What the Genesis Narrative Says about the Human Fall

What, in essence, is the reality to which the 'Fall' metaphor points? In recent decades biblical scholarship has advocated both a 'close reading' of the text and an attention to larger narrative structures. As a result, fresh insights have emerged concerning the early chapters of Genesis which challenge the Augustinian reading and point us in other directions.

2.1 Problems with 'Fall' language

It is important to note that the language of a 'Fall' is nowhere used in the Old or New Testament to refer to what happens in Genesis 3. The term is first found in this connection in the Jewish apocalyptic work known as 2 Esdras (or 4 Ezra), where Ezra exclaims: 'O Adam, what have you done? Though the sin was yours, the fall was not yours alone; it was ours also, the fall of all your descendants' (2 Esdras 7:118, translation from REB Apocrypha). The popularity of 2 Esdras in the early church led to Christian authors adopting the term. However, this text refers only to one specific consequence of Adam's act, namely a fall from potential immortality, and does not contain the broader connotations of later Christian understanding (Goldingay, 2003: 145–46; cf. Colwell, 1988: 249).

Applying the language of 'Fall' to Genesis 3 is from the outset problematic (Brueggemann, 1982: 41). Goldingay notes three drawbacks (2003: 145–47). Firstly, it implies that human beings fell from 'a position of splendor, prestige and exaltation . . . from immortality to mortality.' This Augustinian image goes far beyond anything in the text, and the assumption of prelapsarian immortality is actually contradicted by statements about the tree of life in Gen 2:9, 16 and 3:22 (cf. Ricoeur, 1969: 233; Blocher, 1984: 135; Barr, 1992: 1–21). Secondly, while traditional Fall language implies a life lived in heaven-like union with God before the primal sin, the text itself describes the first human pair 'only as having the opportunity to learn obedience and grow to moral maturity. The tragedy of Genesis 1–3 is not that human beings fell from a state of bliss but that they failed to realize a possibility . . .'. Thirdly, while Augustine saw in the story a change in moral capacity (such that before the Fall human beings were able not to sin, but afterwards they were not), in Genesis 3 'we find the same dynamics of temptation and disobedience on the way to the "Fall" as we ourselves experience after it'.

Further problems arise from a tendency to isolate Genesis 3 from the chapters that follow. Thus Fretheim finds 'Fall' language in its traditional sense 'reductionistic' and inappropriate when applied to Genesis 3 in isolation. A greater appreciation of the thematic links between Genesis 2–3 and the following chapters provides a different perspective: ' . . . Chapter 3 describes the "originating sin," and the chapters that follow speak of a process by which sin becomes "original," that is, universal and inescapable . . .' (Fretheim, 2005: 70; cf. Westermann, 1984: 2–3; Goldingay, 2003: 147). Understanding the place of Genesis 2–3 in a larger narrative requires us to rethink traditional views of both the Fall and original sin.

However, none of this means that we should no longer speak of a Fall. Fretheim himself remarks that, in view of the imagery used throughout Genesis 3 – 11, it would still be appropriate 'to speak of a fall in the sense of a falling "out" or "apart"' (2005: 71). 'Fall' language also remains valid as an affirmation that things are not as God intended.

2.2 Genesis 3 and the nature of the primal sin

When we try to explore the details of Genesis 3 we find several things frustratingly elusive. The account offers no clear explanation for the origin of evil. The nature and presence of the snake (the word traditionally translated 'serpent' means nothing more or less than that) remain enigmatic. (For a variety of views on this see Habel, 1965: 10–14; Blocher, 1984: 150–154; Bechtel, 1995: 17–18; Fretheim, 2003: 73–75; Schwager, 2006: 153–155.) Furthermore, we are not told why a potentially fatal tree is growing in the middle of God's paradisal garden. However, it is clear that this prohibited tree is the key to the nature of the primal sin. It is 'the tree of the knowledge of good and evil'. What are we meant to deduce from this?

In the light of the snake's words in Gen 3:5 ('you will be like God, knowing good and evil'), the first sin has been viewed as a Promethean project, an arrogant grasping at knowledge and the power it brings. As Habel puts it: 'The woman wants the knowledge of good and evil that belongs to the gods, and she sees in the tree the means of discovering the secret . . . In a word the supreme *hybris* of man is exposed' (Habel, 1965: 17; cf. Knight, 1981: 38).

But to understand the transgression as grasping for godlike knowledge and power 'is insufficiently primal, for it assumes a more basic problem, namely, mistrust' (Fretheim, 2005: 71). Furthermore, as Fretheim goes on to point out (2005: 322), it highlights one aspect of our problematic human consciousness at the expense of another: 'Such a perspective, with its emphasis on sin as pride, thinking of yourself more highly than you ought to think, tends to neglect the sin of self-denigration, thinking of yourself less highly than you ought to think. The latter is a fundamental human problem that needs greater recognition.' Habel's identification of 'the supreme *hybris* of man' with the motivation of the woman is particularly unfortunate, for as Keller (1986: 12) observes, the traditional identification of sin with pride and self-assertion has helped reinforce the subordination of women, whose real temptation has often been towards self-negation.

It is important to ask what is meant by 'knowledge of good and evil'. Several options have been proposed and a full discussion would be out of place here (see Westermann, 1984: 242–245; Wenham, 1987: 62–64). Some proposals are ruled out by the text itself, and the range is narrowed if we take as a guide the statement that the fruit of the tree was to be desired to 'make wise' or 'give insight' (Gen. 3:6).

The wider context excludes the possibility that it is knowledge in general that is forbidden. Possession of knowledge and insight on the first man's part is assumed by the Genesis narrative (he is expected to name the animals and birds, and to work the ground – the latter implying some level of technology). In Job 28:1–11 the technological achievements involved in penetrating the secrets of the earth (probably the OT equivalent of space exploration) are celebrated. In Proverbs 8 the same Ms Wisdom who is said to have worked with God on the construction of the universe invites humanity to learn from her (Prov. 8:1–11 and 22–30). Furthermore the image of Ms Wisdom 'delighting' in the human world (Prov. 8:31) implies divine pleasure in humanity's cultural achievements.

The solution that raises fewest problems, and which finds some support from near-parallel expressions elsewhere in the OT, is that 'knowledge of good and evil' means the capacity to distinguish between right and wrong, not in an abstract moral sense but specifically to decide *what is good and bad for human beings* (Goldingay, 2003: 132).

This, of course, is an entirely good thing for people to be able to do. But the story does not portray possession of this knowledge as an end in itself. The end is to 'become like God'. Ricouer comments: 'What is forbidden is not this or that, but a state of autonomy which would make man the creator of the distinction between good and evil.' (1969: 350; cf. Polkinghorne, 1991: 100; Berry, 1999: 34). Fretheim offers a different view: 'The issue of knowledge at its deepest level is an issue of *trust* . . . The primal sin may thus best be defined as mistrust of God . . . which then manifests itself in disobedience . . .' (2005: 74). The two views are not at odds however, for mistrusting God and wanting autonomy from him can readily be seen as two sides of the same coin.

But autonomy, once gained, is clearly something the first human pair cannot handle. Its outworking is fear, shame and discord. Ironically, mistrust increases and relationships disintegrate at all levels (Gen. 3:7–13). It is worth noting that this part of the story tells strongly against interpretations in which the Fall is turned into a 'rise' or maturation process (e.g. Bechtel, 1995). The theme of becoming like God may superficially suggest something of the kind, and a developmental reading allows some interesting psychoanalytic sidelights to be shone on the text, but such interpretations have to ignore the fact that the story is one of catastrophic losses rather than gains.

These negative consequences (manifesting themselves *before* God pronounces judgment in Genesis 3:14–19) should also preclude any idea that the prohibition is an act of miserliness or jealousy on God's part. Rather, the natural reading is that God wanted to protect human beings from consequences they were unable to cope with at this stage in their existence (Ricoeur, 1969: 250; Knight, 1981: 37; Schwager, 2006: 20).

If the foregoing analysis is correct, it also excludes the view that the story simply illustrates the selfishness that drove our evolution (Domning and Hellwig, 2006). Rather, it deals with an originative event that gave a catastrophic twist to our relationship with God.

2.3 Death as a consequence of the primal sin

It has been a widespread belief that human physical death entered the world for the first time through Adam's sin. This belief derives not from Genesis 3 directly but from Paul's statement that 'sin came into the world through one man, and death through sin, and so death spread to all men because all sinned' (Rom. 5:12). The introduction of death in this way is clearly a nonsense in the context of evolutionary theory. One response to this is to interpret death in Romans 5:12 not as physical but 'theological' or 'spiritual' death (e.g. Berry, 1999: 34–5, and sources cited there), as is clearly the case in other NT passages (e.g. Eph. 2:1, 5; Col. 2:13; 1 John 3:14; cf. Luke 15:24). A close reading of Genesis 3 partially supports this interpretation, but also points beyond it.

At first sight the consequences of eating from the knowledge tree do not seem to include the death of which God had warned ('in the day you eat of it you shall surely die', Gen. 2:17). Some writers have suggested we have here another case of 'spiritual death' (e.g. Alexander, 2008: 260–261), but this does not do justice to the OT context. In the OT death is understood in broader terms than the termination of life. Metaphorically it includes anything which threatens, diminishes or impoverishes life: pain, discord, exile, persecution, separation and so on (Wolff, 1974: 111; Blocher, 1984: 171–73). In this sense 'death' appropriately describes the immediate consequence of the primal sin. The first humans' relationship with God becomes dysfunctional: their pathetic attempt to cover their nakedness with fig leaves, their hiding among the trees when God walks in the garden and the man's talk of being afraid (Gen. 3:7–10), add up to a poignant evocation of lost intimacy. In OT terms there is undoubtedly a kind of death here – what Fretheim calls 'the experience of death within life' (2005: 77).

But this loss is then underscored by their expulsion from the garden to prevent access to the tree of life (Gen. 3:22–23). It seems likely that the tree of life, like trees elsewhere in the OT (Ps. 1:2–3; Jer. 17:7–8), is 'symbolic of the life of God' (Wenham, 1987: 62). The sanctuary symbolism contained in the description of Eden and its garden, which has this tree at its centre (Gen. 2:9), strengthens this view (Wenham, 1986: Walton, 2007: 124–5). The imagery speaks of proximity and intimacy with God who is the source of life.

Nowhere in Genesis 2 – 3 is it implied that Adam and Eve were immortal (Barr, 1992: 1–20). It is not even stated that God intended them to live forever by eating from the tree of life, only that this was a possibility for them (Gen. 3:22). Their exclusion from the tree – merciful rather than punitive, given the straits in which they now find themselves – removes this possibility. As Fretheim (2005: 77) expresses it: 'So God makes a further move beyond death within life, namely, exclusion from the tree, so that their mortality is realized.' This reading enables Fretheim to offer the following comment on Rom 5:12–21: 'The upshot of this interpretation is that Paul's understanding of sin and death in Rom 5:12–21, while developing these themes beyond the scope of the story, is right to read the story in terms of an etiology of the full reality of death, if not mortality per se.'

This view supplies what is otherwise lacking in a 'spiritual death' interpretation of Genesis 2:17 and Romans 5:12–21. It allows both texts reference to physical death (alongside other levels) without denying that human mortality was a fact before the Fall.

3. The Fall in an Evolutionary Context

How, if at all, can the Fall narrative be reconciled with evolutionary theory? We will look at two recent attempts to develop integrated models.

3.1 Adam as a Neolithic farmer?

A number of conservative scholars, while not taking the narrative of Genesis 2–3 literally, find grounds in the New Testament for defending the historicity of Adam and Eve. Berry, for example, writes: 'Paul's carefully constructed analogy between Adam and Christ depends on the equal historicity of both (Romans 5:12–19; see also 1 Corinthians 15:21, 45)' (Berry, 1999: 35, quoting John Stott; also Alexander, 2008: 265).

But if Adam and Eve were historical individuals, when did they live? Victor Pearce (1969) uses various details in Genesis 2–4 to arrive at an approximate date, and his argument has been adopted by Berry (1988: 68–71; 1999, 38–9; 2007) and Alexander (2008: 241–243). Pearce's evidence can be summarized briefly as follows: Adam was a farmer (his task in the garden was to till it and care for it); so was his son Cain, while Abel was a shepherd; Cain founded a city, and six generations later Tubal-cain became 'the master of all coppersmiths and blacksmiths'. These (and other) clues suggest a date for Adam and Eve about 10,000–15,000 years ago (Berry), or 6,000–8,000 years ago (Alexander).

By this time modern humans (*Homo sapiens*) had spread all around the globe, so it is impossible for a Neolithic Adam to have been their genetic ancestor. However, in recent versions of the theory this is immaterial, for the crucial claim, as Berry (1999: 39) expresses it, is that Adam 'could be the *spiritual* founder of humankind, since the "spiritualness" in us (i.e. God's image) is not a genetic factor.' On this view, 'God could have gone on to put ("breathed") his image into all members of the species *H. sapiens* alive at the time of Adam.' It is only when thus endowed that *Homo sapiens* becomes fully human from a theological perspective, and can be called *Homo divinus* (a term coined by Stott, 1972: 63). This change from *H. sapiens* to *H. divinus* would be of purely theological significance and not detectable in any way by anthropologists, geneticists or archaeologists.

But if Adam is not the biological ancestor of modern humanity he must be seen as humanity's representative or 'federal head' in order to make sense of the Fall. 'Adam's "federal" headship of humanity extended . . . outwards to his contemporaries as well as onwards to his offspring, and his disobedience disinherited both alike' (Kidner, 1967: 29).

Thus formulated, the 'Neolithic Adam' scenario neatly sidesteps some of the problems that would otherwise beset it. But difficulties remain. Firstly, if Adam is to be located in (pre)history by means of details in Genesis 2–4, why are some details ignored? The narrative refers to the introduction of clothing (3:7 and 21) and to the invention of musical instruments (4:21) – details which, if taken literally, would indicate times much earlier than the Neolithic period: the first use of clothing has been dated at least 100,000, possibly 500,000 years ago (Kittler *et al.*, 2003; Reed *et al.*, 2004) and bone flutes date back at least 32,000 years (Tattershall, 2006: 73). In short, the details do not point consistently to a particular date and Pearce's selection seems somewhat arbitrary. In particular, why focus on Tubal-cain's status as an early metallurgist while ignoring the status of his half-brother Jubal as 'ancestor of all those who play the lyre and pipe'?

Secondly, the name Adam gives to his wife ('Eve, because she was the mother of all living') and the genealogies in Genesis 4 and 5 do seem intended to portray Adam as ancestor, not simply 'federal head' (notwithstanding Kidner, 1967: 29–30).

Also troubling is the view that the 'image of God' (Gen 1:26–27) can be equated in some way with God breathing the breath of life into the first man (Gen 2:7). The Bible nowhere brings these two things together. Furthermore, Middleton's recent and comprehensive study of what Genesis 1 means by the 'image of God' leads to the conclusion that 'the *imago Dei* refers to human rule, that is, the exercise of power on God's behalf in creation'; 'Imaging God thus involves representing and perhaps extending in some way God's rule on earth through the ordinary communal practices of human sociocultural life' (Middleton, 2005: 88, 60). While agriculture and the domestication of animals are likely to have been important aspects of this, it is difficult to believe that human beings were not imaging God before the Neolithic revolution.

The chief appeal of the 'Neolithic Adam' theory is that it fulfils the requirement for an historical Adam which some feel to be implicit in Romans 5:12–21. However, the logic of this position is questionable. As Dunn (1988: 289) points out:

. . . It would not be true to say that Paul's theological point here depends on Adam being a "historical" individual or on his disobedience being a historical event as such. Such an implication does not necessarily follow from the fact that a parallel is drawn with Christ's single act: an act in mythic history can be paralleled to an act in living history without the point of comparison being lost. So long as the story of Adam as the initiator of the sad tale of human failure was well known, which we may assume (the brevity of Paul's presentation presupposes such a knowledge), such a comparison was meaningful.

As to what Paul himself believed about Adam, Dunn is dismissive of 'patronizing generalizations about the primitive mind naturally understanding the Adam stories as literally historical.' He points to Plutarch's *De Iside et Osiride* (32ff.) for evidence of the sophistication with which stories about the dawn of human history could be treated (the literal meaning often being ignored). He adds that the real force of the comparison between Adam and Christ 'is not so much to historicize the individual Adam as to bring out the more than individual significance of the historic Christ' (Dunn, 1988: 290; see also Ricoeur, 1969: 238–9, 271–5).

Without the requirement for a single historical Adam (or Eve) the 'Neolithic Adam' theory is further weakened. In view of its difficulties we will turn to another model for integrating the Fall with evolutionary theory.

3.2 A Fall at the dawn of human consciousness?

Representative of an alternative approach is John Polkinghorne's suggestion (2005: 139) that we take the story of the Fall as 'the symbol of a turning away from God into the self that occurred with the dawning of hominid self-consciousness, so that thereby humanity became curved-in upon itself, asserting autonomy and refusing to acknowledge heteronomous dependence . . .'. Writers who have expressed similar views include C.S. Lewis (1940: 57–76), Keith Ward (1998: 132–33), Allan Day (1998: 137–141), Raymund Schwager (2006) and Francis Collins (2007: 206–210).

Alexander (2008: 240) has objected that such an early date for the events underlying Genesis 2–3 would detach them from the Near Eastern context in which the narrative's local colour would seem to place them. But this overlooks the fact that Eden, with its baffling geography, is probably 'symbolic of a place where God dwells', furnished by him with everything needed for fecundity and plenty (Wenham, 1987: 61; cf. Walton, 2007: 124–5). It is to be expected that the details of this symbolism would be drawn from the ancient Near Eastern world known to the biblical author and his audience.

It is still unclear whether the kind of (self-)consciousness involved here appeared with the emergence of anatomically modern humans (dated to around 200,000 years ago; Renfrew, 2007: 86), or with the emergence of symbolic cognitive processes (perhaps as late as 70,000–60,000 years ago; Tattershall, 2006), or at some point in between. I will decline to speculate on this, given the ongoing debates within the field of cognitive archaeology (e.g. Dunbar, 1996; Mithen, 1998: Tattersall, 2002; Renfrew, 2007; Gamble, 2007).

The most sophisticated elaboration of a Fall at the dawn of human consciousness is that of the Jesuit theologian Raymund Schwager. In Schwager's model the first humans emerged from our hominid ancestors when they experienced 'an intensive, yet provisionally still implicit elimination of limits on the horizons of consciousness'. This was not in itself the origin of fully human consciousness but merely the first step in a process: 'Thus emerged the task of gradually realizing this new human possibility in order to explicitly constitute human consciousness as such.' This lifting of the boundaries of consciousness was, from a scientific perspective, an aspect of the evolutionary process and could be termed 'emergence' (in which a combination of pre-existing elements results in something radically new), but it can also be viewed theologically as a result of God's creative activity (cf. Day, 1998: 138, for a similar point). As such, the experience of self-transcendence was nothing less than a call by which God 'summoned the first humans to embark on a path that would eventually lead them – through an unknown, shared future – to explicit cognition of God and communion with him and among themselves' (Schwager, 2006: 93–94).

Because the goal of human development was to be realized in community, it is important for Schwager that this process involved a group rather than one or two individuals. However, the group which underwent this experience shied away from the divine summons:

> Instead they heeded the voices of their familiar (animal) past and turned the gift they had received into a means of self-assertion. Thus the removal of restrictions on consciousness led to a problematic self-formation of human consciousness, because it included experiences of fear of the numinous and an increased tendency to violent conflicts (2006: 94).

The experience of self-transcendence should have prompted the first humans 'to outgrow the reactions of creatures in the animal world', but their actual response to their new freedom meant that 'the initially positive mechanisms achieved during evolution in the animal realm now became operative in a perverted form' (2006: 52). For Schwager the primal sin can therefore be understood at one level as a choice to continue in ways that had been natural (indeed vital for human evolution), but which became unnatural in the context of newly expanded consciousness. From this perspective he finds evolutionary theory to be 'helpful in making clear how sin can have effects all the way into the self-formation of humans . . .' (2006: 92).

Schwager does not believe we should think in terms of a Fall that occurred at a single moment in time. Rather, he envisages a long process which 'could have begun with a seemingly harmless slipping away from the original gift-like experience . . .' (2006: 52). Day (1998: 139) has also advocated viewing the Fall as a process, 'the gradual emergence of an attitude rather than an individual act'.

As a Roman Catholic theologian, Schwager is concerned to explain the transmission of original sin. He finds a plausible mechanism in René Girard's mimetic theory (e.g. Girard, 1987), in which competitive imitation of others operates 'as a kind of quasi-osmotic contact'. According to mimetic theory, acquisitive imitation spawns various forms of rivalry which easily develop 'into open aggression, even into homicide. In the wake of imitation (mimesis) evil spreads further like contagion, for it draws still other people and all realms of life – even reason – into its domain' (Schwager, 2006: 15). Schwager goes on to offer a compelling reading of Genesis 1–11 in the light of the theory (2006: 16–23).

This view of the spread of sin to all human beings gains some plausibility from the suggestion that language and associated symbolic behaviour could have spread rapidly to all human populations from one group by a form of cultural diffusion (Tattersall, 2006). In light of that possibility it is certainly feasible to suggest that 'fallenness' may have spread by Girardian mimesis. If this hypothesis is rejected, the alternative would be the divine imputation of sin to all humanity (a possibility raised by Day, 1998: 139, though he does not appear to favour it).

Whether Schwager's synthesis succeeds in preserving the Roman Catholic doctrines of the Fall and original sin is for others to decide. I do believe it is compatible in various ways with a careful reading of the biblical text. It coheres with our earlier observations on the progressive nature of the 'Fall' in Genesis 1–11, where we noted Fretheim's view that 'Chapter 3 describes the "originating sin," and the chapters that follow speak of a *process* by which sin becomes "original," that is, universal and inescapable . . .'. It also resonates with Goldingay's observation that 'The tragedy of Genesis 1–3 is not that human beings fell from a state of bliss but that they failed to realize a possibility . . .' The emphasis on violence which mimetic theory brings to Schwager's reading of Genesis 1–11 is also echoed by Goldingay when he notes that the double reference to an earth 'filled with violence' in Genesis 6:11–13 'confirms the hint in Genesis 4 that the essence of sin, in the sense that Genesis uses the word, lies in human violence' (Goldingay, 2003: 165). This is not in conflict with our conclusion that the essence of the *primal* sin was a preference for autonomy over dependency on God, for the Genesis text itself points to a relationship between this primal sin and violence; biblical scholars have noted thematic, linguistic and structural parallels between Genesis 3 and the story of Abel's murder in Genesis 4 (Fretheim, 1969: 93–4; Hauser, 1980: 297–305; Wenham, 1990: 319–20).

Like all proposals for understanding the Fall in an evolutionary context, Schwager's is necessarily speculative. But at the present time it is by far the most sophisticated interdisciplinary approach on offer.

3.3 Irenaeus on the wrong way to rise

We have seen that much of the difficulty in reconciling the Fall with evolutionary theory stems not directly from the biblical text but from the Augustinian patina that adheres to it. Irenaeus of Lyon (c. AD 130–200) suggests openings onto a very different view of Genesis 2–3, and one that is more congenial to evolutionary theory. For this and other reasons some recent writers have preferred an Irenaean to an Augustinian perspective (e.g. Polkinghorne, 1991: 99–100; Hick, 1966: 289–297; Day, 1998: 141). Irenaeus' view of the Fall is complex and only the most relevant strands of his thinking can be picked out here.

Irenaeus believed that the first human beings were not created morally and physically perfect, because at the beginning they were childlike and could not receive perfection (*Against Heresies* IV, xxxviii, 1). In his view it was always God's intention that mankind should acquire maturity 'throughout a long course of ages', by a process which involves men and women being increasingly 'rendered after the image and likeness of the uncreated God' (*AH* IV, xxxviii, 3). While Irenaeus' understanding of the image and likeness of God is exegetically doubtful, there is a good deal in his view of humanity which has contemporary value.

One of Irenaeus' boldest and most imaginative conclusions (for which he creatively brings together Gen. 3:22 and 1 Cor. 15:53–54) is that this process will culminate in redeemed humanity receiving, along with the fullness of God's image and likeness, 'the knowledge of good and evil' (*AH* IV, xxxviii, 4). His idea that this knowledge was ultimately to be part of God's gift may be surprising, but it finds an echo in Goldingay's understanding of Genesis 2:17. By reading Genesis 2–3 in the light of Genesis 22, Goldingay argues that the prohibition was only temporary: 'God is testing Adam and Eve. If they pass the test, as Abraham will, then it can be terminated and they can be given the insight the tree conveys. But they cannot take it. They have to be willing to let God give it . . .' (Goldingay, 2003: 132). With this we can also compare the speculation in C.S. Lewis's novel *Voyage to Venus* (*Perelandra*) (Lewis, 1943: ch. 17).

In Irenaeus' view, therefore, there was no fall from perfection but a failure to ascend by the correct route. The goal of God's plan was deferred by an attempt to accelerate it autonomously. However, this was not the malign and ultimately incomprehensible rebellion of the Augustinian tradition, but a lapse by beings who were no more than children in understanding. God's goal for humanity became attainable once again through the person and work of Christ (see further Tennant, 1903: 282–291; Hick, 1966: 217–221; Hill, 2003: 24–29).

It is a tragedy that in the Western Churches the Irenaean understanding of Genesis 2–3 has been eclipsed by the Augustinian doctrine of the Fall. Irenaeus' history-spanning vision has the potential to be a meeting-place between evolutionary theory and the biblical text, and its recovery is long overdue. Although Schwager does not discuss Irenaeus's view, it is possible to read some aspects of his theory – such as the emphasis on process, and on a failure to respond positively to 'the original gift-like experience' – as a modern evolutionary reformulation of some of the ancient theologian's insights.

4. What of a Cosmic Fall?

In the second century the idea began to develop that the first human sin brought deleterious effects on other parts of creation (e.g. Theophilus of Antioch, *To Autolychus*, II, 17). These effects have been understood in different ways at different times, but generally include such things as disease, floods, earthquakes, volcanic eruptions, animal predation and parasitism. The idea that human sin distorted God's originally perfect creation is generally referred to as the cosmic fall.

The cosmic fall is in even deeper trouble from an evolutionary perspective than the human fall. Not only does Darwinian evolution know nothing of a time when predation was absent from the animal world, it shifts it from being a side-effect of human sin to being an essential ingredient in the long process that gave rise to *Homo sapiens*. Furthermore, the earth had its earthquakes and volcanoes long before it was home to complex life; indeed, it might never have been able to support complex life without them (Ward and Brownlee, 2000: 191–200).

In spite of this, some modern theologians still attribute unpleasant or dangerous aspects of the non-human world to some distortion of the original creation. N. T. Wright describes living 'on an earthquake fault line . . . or by an active volcano' as being 'at the sharp end of the corruption of creation' (Wright, 2004: 151). Others include death and predation in the animal world among creation's supposed abnormalities (e.g. Linzey, 2000).

In order to salvage aspects of the cosmic fall within an evolutionary context, some have proposed locating the distortion of creation before human history, attributing it to rebellious angels (e.g. Lewis, 1940: 121–124; Lloyd, 1998), a view which arguably creates more problems than it solves (Blocher, 1984: 41–43; Southgate, 2008: 31–34).

I have previously discussed the biblical texts on which the idea of a 'cosmic fall' is based, showing that they do not say what they are often assumed to say, and that other texts actually contradict the idea (Bimson, 2006). A good theological critique of the cosmic fall has been provided by Southgate (2008: 28–35). There is no space to repeat the arguments here, but a few comments are in order.

Evolutionary cosmology, geology and biology provide adequate scientific explanations for those features of the world which are often labelled 'natural evil' (Polkinghorne, 2005: 136–146). The question is whether, within an evolutionary framework and without a cosmic fall, there can be an adequate *theological* explanation. The problem, as commonly framed, is that a God who is loving and good would not have created a world that contains such potential for creaturely suffering. A number of suggestions can be offered in response.

Firstly, it can be argued that this potential for suffering (and therefore the existence of real suffering) is inseparable from God's gift of freedom to his creation. Thus Polkinghorne (1996: 45–46) writes of God's act of creation as 'necessarily a costly and vulnerable action in which divine almightiness is qualified by the loving gift of an appropriate degree of independence to the beloved creature . . .'. More recently he has coined the term '*Kenosis of causal status*' to describe his belief that '*the Creator's kenotic love includes allowing divine special providence to act as a cause among causes*' (2001: 104; italics original). While Polkinghorne and others have brought a new sophistication to thinking about this issue, Kaiser (1991: 15–18) has shown that 'the relative autonomy of nature' is a theme found in the Bible itself and in intertestamental Judaism and early Christian texts.

Secondly, it is entirely reasonable to suppose that 'a creation evolving according to Darwinian principles' – with all the costs that involves – 'was the only way in which God could give rise to the sort of beauty, diversity, sentience, and sophistication of creatures that the biosphere now contains' (Southgate, 2008: 16).

Thirdly, it seems likely that such complex life could never have evolved on a planet without plate tectonics (Ward and Brownlee, 2000: 191–200). In that case the potential for earthquakes, volcanic eruptions and tsunamis is inseparable from the extraordinary beauty and diversity of life on earth, including the existence of human beings. In a phrase of Polkinghorne's, creation is 'necessarily a package deal' (2005: 144). Its values are not attainable without its disvalues.

But would God have described such a world as 'very good', as we read in Gen 1:31? Rather than meaning that the original creation was devoid of harms or disvalues, the word 'good' in this verse (and in its previous six uses in Genesis 1), probably means 'good for achieving its purpose' (Rogerson, 1991: 61). If values such as variety, beauty and fruitfulness were among God's goals in creating, then the world as we know it is indeed very good.

Finally we must note that no theodicy of evolutionary creation can be complete without an eschatology in which the whole of creation is renewed through Christ's redemptive activity (Rom. 8:19–22; Eph. 1:10; Col. 1:20). On this theme Southgate's recent treatment (2008: 78–91) offers some valuable insights.

5. Conclusion

The Fall of the first human beings, as traditionally understood, was a fall from finite perfection resulting in the loss of their paradisal state. This is clearly incompatible with a Darwinian understanding of human origins, but that does not automatically mean that the Fall is a concept that must be abandoned entirely. Rather, it is the traditional (i.e. Augustinian) understanding that conflicts most strongly with an evolutionary perspective. For some, the Augustinian view of the Fall will be a central, non-negotiable doctrine. However, nothing in either the Old Testament or the New requires this view of the Fall, and the narrative in Genesis 2–3 is actually opposed to it. The idea of a cosmic fall faces even bigger problems in an evolutionary context, and is also biblically and theologically indefensible.

Stripped of its accretions the biblical narrative itself speaks of a freely chosen move by human beings away from God to autonomy, in which relationship with God was catastrophically distorted. Indeed, relationships at every level became dysfunctional. At the human level this spiralled through violence to the point at which 'All humanity had ruined its journey on the earth' (Gen. 6:12 as translated by Goldingay, 2003: 165).

Looking at ways in which such an account of humanity might be integrated with an evolutionary understanding of human origins, we found the model developed by Raymund Schwager more attractive than the 'Neolithic Adam' model. Not only is Schwager's view more sensitive to the nature of the Genesis narrative (understood as a symbolic story or extended metaphor rich in mythological motifs), it also points to ways in which the nature of sin and its spread may be understood psychologically and anthropologically.

These are of course mere possibilities and many questions remain. We cannot penetrate with any confidence behind the narrative in Genesis 2–3 to the events it skillfully depicts for us.

8

Theological Ethics After Darwin

Michael S. Northcott

Charles Darwin's description of natural selection has had profound effects on accounts of the origin and nature of ethics. For Darwin himself, his observations of the suffering, violence and waste entailed in the processes of natural selection led him to doubt traditional Christian accounts of the goodness of created order, and of the wise beneficence and goodness of a divine Creator. Herbert Spencer, often called the father of social Darwinism, observing the roles of competition, predation, randomness, struggle, and violence in Darwin's account of natural selection, suggested that human societies ought to be organized in such a way as to maximize competition, randomness and struggle even at the cost of diminishment in equity, peace and social justice, for to act otherwise would be to encourage the weak to flourish and so undermine the fitness of the human species (Spencer, 1873). Darwin himself expressed similar sympathies in some of his later works. And present-day social Darwinists, drawing on neo-Darwinian accounts of the roles of randomness and selfishness in the survival of individual genes and individuals of species, argue that societies that promote competition rather than cooperation are more likely to evolve into societies that advance human flourishing (Ridley, 1997).

These moral iterations of Darwinism have had the paradoxical effect of strengthening the divide in Enlightenment philosophy between accounts of human moral life and descriptions or observations of biological or physical reality. If nature is intrinsically brutal and violent then human morality must be understood as a unique feature of the human condition, related to linguistic and rational faculties that radically distinguish humans from all other animals. Thomas Huxley wrote:

> The practice of that which is ethically best--what we call goodness or virtue
> – involves a course of conduct which, in all respects, is opposed to that which
> leads to success in the cosmic struggle for existence. In place of ruthless self-
> assertion it demands self-restraint; in place of thrusting aside or treading down
> all competitors, it requires that the individual shall not merely respect, but
> shall help his fellows; its influence is directed, not so much to the survival of
> the fittest, as to the fitting of as many as possible to survive. It repudiates the
> gladiatorial theory of existence. It demands that each man who enters into the
> enjoyment of the advantages of a polity shall be mindful of his debt to those
> who have laboriously constructed it; and shall take heed that no act of his
> weakens the fabric in which he has been permitted to live. Laws and moral
> precepts are directed to the end of curbing the cosmic process and reminding
> the individual of his duty to the community, to the protection and influence
> of which he owes, if not existence itself, at least the life of something better
> than a brutal savage. (T. Huxley 1894: 41).

For Huxley 'life was a continual free fight'; beyond the confines of the family and the polity it was a 'Hobbesian war of each against all' (T. H. Huxley, 1888). In such a situation there can be no moral lessons to be learned from observing the lives of ants, badgers or locusts, as proposed in the Book of Proverbs. The consequent bifurcation between moral philosophy and the nonhuman world exacerbates anthropocentric tendencies already present in Cartesian and post-enlightenment accounts of reason. If moral worth is only present in and recognizable by rational human minds then the nonhuman world is devalued in modern, post-Darwinian ethics as compared to the ethics of Moses or Christ. Whereas in Jewish and Christian ethics the pursuit of the good life for humans includes respect for creation and for other creatures as objects of divine concern, in most modern denatured accounts of ethics, human concerns and values trump other than human considerations such as the suffering of nonhuman creatures or the ecological degradation of their habitats.

Social Darwinians suggest that humans, as the 'highest' form of evolved life, are right to take up with the world in such a way as to put their interests above those of all other species on the grounds that this is the progressive outcome of evolution. In this perspective, the re-engineering of the world, and even the geo-engineering of the climate, is simply another consequence of the progress of evolution, although it may lead to the destruction of ecosystems and alter the course of evolution by extinguishing myriad species. And yet such an approach is at variance with a core feature of Darwin's own moral perspective. From his observations of other animals as recorded in his journals and in *The Descent of Man*, Darwin argued for the existence of moral worth and moral sentiments in humans and other animals.

In this essay I will argue that the moral implications of Darwin's theory of natural selection depend crucially upon the extent to which open-ended randomness, or 'chance', may be said to characterize evolution. In so doing I will draw on the work of Samuel Butler who was a notable contemporary opponent of this feature of Darwin's account of evolution, and of Simon Conway Morris whose account of a 'convergent creation' suggests that its outcomes are not open-endedly random. I will also show that in the last forty years ethological studies of animals reveal a far greater area of common ground between the moral lives of humans and other animals than most Enlightenment philosophers – and most Darwinians – have been prepared to admit. In conclusion I will suggest that resisting randomness, and acknowledging the existence of moral worth beyond the human species, are important prerequisites for a Christian account of created moral order that is consistent with the key biological tenets of Darwin's theory of evolution and with his observations of the overlap between moral sentiments in humans and other animals. And I will suggest that an approach to ethics that embraces the theory of evolution as revised by Butler, and more recently Conway Morris, enhances our understanding of the moral life. It provides a narrative of creation *as* evolution that affirms the central moral responsibility of humans, as taught by Moses, Christ and the Apostles, to love and care for the poor, the suffering and the weak, and that affirms the extension of moral responsibility by St Anthony, St Francis and Albert Schweitzer in subsequent eras to other species.

The Way of All Flesh?

According to Samuel Butler, author of *Erewhon* and *The Way of All Flesh*, the principal and most contentious idea advanced in *On the Origin of Species* is that luck and not cunning has generated the range of species, including humans, that have descended from their forbears in the evolution of life. Butler suggests that the implication that plants and animals are created by accident is a profound challenge to accounts of divine creation since it indicates that luck alone, and not created order, is responsible for the material and organic unfolding of life on earth (Butler, 1887). For Butler, Darwin's description of evolution is more mechanistic and materialistic than that of his predecessors, and most notably Lamarck, because Darwin failed to recognise the agency of the animals themselves in beneficially shaping the history of life (Bowler, 2007, 147). And in 'Darwin Among the Machines' Butler argued that this materialism might lead to a progressive dominion of machines over humanity (Butler, 1863).

Butler believed that Darwin's eschewal of creativity or desire in the unfolding of life was also a profound challenge to moral philosophy for it undermined the moral ends, narratives and virtues that shape the lives of individuals. And if they are accidental then they are no part of the divinely created ends and ordering which God set into the structure of the universe; they are not intrinsic to the nature of being. And if so, then moral ends, laws, narratives and virtues cannot be properly informed by experience, observation and rational reflection on the nature of organic life.

Butler did not resist the theory of organic evolution and progress in the generation of species across geological eras. His objection was to Darwin's more specific claim that species evolve across time and space without the aid of the developing designs and desires of living creatures because they are 'favoured' with luck. Butler argued that Darwin's description of the evolution of life in *Origin* makes it accidental in a way not implicit in the evolutionary theories of Erasmus Darwin or of Lamarck (Butler, 1887: 90–7). Consequently Darwinism, and more especially social Darwinism, subverts the human moral enterprise because it promotes the idea that living the good life is a matter of luck rather more than of human intelligence and divine grace. Virtuous sentiments and actions become mere biological or cultural emanations and are no longer directed towards the ultimate good emanating from the divine mind, and manifest in creation through its providential ordering. As Butler puts it, Darwinism promotes

> an essentially mechanical mindless conception of the universe; to natural selection's door, therefore, the blame of the whole movement in favour of mechanism must be justly laid. It was natural that those who had been foremost in preaching mindless designless luck as the main means of organic modification, should lend themselves with alacrity to the task of getting rid of thought and feeling from all share in the direction and governance of the world (1887: 140).

In other words the Darwinian description of natural selection is suspect because it eschews mind from its account of biology. And this denial of a 'causative connection between mental and physical processes' in biology leads to a 'purely automatic conception of the universe, as of something which will work as if a penny were dropped in the box' (Butler, 1887: 143). This advocacy of mechanicalism not only removes the divine mind from creation, it also underestimates the role of mindfulness in the evolution of species and societies.

Against mechanicalism, and the blind and brutal role of instinct in the struggle for survival, Butler argued for the role of animal and plant 'cunning' in shaping the course of evolution, and by cunning he meant intuition or intelligence. In so doing Butler advanced a 'general theory of the mind-body relation' (Pauly, 1982) that resisted both the mechanicalism of Darwin, and the mind-body dualism of Darwin's philosophical predecessors – especially René Descartes. Butler also proposed a more teleological, and hence Lamarkian, account of evolution than that of Darwin.

The word chance occurs fifty-eight times in the *Origin* and Butler was not alone in resisting the crucial role given to chance by Darwin. The American pragmatist Charles Pierce advocated a Lamarkian argument to counter the anti-teleological character of Darwinism. Pierce argued that habits could become instincts and that these could be transmitted inter-generationally, and become part of the mindfulness that Butler also affirmed against Darwin's emphasis on purely material processes (Pauly, 1982). The American Protestant theologian Charles Hodge, while fully accepting Darwin's proposals that species undergo development over time, and that natural selection explains important aspects of these changes, also resisted the Darwinian idea that these changes are 'entirely the result of random occurrences' (Noll and Livingstone, 2003). For Hodge it was this claim that gave Darwinism its 'peculiar character and importance'. The consequent rejection of teleology and the doctrine of final causes meant that for Hodge, as for Butler, Darwinism is the equivalent of atheism (Hodge, 1874). Hodge's teacher B.B. Warfield similarly argued that evolution could not be random since it represents the unfolding of developments produced by forces within the original divine creation (Noll and Livingstone, 2003).

That the dispute between Butler and Darwin is at least in part a theological dispute is indicated in the extent to which Darwin's understanding of evolution was shaped by the natural theology of Thomas Malthus. When we ask by what principle Darwin established the random unfoldings of mechanical evolution in the absence of the immanent workings of mind(s) we find that the answer is supplied by the population theory of Malthus. Malthus proposed that societies are governed by a law of struggle which limits numbers to the food supply available to it. By this means Natural Selection preserves 'Favoured Races in the Struggle for Life', in the words of the subtitle of the *Origin*. That this is a Malthusian perspective is confirmed both in Darwin's notebooks in the 1830s, and in the references to Malthus in *Origin*. But while neo-Darwinians such as Stephen Jay Gould argue that the outcomes of evolution are random and that if the tape of life were played again there would be different outcomes, is it fair, as Butler does, to ascribe the same view to Darwin?

Perhaps the clearest evidence that Darwin held the strong view of chance that Butler ascribes to him lies in the origin of the phrase 'natural selection' which Darwin adopted from his observations of the work of plant breeders. Natural selection is defined with reference to *artificial* selection, that is selection by a plant or animal breeder. Natural selection is accidental to the extent that it depends upon random interactions between individuals, species and environments, whereas for Butler human plant and animal selection is intentional. Robert Young (1985) argues that Darwin's focus on the workings of natural selection through population pressure and environmental constraints in contained and isolated land areas, such as the Galapagos islands, favours his adoption of the language of struggle and violence to describe evolution. And this is why those who characterize Darwin's description of nature in Tennyson's phrase as 'red in tooth and claw' are not wide of the mark. Darwin himself characterizes the processes of evolution as a 'war of nature' though he consoles his reader with the thought that 'the war of nature is not incessant, that no fear is felt, that death is generally prompt, and that the vigorous, the healthy, and the happy survive and multiply' (Darwin, 1859: 80).

Malthus' influence on Darwin also helps explain the direction in which Darwin's thoughts turned when he came to consider the moral implications of Natural Selection in *The Descent of Man*. Malthus' pessimism about the progress of human society in the eighteenth century arose in part from his observation of the miserable condition of the poor, evicted from the land and herded in squalid urban slums. He judged that the problem of too many mouths to feed could best be answered by *laissez faire* social policies that allowed the natural law of competition and struggle to determine the welfare of the whole (Malthus, 1798). The corollary he took from mass hunger in Victorian Britain was that it was Nature's device for controlling the putative tendency of the poor to outbreed the wealthy. Interfering in this device would therefore be counter-productive. As grandson of Josiah Wedgwood, Darwin was a rich landowner who believed that increasing rents through the stocking of land with sheep, and the forced removal of peasants from farms to factories, were as necessary to the progress of human society as the progressive evolution of species to the origin of *Homo sapiens*. Darwin's theory of progressive evolution made of nature a 'self-improving workshop' and for this beneficiary of one of the industrial revolution's most successful manufacturing businesses 'the creation of wealth and the production of species obeyed similar laws' (Desmond and Moore, 1991).

The Descent of Morality

While avoiding moral arguments in the *Origin*, Darwin explored more fully the moral implications of his theory in his later *The Descent of Man*. In the *Descent* he argued that individual conscience develops through social instincts that benefit human groups, those groups with well-developed social instincts have better survival chances. As Darwin put it 'those communities which included the greatest number of the most sympathetic members would flourish best and rear the greatest number of offspring' (Darwin, 1871: 163). Parents that express better care of their progeny will be more successful in reproducing themselves than those less careful and so over time evolution will favour the better carers. This is as true of the species ancestors of *Homo sapiens* as it is of humans themselves.

Darwin also sprinkled his later work with progressivist views, indicating that he shared his grandfather Erasmus Darwin's belief in the link between the moral and social progress of humans in history and the processes of evolution. Darwin shared with Malthus the view that support for the insane, the poor and the sick in Victorian England through institutions such as asylums, and practices such as vaccination, represented forms of care which were 'wrongly directed' and which would assuredly lead to 'the degeneration of a domestic race' (Darwin, 1871: 150). For Darwin, evolution from savage to civilized was proof of natural progress in human development. Interference in those natural processes which favour the children of the poor over the rich, or of the indigent over the intelligent and industrious, would subvert the moral as well as the civilizing progress of the human species. That the more civilized are superior to savages is evidenced not only in that civilized men are more cultured in their pursuits than savages; all comparison had shown that they are 'physically stronger' as well (Darwin, 1871: 153).

Herbert Spencer was among the most prominent advocates of an evolutionary approach to ethics in Darwin's lifetime, albeit that Darwin himself despised Spencer. For Spencer the biological promotion of fitness in individuals and species has a moral function such that biological or species fitness acquires moral authority. The nature of this mechanism is struggle between individuals and the restraining power of population pressure. This means that the natural state is one of war, warfare being the equivalent of predation in the animal world with fitter tribes wiping out less fit ones (Spencer, 1873: 193). Industrial competition performed analogous functions in Victorian cities and hence charitable interventions were misguided if they resulted in the inferior not receiving in their own bodies the effects of their inferiority since 'the struggle for life and the survival of the fittest must be left to work out their effects without mitigation' (Spencer, 1898: 533). However for Spencer, as for Darwin, warfare itself has a different and retrogressive effect in industrial as compared to tribal societies because industrial warfare takes the fittest young men and slays many of them on machine-enhanced battlefields leaving behind the weak to perpetuate the race (Darwin, 1930: 151; Spencer, 1898: 539).

The political import of social Darwinism was not all in this socio-biological direction (Hawkins, 1997). Other influential advocates of evolutionary approaches to ethics, such as T. H. Huxley, argued that Victorian poverty was squalid and immoral and that there was nothing in the history of human evolution that suggests it is inappropriate for charitable individuals and institutions to intervene to ameliorate it. While Huxley concurred with Darwin that animal and human morality originates in instinctive behaviour undergirded by reasoning powers and relational reflexes, nonetheless he argued that evolution does not necessarily favour virtue or the Golden Rule. Whereas for Spencer too much altruism can foster reproduction of the less fit, for Huxley humanity has progressed through the species struggle to a point where a kind of morality is possible which is superior to and above this biologically driven struggle. The purpose of human ethical life is not to sink into the cruel and amoral character of the cosmic process which has birthed human life but 'to pit the microcosm against the macrocosm and to set man to subdue nature to his higher ends' (Huxley, 1894: 83).

The argument that told against the first wave of evolutionary ethics was not its progressive view of history but its association with eugenics. After the discrediting of the eugenic evils sponsored by racists in the Southern States of the United States, and by the Nazi regime in Germany, Darwinian approaches to ethics seemed for many fatally flawed. But others, such as Julian Huxley, remained fierce advocates, though the revival or 'second wave' of evolutionary ethics is more often identified with the publication of E. O. Wilson's *Sociobiology* (1975). Huxley was much influenced by the French philosopher Henri Bergson and argued that evolution was a progressive and upward move of life from lower to higher forms, and from simpler to more complex species. Since humanity is at the top of the evolutionary tree, it is appropriate that humans take charge, as rational creatures, of the course of evolution. In this perspective eugenics, and other kinds of scientific planning of human life, are devices by which humans may foster moral and social progress in their own evolution by scientifically improving their own genome (Huxley, 1942). It is as if evolution has been transformed by the rise of modern rational humankind so that instead of its former upward path being the fruit of automatism and accident, its future path may now be one of artifice as humanity becomes in effect nature's principal breeder.

In his more recent version of social Darwinism, socio-biology, E. O. Wilson attempts to distance himself from the views of Huxley and others in relation to eugenics. Wilson offers a genetic argument for the development of cooperative behaviours in which he proposes that individuals who act cooperatively with others enhance the likelihood that the genes of their group will. Such behaviours in other words make for biologically 'fitter' groups. On this view moral behaviours and beliefs about right and wrong have evolved through interaction between the biological environment, social interaction and the developing human brain (Wilson, 1975: 12–19). Opportunities and threats in relation to human survival provoke the evolution of emotional centres in the brain that enables human beings to respond to their environment in ways that promote their survival. Anger aids fight and fear promotes flight in relation to predators. Compassion and joy aid companionship, cooperation and familiarity which in turn promote reproduction and hence survival. The natural selection of emotional responses to the environment is the origin, according to Wilson, of human moral sentiments.

Despite his protests to the contrary Wilson reprises many of the problems in the thought of his social Darwinist predecessors (Hawkins, 1997: 300). Hence he proposes that men and women have evolved differently because of their different roles in hunter-gatherer societies. Sexual behaviour among men is therefore more predatory than among women since men are not programmed in evolutionary terms to fidelity to one partner. Furthermore men are more aggressive than women because of the behaviours their evolutionary roles required of them. Therefore no matter how much effort societies expend in educating men and women to the same level and in reducing sexism in the workplace, it is likely that 'men are likely to maintain disproportionate representation in political life, business and science' and play a lesser role than women in many of the formative aspects of parenting (Wilson, 1978: 133).

Michael Ruse rejects socio-biology because its advocates have transformed Darwinian and neo-Darwinian accounts of the random nature of the processes of Natural Selection into a progressive and hence purposive account (Ruse, 1999). If natural selection does not automatically produce greater complexity or 'higher' beings then the attempt of Julian Huxley and other sociobiologists to found ethical judgements on random processes makes no sense (Huxley, 1947). It is better to acknowledge that there are no biological or evolutionary foundations to morality. For Ruse the human moral sense cannot be said to have any natural foundations since this would suggest that morality is the product of random processes of evolution. Instead the development of certain moral sentiments are indicative of the complex character of human society and are 'put in place by evolution to make us work more efficiently as social animals' rather than characteristic of the evolutionary process itself (Ruse, 1999: 447). But even as nuanced in this way, evolution is still performing the role of source of morality, and morality is consequently reduced to the accidental status it has in the Darwinian mainstream. Perhaps Ruse's position is better stated in the claim that there was nothing inevitable about evolution having put morality in place. Things could have gone another way, and moral animals like humans might not be here at all.

A Convergent Creation?

If first we assume that humans are *meant* to be here, and that the divine Creator worked immanently through evolutionary processes to bring humanity about, the moral implications of Darwinism look very different from those offered by social Darwinists, or even by Ruse. The logic of this position is that human beings evolved through a set of processes stretching back to the pre-Cambrian era more than 600 million years ago in which relatively simple life forms crawled along the floor of a planet mostly covered in tropical oceans. The history of life since then has included successive waves of speciation punctured by five massive waves of extinctions. But, as Simon Conway Morris shows in his account of a convergent creation, at various stages in the evolutionary tree certain crucial features of the human form – eyes, ball joints, bipedalism – have developed along branches of evolution that turned out to be dead ends (Conway Morris, 2006). It is as though life has been trying all along, in its repeated creation of certain highly complex forms that are requisite for human life, to bring forth the human species.

In the light of this account of a convergent biological history Christians may reasonably judge that the resultant emergence of *Homo sapiens* at a time of maximal species diversity, and more recently of unprecedented climate stability, is the outcome of divine beneficence and providence immanently at work in a creation that is fitted to the evolution of humans and to their present flourishing. This is not a 'value' claim justified by comparative observations between this and other periods of life. And it is therefore not evidence of moral progress either. It rests rather upon a combination of a Christian doctrine of divine creation and the Darwinian account of natural selection of the kind advanced by R. J. Berry in the opening chapter of this volume. And here is the heart of the difference between my own account of the moral and theological implications of Darwinism, and that of social Darwinists. Without a *narrative* of the nature of reality to supplement the factual evidences left in the fossil record as read by Darwin or Gould or Conway Morris, there is no justification for the view that this world is better than another or that humans are a 'higher' species than others. To that extent, then, we can agree with Ruse. It is the metanarrative that cosmic progressivism or sociobiology adds to evolutionary description which warrants such readings of the moral and social implications of biological evidence. Sociobiologists cannot justify the claim that because evolution favours more successful child-rearers successful child rearing is *morally* good or a necessary outcome of the claimed upward progress of evolution and the human species. This is where such arguments always fail, and the latest or 'second wave' of sociobiology is no exception to this. Science cannot empirically justify moral positions without appeal to something other than empirical observation and factual description.

Let us now return to Butler. His argument that luck is the crucial feature of Darwinian natural selection that Christians should resist turns out to have been remarkably percipient. It is not that he wishes to replace luck with design however. Instead both play a role in evolution for Butler, as they do in human moral life. As he puts it 'in theory we should admit that both design and chance, however well defined, each have an aroma, as it were of the other' (Butler 1887: 154). But if there is an admixture of these two elements in the processes by which successive and varied species have evolved then desire and intelligence – or cunning – must be present in plants as well as animals.

Some would suggest that this presents an insurmountable obstacle to Butler's position. To answer this point Butler turns to the work of his friend, the botanist Alfred Tylor. Tylor's observations of plants had led him to discern under the individuality of an organism

> the necessity for some co-ordinating system to enable the parts to act in concert, and the probability that this also necessitates the admission that plants have a dim sort of intelligence. Moreover, inasmuch as my experiments show that many plants and trees possess the power of adapting themselves to unfamiliar circumstances, such as, for instance, avoiding obstacles by bending aside before touching, or by altering a leaf arrangement, it seems probable that at least as much voluntary power must be accorded to such plants as to certain lowly organised animals. Finally, a connecting system by means of which combined movements take place is found in the threads of protoplasm which unite the various cells, and which I have now shown to exist even in the wood of trees (Butler 1887, 253; citing Alfred Tylor, *On the growth of trees and protoplasmic continuity*).

The import of this for Butler is that form, habit and opinion concerning advantage are all functionally interdependent in the modifications that individuals, and hence species, adopt in the course of their evolution: 'form is mind made manifest in flesh through action: shades of mental difference being expressed in shades of physical difference, while broad fundamental differences of opinion are expressed in broad fundamental differences of bodily shape' (Butler 1887 255). In a recent essay on plant intelligence Colin Trewavas suggests, like Tylor and Butler, that plants do manifest intelligence in their responses to environmental stimuli, nutrients and other species. But the idea of plant intelligence is counter-intuitive because plants do not move and human beings tend only to ascribe agency and intelligence to moving beings (Trethawas, 2003).

The account Butler gives of evolutionary processes anticipates in some respects the theory of convergent evolution of Conway Morris. And like Conway Morris, Butler resists the kinds of arguments from design that have characterised creationist attempts to resist Darwinism in the last 150 years. Butler rejects the 'old, far-seeing *Deus ex machina* design as from a point outside the universe, which indeed it directs, but of which it is no part' on the grounds of the mindfulness of organism (Butler 1887, 265). But he also rejects it because such a deity is alien to his own religious sensibilities. Butler had long abandoned the religion of his clerical parents and forbears when he wrote *Luck or Cunning*. He was critical of those within the established church, such as the authors of *Essays and Reviews*, who as liberal modernists had sought to ally a rationalist faith with Darwin's account of evolution. But Butler did not give up on what he saw as the essence of Christianity, which was also the essence of his argument in *Luck or Cunning*, and which he summarised as the insistence 'on the omnipresence of mind and intelligence throughout the universe to which no name can be so fittingly applied as God' (Butler, 1886).

Butler's efforts to retrieve creativity and mindfulness in describing evolution provide a suggestive way of addressing the question of the moral import of evolution. If social Darwinists are wrong to read off moral progress from the mechanistic character of Darwin's account this is in part because the attempt commits them to the naturalistic fallacy. If evolution proceeds by autonomous mechanism then even though life may appear to have produced greater complexity in the ends and forms of organisms as now constituted the autonomous character of evolution does not permit of its being endowed with moral goodness or virtue. But if Butler is right, and evolution is incipiently mindful, then this mindfulness can be said to be a reflection of the divine mind in the history of life as well as of the heritable memory of the instincts and intents of species. And this is a position not unlike that later developed by Teilhard de Chardin, who in *The Phenomenon of Man* suggests that it is not easy to relate the notion of the good to the general trend of evolution unless that trend is admitted to express something like the workings of the divine mind (Teilhard, 1972). Traditionally Christians have described the continuing creative activity of the divine in terms of the ongoing and sustaining activity of the creator Spirit.

Butler himself summarizes the implications of his account of evolution as follows:

> What, then, remains, but the view that I have again in this book endeavoured to uphold – I mean, the supposition that the mind or cunning of which we see such abundant evidence all round us, is, like the kingdom of heaven, within us, and within all things at all times everywhere? There is design, or cunning, but it is a cunning not despotically fashioning us from without as a potter fashions clay, but inhering democratically within the body which is its highest outcome, as life inheres within an animal or plant (Butler, 1887: 265).

And he concludes:

> Bodily form may be almost regarded as idea and memory in a solidified state – as an accumulation of things each of them so tenuous as to be practically without material substance. Action arises normally from, and through, opinion. Opinion, from and through, hypothesis. "Hypothesis" as the derivation of the word itself shows is singularly near akin to "underlying, and only in part knowable, substratum; and what is this but "God" translated from the language of Moses into that of Mr Herbert Spencer? The conception of God

is like nature – it return to us in another shape, no matter how often we may expel it (Butler, 1887: 266).

Butler's argument here recalls the proposal of the Anglican divine Richard Hooker that moral purposiveness and order are manifest beyond conscious mind. As Hooker suggests,

> all things that are have some operation not violent or causal; nor doth any thing ever begin to exercise the same without some foreconceived end for which it worketh indicates a view of natural dispositions or ends, such that they can be seen at work in rivers or trees as much as in animals, rational or otherwise (Hooker, 1888: 188).

For Hooker, the doctrines of divine creation and of the incarnation of the divine in embodied organic life, indicate that divine intentionality and moral order are manifest in the biosphere and in the ends of creatures. However for Butler the divine is at work in creation in embodied form in the instincts and desires that have shaped the evolution of organic life over billions of years. Butler resisted both scientific naturalism and the predilection of Hooker, like Paley and Malthus, to locate divine agency in creation primarily in its primeval origination. Butler was also no liberal Anglican progressivist. Instead of making peace with Darwinism, he struggled for a third position in which both Darwinism and liberal rationalist Christianity are revised by a cosmic story of the mindfulness of life.

But how might Butler's revision of Darwin's theory of evolution contribute to an account of the moral life more satisfactory than that of the sociobiologists? I will suggest in the final section that the answer lies in recent ethological discoveries of the place of moral sentiments and mindfulness in the lives of other animals.

More than human morality

From his field observations of animal behaviour Darwin believed that a moral sense or conscience is present in other animals and he noted what he identified as altruistic behaviours both within and between species (Darwin, 1897). The most striking for Darwin of such behaviours were the role of whole castes of sterile bees in helping fertile bees to reproduce. Why the sterile bees behaved in this seemingly altruistic fashion was a problem which vexed him for many years and in the sixth edition of *Origin* Darwin acknowledged that the wide extent of such altruistic behaviours in insects and other animals might even prove fatal to his whole theory of natural selection by violent struggle (Darwin, 1867: 15).

Against the moral pessimism of Darwin, Huxley and Spencer, their contemporary Peter Kropotkin of Russia argued that altruism was intrinsic and not epiphenomenal to the history of life. Kropotkin did not believe that all that stood between men and war was the State. On the contrary he believed strongly in the capacity of human beings, and other animals, for mutual aid and altruism and lectured widely in Europe and North America on anarchism and socialism (Kropotkin, 1902). But this was not only a political dispute. Kropotkin argued that he and other Russian mutualists were better able to discern the role of mutual aid and altruism in the behaviour of animals because they drew on zoological observations of animals in the large and cold Russian continental landmass where species more often struggle against natural obstacles than each other, whereas Darwin had studied the behaviours of animals in islands or coastal zones where overcrowding was more of a problem (Dugatkin, 2006: 33).

Kropotkin's account of the role of altruistic behaviours in the flourishing and survival of species is taken up in the twentieth century by animal ethologists such as Marc Bekoff and Frans de Waal. The science of ethology, the systematic study of the behaviour of animals in the wild, suggests that the grain of the universe, as manifest in the history of life, is more mindful and compassionate than Darwin and many of his heirs allow. Contemporary proponents of the science of 'cognitive ethology' suggest that altruism and cooperation in other animals are not just instinctive but are related to desires, emotions, and prospective and retrospective planning (Allen and Bekoff, 2007). David Griffen, who first coined the phrase cognitive ethology, rejects the common modern refusal to attribute certain states of consciousness – such as the capacity to anticipate, plan and remember, and to envisage a self – to other animals (Griffen, 1978).

Frans de Waal argues that studies of chimpanzees, dolphins, dogs, gorillas, pigs, pigeons and parrots reveal a range of behaviours that are 'good natured' in the sense that they manifest analogies with human moral capacities, including grief, identification with the pain or suffering of other individuals, and preparedness to make self-sacrificial efforts to reduce such suffering (de Waal, 1996). Many of these capacities are manifest in facial expressions, in actions such as stroking or feeding, and in complex kinds of vocal communication that are analogous to human language. De Waal assembles an impressive range of field and laboratory observations of which one of the more striking is the account of a group of lemurs in the process of helping one of their young who had mounted an electric fence, received a shock and been thrown off. Infant lemurs who do not normally groom one another groomed the injured infant intensively after its injury. Its grandmother who did not normally allow infants to ride on her back carried the infant for some time after the incident, and also persuaded its reluctant mother to carry it for longer. Gould and Gould assemble a similar and considerable array of such behaviours including for example descriptions of dolphins working together to support a wounded individual, of whales allowing themselves to be beached rather than abandoning an individual already so caught, of vampire bats diverting food from their own progeny to feed other starving members of their community (Gould and Gould, 1999).

Ethological descriptions of the behaviour of other animals indicate that animals, as well as humans, manifest a range of capacities for self-sacrifice and care for others that subvert naïve accounts of the evolution of morals as group survival strategies. Drawing on such studies, the moral philosopher Alasdair MacIntyre argues that the virtues manifest in the caring, communicative, nurturing and planning behaviours of many animals suggests a far greater diffusion of moral order in the biosphere that has been conventionally acknowledged by modern moral philosophers. He also proposes that core features of human moral formation and identity are intimately connected with the experiences of nurture and care at the beginning of life and in periods of greater biological dependency such as illness (MacIntyre, 1999). This recognition represents an important revision of accounts of the moral life which over-emphasize individual autonomy, rationality and sentiment. Compassion and care for the weak in kin and in non-kin turn out to be far more widespread features of the moral order than most modern moral philosophers have allowed. That these behaviours also have an evolutionary function does not gainsay that they are moral. On the contrary the recognition that the biosphere is divinely created and sustained obviates any binary divide between biology and morality, the body and mindfulness (Northcott, 2003).

In Butler's and Conway Morris' narratives of evolution, humans dwell in a created order that is not vacant of divine or creaturely mindfulness and purposivenes but directed to the creation of beings who mirror the divine nature that Christians call love. Hence it is no coincidence that many of those features of human moral life that are so admired in the Christian and post-Christian West, including compassion, self-sacrifice, and care for the sick and the weak, are not contrary to the evolutionary path on which history is set by the divine mind, and are at times glimpsed in the lives of other animals. It is however still not possible to read off the moral order from the biological order without the aid of a narrative of created order informed by revelation. This was the error of natural theology as pursued by Malthus and Paley, and it finds its way into many of the iterations of Darwin's Malthusian theory of evolution. But when Christians read the book of nature alongside the book of the Word of God they are able to discern significant analogies between the created order and the revealed moral order. When they find that God works to bring order through suffering *and* suffering-with (compassion) they will not, like many Darwinians, conclude that a world in which there is predation and pain cannot be a world that is created and sustained by the God who took on the flesh and bones of an organic body in the incarnation of Jesus Christ, and trained the people of God in compassion and care for the weak.

9

Natural Evil after Darwin

Neil Messer

In this chapter, I shall attempt four things: first, to identify and map the 'problem of evil' in the particular form in which Darwinian evolution seems to raise it; secondly, to give a brief account of some responses to that problem that are representative of mainstream ways of framing and addressing the issue; thirdly, to suggest that these responses share some important theological difficulties; and finally, to propose and defend an approach to the problem of evolutionary evil that I shall claim is more satisfactory from the perspective of a Christian tradition grounded in the Bible.[1] My own approach to the problem will be developed in dialogue with the greatest twentieth-century theologian of the Reformed tradition, Karl Barth. This might seem a surprising path to take, since Barth is widely regarded as an unhelpful partner in the dialogue of science and theology, not least because of his insistence on the primacy of divine revelation in theology and his robust opposition to natural theology (Brunner and Barth, 1946; Barr, 1994; Clayton, 1997: 66–7). However, I have argued elsewhere that Barth's theology, far from closing off the possibility of dialogue with the natural sciences, offers rich resources for re-framing that dialogue in ways that avoid some of the pitfalls to which

[1] Sincere thanks are due to Chris Southgate, who gave a valuable critique of an early draft of this chapter, offered further helpful comment in subsequent email discussion and was kind enough to send me an advance proof copy of his recent book (Southgate, 2008). I cannot expect him to be convinced by the end product presented here, but its final form owes a good deal to his generosity.

more mainstream approaches are prone (Messer, 2007: ch. 3). In the
present chapter, I shall attempt to show that this potential for the fruitful
re-framing of the dialogue extends to the discussion of evolutionary
evil.

1. Mapping the Problem of Evolutionary Evil

Believers who wish to hold together a Christian doctrine of creation
with a Darwinian theory of biological evolution appear to be committed,
at the very least, to the conviction that the world which God made
and pronounced 'very good' (Gen. 1:31) is a world that has a process
of evolution by natural selection built into it. Often, Christian writers
on science and theology make a stronger claim along the lines that
this evolutionary process is the means that God has used to create all
biological life, including human beings. One form of this stronger claim
was expressed in what became the standard 'liberal' Anglican response
to Darwinism in the later nineteenth century: 'He did not make the
things, we may say; no, but He made them make themselves' (Temple,
1884: lecture IV). A more recent example can be found in the work of
Arthur Peacocke: 'The processes themselves, as unveiled by the biological
sciences, *are* God-acting-as-Creator, God *qua* Creator' (Peacocke, 2001a: 23;
emphasis original). One obstacle that modern evolutionary biology seems
to place in the way of either the weaker or the stronger claim is that a
process of evolution by natural selection inevitably entails 'ills' or 'evils':
the pain, suffering and death of individuals, human and nonhuman,
and the extinction of countless whole species. These intrinsic features
of the evolutionary process have seemed to many commentators from
Darwin onwards to be incompatible with the Christian confession that
the cosmos is the work of an all-powerful and perfectly loving Creator.
Thus, Darwin wrote to his American collaborator Asa Gray (himself an
orthodox Christian):

> I own that I cannot see as plainly as others do, and as I should wish to do,
> evidence of design and beneficence on all sides of us. There seems to me too
> much misery in the world. I cannot persuade myself that a beneficent and
> omnipotent God would have designedly created the Ichneumonidae with the
> express intention of their feeding within the living bodies of Caterpillars, or
> that a cat should play with mice (F. Darwin, 1887, vol. 2: 312).

More recently, the philosopher of biology David Hull wrote in similar
vein, but in a markedly less eirenic tone: 'The God of the Galapagos is
careless, wasteful, indifferent, almost diabolical. He is certainly not the
sort of God to whom anyone would be inclined to pray' (Hull, 1991: 486).
Darwinian evolution, in short, seems to pose its own particular form of

the 'problem of evil', a problem neatly formulated by the eighteenth-century philosopher David Hume: 'Is [God] willing to prevent evil, but not able? then is he impotent. Is he able, but not willing? then is he malevolent. Is he both able and willing? whence then is evil?' (Hume, 1991: 157).

What are the theological difficulties created by these features of the evolutionary process? In general terms, two can be stated. The more familiar theological difficulty raised by evolutionary evils is that *a loving God would presumably not impose suffering on his creatures if it could be avoided*; should an all-powerful God not be capable of creating a world in which evolutionary ills did not exist? This kind of theological difficulty is in view in much of the standard discussion of evolutionary evil, as we shall see. However, a second kind of theological difficulty seems to go deeper: *the kind of world disclosed to us by evolutionary biology appears very different from the kind of world depicted in key biblical sources of the doctrine of creation.* The creation narratives of Genesis 1 and 2 flesh out the meaning of God's declaration, that the creation is 'very good', by depicting a world of plenty and peace. God's creatures have all that they need to live and flourish, and have no need to kill one another for food or in self-defence. By contrast, the world disclosed to us by Darwinian evolution is one that has at its heart the 'struggle for existence' (Darwin, 1859: ch. 3). For example, some animals need to prey on others for food, and the struggle between predator and prey is bound to end badly for one or the other: either the prey dies a bloody death, or the predator starves. Furthermore, the 'struggle for existence' is very often driven by a scarcity of resources that seems a far cry from the plenty depicted in the creation narratives.[2] It seems clear, moreover, that throughout the history of life on earth, it has been this kind of world: there was never a golden age of peace and plenty in any era about which evolutionary biology can tell us.

The problem of evolutionary evil is advanced by some as a reason for holding that there is no God; by others, as an argument for agnosticism about God's existence (Huxley, 1894: 195–202); by others again, in support of the view that there might be a God, but not the all-powerful, perfectly

---

[2] Darwin held that the 'struggle for existence' was central to natural selection. In this, as Michael S. Northcott discusses elsewhere in this volume, he was influenced among other things by the political economy of Thomas Malthus (Desmond and Moore, 1992: 264–8). It is of course true that the driver of natural selection is not the 'struggle for existence' *per se*, but differential reproductive success, and in some instances of natural selection, reproductive success is not influenced by a violent or competitive 'struggle for existence'. Be that as it may, violence and competitive struggle are pervasive features of the evolutionary history of life on earth, as in the examples I have cited and in the many others documented by Southgate (2008: ch. 1) and his sources. Insofar as this is so, the jarring contrast with the vision of a 'very good' creation offered in biblical texts such as Genesis 1–2 remains.

good God whom Christians worship. How have Christians attempted to respond?

2. Some Responses to the Problem

Responses to the problem of evil are often classified into 'theodicies' and 'defences' (Phillips, 2005: 34).[3] *Theodicies* are attempts to demonstrate that God is just by giving an account of God's purposes in creating a world with the capacity for evil. Those who produce *defences* settle for the less ambitious goal of showing that it is not incoherent or self-contradictory to acknowledge the existence of evil in the world, but still believe in a perfectly good, all-powerful God (cf. Murray, 2008).

According to evolutionary biology, from its very beginnings the history of life on earth has been characterized by the death of individuals, the extinction of whole species and (as soon as it produced sentient organisms) pain and suffering. This creates difficulties for what John Hick (1966: part II) called the 'Augustinian type of theodicy' (after the fourth-century bishop and theologian Augustine of Hippo) – the claim that the existence of evil in the world results from the freely-chosen fall into sin of the first human couple. This account generates one version of the so-called 'free-will defence': God did not intend the existence of evil, but by our misuse of our God-given freedom, we have brought it into the world. We, not God, bear the responsibility for that. This line of thought might invite the retort: Was it not irresponsible of God to make creatures with the capacity to bring evil into the world, knowing how terrible the result might be? To this retort, the free-will defence could offer the reply that the great good of having creatures with free will, capable of choosing to love and worship God, was worth the price – or at least, we cannot say that it was *not* worth the price.

Hick rejected 'Augustinian' theodicy in favour of another type, which he called 'Irenaean' after the second-century church father, Irenaeus of Lyons. In Hick's account, the sin and suffering of this world are an unavoidable part of the process whereby free personal beings grow towards perfected relationships with a loving God. Beings capable of a loving personal relationship with God simply cannot be created instantaneously: they must be formed through a process of struggle. The world as we experience it is a 'vale of soul-making', through which we must pass on our journey towards God; the evils of this world will be

---

[3] Note, though, that Phillips considers the distinction more or less irrelevant, since he finds both theodicies and defences deeply unsatisfactory for reasons that will be touched on later in this chapter.

richly compensated for by the surpassing glory of eternal life with God (Hick, 1966: part IV).

His main reasons for rejecting 'Augustinian' theodicies were philosophical and theological, but he also thought that evolutionary biology makes a historical Fall implausible (Hick, 1966: 178–82, 281–9). Others have disagreed (e.g. Berry, 1999),[4] but in any event, Darwinism does make it dauntingly difficult to attribute *all* of the world's evil to original sin: the suffering, death and extinction associated with the evolutionary process went on for billions of years before humans appeared on the scene and started sinning. This observation is one aspect of the more general idea that has developed with the rise of modern science, that much of the evil in the world results from natural processes, not human choices or actions. That is why it is customary, in discussions of the problem of evil, to sub-divide it into *moral* evil, brought about by human choices and actions, and *natural* evil, not caused by human activity.

It is perfectly possible to construct free-will defences that do not depend on a historical Fall. However, if the division between moral and natural evil is accepted, then the theological problem of *evolutionary* evil must be filed under 'natural evil', and it seems clear that in addressing *this* problem, free-will defences are beside the point. Those who develop evolutionary theodicies and defences, therefore, set themselves the problem of showing that God is not guilty of building avoidable evil into the natural processes of the world.

Recent attempts to address this problem have been helpfully surveyed by Christopher Southgate (2002; 2008: ch. 3). One move sometimes made is to re-frame the problem by denying one or other of the components of the dilemma stated by Hume. For example, God might be understood as the ground of being, the origin of both the beauty and the violence of the cosmos, but not 'link[ed] . . . to a transparent good of any sort' (Southgate, 2008: 21, citing Wildman, 2007). Or some version of process theology might be adopted in which God is not the transcendent Creator of classical Christian thought, but 'one entity among others . . . [a] fellow-suffering God, who does not coerce but merely seeks to persuade other beings in the direction of love' (Southgate, 2008: 23–4, citing Whitehead, 1929). Southgate rightly concludes, though, that such moves incur unacceptably high costs for Christian theology, and are 'road[s] not to be taken' (2008: 25).[5] If they are not, then broadly speaking we are left with theodicies and defences that depend on something like the following three arguments.

---

[4] But for a critique of Berry's argument, see Messer, 2007: 185–8.
[5] As we shall see in section 4, he also rules out the kind of approach that I shall propose later in this chapter. There, of course, I part company with him, but I am in full agreement with him about the other roads that he judges are 'not to be taken'.

(i)   The core argument, present in some form in most mainstream attempts to address the problem of evolutionary evil (e.g., among many others, Peacocke, 2001; Rolston, 2001: 58–61; 2003; Tracy, 1998; Attfield, 2006: 121–50), is this. A world that can produce all the rich variety of life that we see in ours (including, but not only, complex, conscious and intelligent life capable of freely chosen relationship with God) *has* to be a world in which there is pain, violence, death and destruction. Even an all-powerful God could not cause such a rich variety of life to be made except by some kind of evolutionary process that inevitably has such evils associated with it. The good realized in such a world is so great that it is worth the cost – or at any rate, we cannot say that it is *not* worth the cost. Southgate (2008: 41–8) has mapped various forms of this claim, which he calls the 'only way' argument. It is worth noting that any theodicy built on this argument has some kind of family relationship to Hick's 'Irenaean' theodicy, even though many versions do not refer directly to Hick.

(ii) Set alongside this core argument, in many recent evolutionary theodicies, is the claim that God shares in the suffering of creation. As Arthur Peacocke puts it, '*God* also suffers in, with, and under the creative processes of the world with their costly unfolding in time' (Peacocke, 2001: 37; emphasis original). The thought is presumably that if God is not aloof from the suffering of the world, this helps to assure us of God's love. This element of the argument can easily get us into deep waters in our talk of God. One difficulty often pointed out is that it is not clear how God's suffering, in and of itself, helps us in *our* suffering; furthermore, if we claim that suffering is part of God's own being, that could even lend a status and validity to evil that it ought not to be given (Gunton, 2002: 125–32). Nonetheless, this discussion reflects an insight too important to be lost, which I shall re-visit in the final section.

(iii) The evolutionary process has had countless 'victims', human and non-human creatures that have suffered and died without receiving any proportionate benefit in this age. Because of this, evolutionary theodicies tend to include an eschatological claim: that God promises a good and everlasting future age whose blessedness will richly compensate the victims of evolution and far outweigh all the sufferings of this present world (Southgate, 2002; 2008: 16).

The first of these arguments, which I called the core argument, depends on a strong claim that in any conceivable universe that an all-powerful God could create, it would be impossible for a world with the goods that we find in ours to be made except by some kind of process that entailed pain, waste and destruction. Even if such a strong claim can be defended, it is also worth observing that the core argument is commonly addressed to the first aspect of the problem of evolutionary evil that I identified earlier, the apparent incoherence of believing in an all-powerful and perfectly good God given the existence of natural evil. It is less clear that it helps with the second aspect, which I claimed was a deeper theological difficulty: the sharp contrast between what a biblically-based Christian tradition means by a 'very good' creation and the kind of world disclosed to us by evolutionary biology. I shall return to this second aspect of the problem in the final section, but first, I must take note of some further difficulties to which mainstream theodicies and defences are prone.

3. Some Difficulties with Recent Responses

One assumption that appears to be in the background of many recent evolutionary theodicies and defences is that theological language functions in the same way as natural-scientific language. The claim, 'God created the universe', is an explanatory hypothesis of the same sort as the claim, 'evolution by natural selection has given rise to all the living things that we see in the world'. Thus, in a recent book, Arthur Peacocke (2001b: 29) quotes with approval the view that

> many Christian beliefs are potential explanations: they tell me why certain data that need to be explained are the way they are; they account for certain facts about human existence. When I believe them, I believe they do a better job of explaining the data than other explanatory hypotheses of which I am aware (Clayton and Knapp, 1996: 134).

But it is not clear that scientific and theological language *do* function in the same way or for the same purpose. The Christian doctrine of creation characteristically takes the form of a *credal* statement (Gunton, 1998: 8): in the words of the Nicene Creed, 'We believe in one God, the Father, the Almighty, maker of heaven and earth, of all that is, seen and unseen.' This language is the response of a believing and worshipping community to the revelation of God in Christ, as that revelation is witnessed to by the Scriptures of the Old and New Testaments. In other words, theology is *not* the same kind of activity as biology. It is 'faith seeking understanding', to borrow a famous phrase associated with the mediaeval theologian Anselm of Canterbury: a kind of inquiry that is every bit as rational and rigorous as a natural-scientific investigation, but *different*. And this at any rate suggests that considerable care will be needed when we try to relate these two different kinds of rational investigation to one another. If we are not careful, it will be easy to confuse ourselves.

One kind of confusion to be found in the literature about the problem of evil has been diagnosed by D. Z. Phillips. This is the assumption that 'God is a moral agent who shares a moral community with us' (Phillips,

2005: 35), so that we can call God to account in terms of the moral standards and criteria that operate within the creaturely world that we inhabit, and we can make judgements about the moral character of God just as we would of a human being. If we attempt such judgements, we are in effect assuming that God is *an agent of the same kind as us, only greater*. Now if we find ourselves speaking of God in that way, we will no longer be speaking of the God of Christian theology. At best we might be speaking of the greatest being *in* the universe, not the transcendent Creator *of* the universe (Oliver, 2008). This reduced 'god' can be no more than a *participant* in the processes of physical cause and effect in the universe, albeit the greatest and most powerful participant. Among other things, this means that such a 'god' (unlike the God whom Christians worship) will be a 'god-of-the-gaps': to the extent that it is possible to give a full causal explanation of physical events without appealing to that 'god's' intervention, we will – to borrow the famous phrase attributed to Laplace – have no need of the hypothesis that such a 'god' exists.

Furthermore, the language of 'theodicies' and 'defences' makes clear what kind of judgement about God we have in view. Our moral evaluation of God has a forensic aspect to it: we are in a courtroom drama in which God stands accused of culpable negligence, wanton cruelty or worse. Theologians who develop theodicies and defences within such a frame of reference act as God's defence counsel, trying to get God acquitted of all charges. It is worth noting the oddness of this way of speaking from the perspective of the Christian tradition, which is more accustomed to thinking of God as *our* Judge. Even if it is sometimes necessary to engage on its own terms with the kind of God-talk that puts God on trial (so to say), we need to remain constantly aware that this is not Christian theology's characteristic mode of speaking – and at the very least, it has significant intellectual and spiritual dangers.

Finally, it is worth observing the kind of moral argument often used to defend God within this kind of discourse. As I noted in the last section, it is often claimed that the good achieved by creating the kind of world that we experience outweighs the evil. In other words, evolutionary theodicies and defences often rely on *consequentialist* moral reasoning – the kind of moral reasoning that assesses the rightness or wrongness of actions solely in terms of their consequences (Phillips, 2005: 35–46). This chapter is not the place for a discussion of the philosophical merits of consequentialism, but it is fair to say that not many Christian theologians would defend it as a *theologically* adequate approach to moral reasoning. If our responses to the problem of evolutionary evil commit us to making a consequentialist moral assessment of God's actions, this could be a sign that something has gone badly wrong.

The problem of evolutionary evil must be faced, but I have suggested that familiar ways of addressing the problem have some major theological difficulties. In the final section, therefore, I shall sketch out an alternative way of thinking about the problem within the framework of the Christian tradition, a way that might avoid some of the difficulties that I have diagnosed.

4. An Alternative Approach to the Problem

In the alternative approach that I propose, the first step is to focus on the *second* aspect of the problem of evolutionary evil, as I mapped it earlier, rather than the first. That is, we should concentrate our attention on the apparent contradiction between the world disclosed to us by evolutionary biology and the creation that God, in the first Genesis creation narrative, pronounces 'very good'. Why concentrate on this aspect of the problem, rather than the more familiar question whether an all-powerful God could have avoided some of the evil that we find in the world? There are two reasons. First, setting up the question in the more familiar way too easily becomes part of the problem. If the question is whether God is guilty of creating a world that contains avoidable evil, then an obviously attractive answer is that the evil we find in the world was unavoidable *given that* God wished to create this kind of world. But that answer is, of course, open to the challenge: Given the evil, wouldn't it be better not to have this kind of world? Would it not be better for God to have created a different kind of world, without evil in it, or even to have created no world at all? The price of this kind of world is too high, as Dostoevsky's character Ivan Karamazov thought (Dostoevsky, 1912: 251). And the attempt to meet that challenge leads all too easily to the kind of consequentialist calculation in which *this* much benefit (of conscious, complex, loving life, etc.) is held to justify *this* much evil. Now I have already suggested that this is a radically distorted way of speaking of God. There is a danger that if Christians pursue this line of thought too far, they will find themselves defending an idol of their own making rather than the God of Christian revelation.[6]

The second reason for focusing on the second aspect of the problem rather than the first is that it offers a way of starting from the place where Christian theology most characteristically starts: the Christian community's confession of faith in response to the biblical witness. This is not where evolutionary theodicies always start. That is not to say, of course, that they ignore the biblical witness or the Christian tradition's reflection on that witness, but the *starting* point is sometimes elsewhere: for example, in scientific data about the world (e.g. Peacocke, 2001a), or a philosophical challenge like that of David Hume (1991: 157). In effect,

---

[6] David Bentley Hart (2005: 36–44) suggests – with reference to Ivan Karamazov, among others – that protests *against* some theodicies demonstrate Christian insights, of which the authors of the theodicies themselves have lost sight.

I suggested in the last section that such choices of starting point can lead to serious theological confusion; if I am right, then it seems worth at least *trying* to begin where Christian theology most habitually starts.

If we do so, then the central problem that we face concerning evolutionary evil is this. The Scriptures witness to a God who created all that is, and who pronounced the creation 'very good' (Gen. 1:31). Furthermore, the Genesis creation narratives and other biblical texts flesh out what we are to understand by 'very good': as I noted at the beginning of the chapter, what they depict is a world of peace and plenty. But this is not the world disclosed by evolutionary biology, which is a world deeply marked by scarcity, competition and violence – by the 'struggle for existence'. If in any sense the Christian doctrine of creation and Darwinian evolutionary biology are referring to the same world, then we seem to be faced with a contradiction.

The great Reformed theologian Karl Barth was well aware of this contrast. One place in his extensive writings where an acknowledgement of it can be found is in his discussion of human responsibilities in respect of non-human animals, part of his treatment of the 'ethics of creation' (Barth, 1961: 348–46). Barth notes, as I have, that the Scriptures speak of the peace of creation; he further notes that biblical texts such as Isaiah 11:6–9 and Romans 8:18–25 promise that this peace will be restored by God at the *eschaton*, the end of all things. But both the stories of creation 'in the beginning' and the promise of eschatological fulfilment 'at the end' lie *beyond* the horizon of the world's history, and are not accessible to human investigation. Only revelation can tell us about the peace of creation and final fulfilment; evolutionary biology certainly cannot. History, says Barth, *begins* with the story of sin and the Fall (Gen. 3), and it is the *fallen* world we inhabit that has the 'struggle for existence' at its heart, a struggle that 'does not correspond with the true and original creative will of God, and . . . therefore stands under a *caveat*' (Barth, 1961: 353).[7] This means that history, right back to the beginning of time as it is open to scientific investigation, is characterized not by peace and plenty, but by scarcity and violent struggle. When I remarked earlier that evolutionary biology shows us that there was never a golden age, I was echoing Barth: 'There never was a golden age. There is no point in looking back to one. The first man was immediately the first sinner' (Barth, 1956: 508).

It might appear that Barth is offering the kind of 'Augustinian' theodicy that I said earlier is called into question by evolutionary biology. In at least two respects, though, this is certainly not the case. First, the creation

---

[7] Barth uses the phrase 'the struggle for existence' in what is almost certainly a deliberate allusion to Darwinism: the original German phrase (*der Kampf ums Dasein*) is the phrase used in German translations of the *Origin* from 1860 onwards (e.g. Darwin, 1867: ch. 3).

and fall narratives are not *within* history.[8] By saying that history begins with the Fall, he is in effect saying that the history of the world has *always* been a fallen history: 'There never was a golden age'. So the story of creation and fall is not a piece of history that could be contradicted by the different history supplied by evolutionary biology. Secondly, in this discussion Barth is not attempting an *explanation* of the origins of evil. It is probably true in general to say that he thinks the question of the explanation of evil is by no means the most important one to ask: he is more interested in asking what God has done about evil and how we are to respond to what God has done.

One potentially misleading aspect of Barth's discussion, though, must be addressed. In this discussion, because he says that the 'struggle for existence' becomes evident in the history that begins with the Fall, he might appear to be claiming that all evolutionary evil is caused by human sin – a claim that I suggested earlier is unsustainable in the light of evolutionary history. In fact, it is clear from other discussions that Barth does not think all evil is caused by sin. In a well known, difficult and much misunderstood account, he identifies evil as 'nothingness' (in German, *das Nichtige*; Barth, 1960: 289–368). By 'nothingness', he does not mean 'nothing'; rather, 'nothingness' is what God rejected, and *did not will*, in creating everything that exists and pronouncing the creation 'very good'. As such, 'nothingness' has a strange, paradoxical, negative kind of existence: it is the chaos, disorder and annihilation that threatens God's creation, and to which God is opposed. Sin is one form that 'nothingness' takes, but it also takes the forms of suffering and death. Furthermore, it is clear that not only humanity, but the whole of God's creation, is threatened and opposed by 'nothingness'. Whatever in the evolutionary process is opposed to God's creative purpose is to be identified with 'nothingness': it is an aspect of the chaos and disorder threatening the creation.

The biblical witness, in short, requires us to say of the world we inhabit *both* that it is created *and* that it is fallen; *both* that it is the work of God, pronounced 'very good', *and* that it is badly astray from what God means it to be. Even though, in this world, the 'goodness' and the 'fallenness' are so closely entangled that they cannot be separated – scientifically speaking, the aspects I have identified theologically as 'fallen' are essential to the process that generates what we plausibly call 'good' – they must nonetheless be distinguished. This is a difficult, and inevitably somewhat mysterious, distinction to make, and is rejected by some critics on the grounds that if it is adopted, 'consideration of the really hard ambiguities of creation can never develop' (Southgate,

---

[8] In following Barth here, I take issue on this point with those scholars (e.g. Berry, 1999) who do still wish to argue for a Fall *within* history; see, further, John Bimson's chapter in this volume.

2008: 34). But nonetheless, it seems to me to be a crucial distinction, offering the beginning of a way to make theological sense of both the beauty and the horror that commentators since Darwin have discerned in the evolutionary process, while avoiding the theological problems of mainstream approaches. It is also worth noticing that this account tends to blur the sharp distinction usually made between natural and moral evil. There could be closer links than we sometimes think between the violence of the 'struggle for existence' and at least some aspects of human sin (Messer, 2007: 133–215).

I have claimed that my approach avoids some of the problems that I found in more mainstream evolutionary theodicies, but it might by now appear to have some serious theological difficulties of its own. First of all, the evolutionary process, deeply marked as it is by the struggle for existence, has made us the way we are. Yet I have followed Barth in identifying the violence and scarcity of the struggle for existence with the fallenness of the world. Does that mean that God has used an evil process to create us?

My earlier comments about language and God-talk should caution us against drawing this conclusion in any simple way. To say 'God is our maker' is to use language in a rather different way than to say 'natural selection has made us the way we are'. The language of 'making' in the two sentences does not mean exactly the same thing, though it is of course (analogically) related. To say 'God made us by means of a process of natural selection' is to risk confusing the two kinds of language. We are talking about the same 'us' in both, but we are saying different kinds of thing about 'us'.

But this leads to a second difficulty: if I insist on distinguishing between theological and scientific claims in this way, do I not risk driving too wide a wedge between them? I seem to be close to saying that God might have made us and the world 'very good' in some unspecified sense, but that the causal processes that have produced what I see in the mirror every morning are, to some extent at least, evil. If that is the case, it might seem that the material world, including the physical nature of humankind, is irretrievably shaped by evil, and that salvation will have to mean *escape* from this flawed material world and its 'struggle for existence'. Furthermore, I have said that in the history of the world, it was always like this: there was never a golden age. If I say that, do I not risk making God's good creative purpose and the flawed evolutionary process into two co-eternal powers vying for the upper hand in shaping us? In other words, I might seem to have re-invented two of the oldest heresies in Christian history: a form of Manichaeism, in which there is a cosmic conflict between equal powers of light and darkness, and a form of Gnosticism, in which the material world is irretrievably flawed and salvation lies in escaping from it.

The reason we do not have to say either of these things lies in what God has done to address our predicament, according to the Christian confession. God in Christ has taken upon himself human existence in the material world. This is the important – indeed, crucial – insight that I said earlier is struggling to get out when evolutionary theodicies refer to God's co-suffering with the creation. As Barth puts it, 'in the incarnation God exposed Himself to nothingness even as this enemy and assailant. He did so in order to repel and defeat it' (Barth, 1960: 311). The way in which God in Christ 'repelled and defeated' this enemy, of course, is summed up by the early Church's proclamation 'that Christ died for our sins in accordance with the scriptures, and that he was buried, and that he was raised on the third day in accordance with the scriptures' (1 Cor. 15:3, 4).

Because *this* is the heart of the Christian good news, Gnosticism is not an option: the Christian gospel promises not an escape from the material, but its healing and transformation. This good news also gives Christians good reasons not to be Manichaeans, even in the face of the pervasive influence of the evolutionary struggle for existence. The Christian tradition understands the resurrection of Christ as the in-breaking of God's promised new age into human history, the first fruits of what God promises to do to 'mak[e] all things new' (Rev. 21:5). So if we respond in faith to the Christian proclamation of the resurrection, we are (among other things) affirming our belief in God's promise of a new age, expressed in Isaiah's vision of the peaceable kingdom where the leopard lies down with the kid and the lion eats straw like the ox. We can hardly begin to imagine what such a world might be like, but part of what Christians affirm when they declare their faith in the resurrection is the hope that God's peace, not the struggle for existence, will have the last word. And because God's good future has broken into our present with the resurrection of Christ, we are able to see the past and 'the beginning' in a true light too. It is because of this that we can recognize that the struggle for existence did not have the first word, any more than it will have the last. If we respond in faith to the preaching of the resurrection, part of what we are affirming is that God's good creative purpose is prior to the flawed everyday reality of the struggle for existence.

Perhaps the hardest challenge to the account I have been developing is posed by Christopher Southgate (2008), who sets out to speak of the goodness of God in a way that is both faithful to the biblical witness and able to engage constructively with the natural sciences. This means that he is alert to the second aspect of the problem of evolutionary evil that I identified in section 1: the dissonance between the biblical vision of the goodness of creation and the view of life disclosed by evolutionary biology. He is impressed by the central insight of Darwinism, that all life as we know it is the product of an evolutionary process that includes the struggle for existence. He infers from this that the 'good' and the 'groaning' (cf. Rom. 8:22) in God's creation are both outcomes of the evolutionary process, inseparably bound together (2008: 1–2, 47–8). For that reason, he not only denies (as I do) that the literal, historical fall of a first human couple could account for evolutionary evils. As I have already noted, he goes further – rejecting *any* attempt to associate the suffering and destruction resulting from the evolutionary process with the 'fallenness' of the world, and taking T. F. Torrance (1981), Michael Lloyd (1998a, b) and Ted Peters and Martinez Hewlett (2003), among others, to task for making versions of such a claim (Southgate, 2008: 28–35, 54). Clearly, if he is right, then the argument I have been developing – that the evolutionary struggle for existence stands under God's *caveat*, and the suffering and destruction that result from it are aspects of what God *did not will* in creating the world – is also ruled out. According to Southgate, the work of evolutionary theodicy can only get started once appeals to 'fallenness' are set aside. Because he rejects such appeals, he is committed to what I described in section 2 as the core argument of mainstream evolutionary theodicies: the only way in which God could create a world like ours is by an evolutionary process involving suffering and destruction (Southgate, 2008: 47–8). He adds to that core argument several further elements: God's 'co-suffering' with creation (50–4, 56–7); the centrality of the Cross as 'the moment of God's taking ultimate responsibility for the pain of creation, and – with the Resurrection – to inaugurate the transformation of creation' (16); the hope that God will compensate the victims of evolution in the age to come (82–90; cf. also Russell, 2008: ch. 8); and some intriguing and thought-provoking reflections on the calling of humanity to participate in the healing of creation (Southgate, 2008: 92–133).

My disagreement with Southgate has something to do with differences of emphasis, at least, about how much – and what – theology ought to learn from the natural sciences. These differences can be illustrated by Southgate's treatment of eschatology. His evolutionary theodicy, as I have noted, includes the eschatological claim that in God's good future, the victims of evolution will be compensated for their suffering and lack of fulfilment. Rightly recognizing that any Christian talk about heaven requires a good deal of reticence, he nevertheless offers some cautious and tentative reflections on the nature of this eschatological compensation. He argues that heaven for any creature must be the fulfilment of *what it is to be that creature*: leopard heaven must be the fulfilment of 'leopardness', and so on. Thus far, I agree. But I differ from him about how we can learn what the fulfilment of leopardness, in God's good purposes, might mean. The evolution of leopards has produced exquisitely well-adapted hunters and killers of (for example) antelopes, which have been equally finely honed by evolution to escape from leopards. Southgate (2008: 88) infers from this that 'it is very hard to imagine any form of being a predator that nevertheless does not "hurt or destroy" on the "holy mountain" of

God (cf. Isa. 11:9)', and he turns instead to a poem of James Dickey (2002), in which eschatological fulfilment for predators consists in the ultimate perfection of their hunting and killing skills. Heavenly fulfilment for their prey consists in being the victims of this perfected lethal violence, and accepting their fate. What makes this different from the present world is that it does not hurt the prey to be killed, and they do not stay dead – so they are able to get up and have it happen to them all over again, for all eternity. The use of this poem is not an arbitrary move on Southgate's part: it is entirely consistent with his argument up to this point, and some such conclusion is probably required given the earlier stages of that argument. But a heaven that has a place for lethal violence and eternal victimhood seems to me to be a strange reading of the Christian hope.[9] By contrast, my account in this chapter has been *shaped* by Isaiah 11, among other biblical texts. This leads me to conclude that in God's good future, it must be possible for leopards to be ultimately fulfilled without hunting and killing kids, and for kids not to be the victims of lethal violence – even though, like Southgate, I learn from biology that *in the present age*, a non-predatory leopard is an impossibility.

Southgate's project has a good deal in common with mine, even though we differ in some crucial respects. He is attempting to make sense of the tension between a biblically-informed vision of the goodness of creation and the view of life disclosed by Darwinian evolutionary biology, as I have also tried to do in this chapter. Neither of our approaches is without its theological costs. Mine appears to offer less by way of explanation of the origins of natural evil, which will make it unsatisfying to some. It also seems to limit the scope for dialogue with the natural sciences – though as I have suggested, it by no means closes that dialogue off, and I would hold that theology's engagement with science is best served when theologians are as clear as possible about the kinds of work that science can, and cannot, do in theological reasoning. Conversely, Southgate's determination to incorporate scientific insights leads him to make two theological moves that I have criticized. One is to deploy what he calls the 'only way' argument, which I identified earlier as the core argument of mainstream evolutionary theodicies. I argued in section 3 that this theological move risks serious distortions of our God-talk: it seems to me that there is some tension between Southgate's use of it and his clear intention to speak of God's goodness in a way that is rooted and grounded in Scripture and Christian tradition. The other move of his that I have criticized is the reluctance to allow his eschatological vision to be

---

[9] It might be asked whether the heavenly vision of 'the Lamb that was slaughtered' (Rev. 5:12) does not express a heaven of eternal victimhood. But that is precisely the point: the willingness of the Son of God to suffer lethal violence at the hands of human creatures is the means by which God breaks the cycle of violence and victimhood in a fallen creation and makes possible a good future of peace.

formed by biblical texts that promise an end to violence and predation –
a reluctance which makes it thinkable that in God's good future, some of
God's beloved creatures will continue to be the victims of lethal violence
for all eternity, and will be content with their lot. Southgate has mapped
out one route through the problem of evolutionary evil with considerable
intellectual honesty, rigour and flair. In the end, however, I am unwilling
to follow him, because – while acknowledging the difficulties of my own
approach – I judge the theological costs of his to be higher.

5. Conclusion

Having found fault with mainstream approaches to the problem of
evolutionary evil, I have proposed an alternative approach, which begins
by viewing the problem through the lens of the biblical witness to Jesus
Christ. When we do so, we discover, first, that we are committed to
understanding the material world as God's good creation; secondly, that
the 'struggle for existence', however deeply it structures the world as we
experience it, is not the most fundamental reality; thirdly, that the peace
of creation and of God's promised good future is a deeper reality than
the struggle for existence – it is both the first word and the last, so that
the struggle for existence, which so deeply marks our present life in the
world, 'stands', as Barth (1961: 353) puts it, 'under a *caveat*'.

This picture does not offer much by way of explanation of how the
struggle for existence comes to be such a pervasive feature of our present
reality, but it does put that struggle theologically in its place. In any case,
I have already suggested that according to this approach, the question of
explanation is by no means the most important one to ask. Much more
important is to ask what God has done to address our predicament, and
how we are to respond. The answer to the first of these questions is
seen in the life, death and resurrection of Jesus Christ. The second is
the question faced by every person who hears the proclamation of the
Gospel, and by all Christian believers and communities seeking to live
their lives in the light of that proclamation; and that fact might suggest
the kind of answer that is called for.

10

Natural Theology after Darwin: Contemplating the Vortex

David Grumett

Why has Charles Darwin's theory of evolution so often been seen as a threat to Christianity? The narrative of progress it unfolds is consistent with the Christian–Whig historiography which dominated Victorian thought and the modern historical imaginary more widely, as shown by Amy Laura Hall in her examination of Charles Kingsley earlier in this collection. Such historiography has also accepted that humankind will endure suffering in its pursuit of progress because of its sinful condition. The image of humanity occupying the peak of the natural order, which evolutionary theory could be seen as presenting, resonates, moreover, with a dominant strand in Christian theology stretching back through Aquinas to patristic writers. One of these, Gregory of Nyssa, even presents the ability to stand upright with free hands as a defining feature of humanity, anticipating in his treatise 'On the Making of Man' the classic diagrams of humans evolving from apes crawling on all fours to *Homo sapiens* striding upright, bearing a tool or weapon, and gazing straight ahead (1988: §8). Furthermore, evolutionary theory echoes another medieval Christian tradition of relating humans and animals symbolically and morally. This extends from desert hermits living in close fellowship with wild animals, through the moralizing of illuminated bestiaries, to Francis of Assisi preaching to attentive birds and fishes. This attribution of human characteristics to animals is more quaintly evident in Darwin's chapter from *The Descent of Man* 'On the affinities and genealogy of man', such as in his assertion that ants 'feel sympathy' for each other (2003:

147). Finally, by espousing a linear, developmental and Christian model of history rather than the classical pagan view of time as cyclical and repeatable (Cullmann, 1962), evolutionary historiography parallels the Christian vision of new events occurring in the world and transforming the world as a consequence of the life, death and resurrection of Jesus Christ.

The task of natural theology has classically been seen as being to establish grounds for belief in God's existence and attributes using reason and observation of the world. It therefore connects unavoidably with major new scientific theories such as evolution that seek to explain why the world is constituted as it is. Although the methods of natural theology do not depend on scripture or other forms of revelation, they might well draw inspiration from these and are in no way incompatible (Barr, 1993). In this chapter, I wish to question the idea that Darwin's theory of evolution, especially as developed in the *Origin*, presents natural theology with insurmountable problems. In comparison with the authors of some preceding chapters, I will range widely, since several of their topics – creation, anthropology and theodicy – are implicated in the task natural theology sets itself of discerning evidence for God's existence and activity in the rational and physical patterning of the world that human beings inhabit.

It seems important to approach the topic of natural theology after Darwin with a certain naivety about both historical controversies and current debates. The cacophony of popular argument surrounding the theological implications of Darwinism, and more recently neo-Darwinism, has frequently generated more heat than light. Yet curiously, opposing protagonists have often presented mirror images of each other. Compare, for instance, the evangelical dogmatism of Richard Dawkins' dismissal of religion as a 'mind virus' and the idea of its convergence with science as a 'shallow, empty, hollow, spin-doctored sham' (2004: 162–72, 179), with the posturing of Pope Pius IX, who in concluding his *Syllabus of Errors* (1864) condemned the proposition that the 'Roman Pontiff can, and ought to, reconcile himself, and come to terms with progress, liberalism, and modern civilization'.

The polarization of debates about evolution and natural theology is illustrated by interpreters of Pierre Teilhard de Chardin, on whose evolutionary theology the second half of this chapter will focus. Teilhard has been excoriated by neo-Darwinists like Peter Medawar (1996) and Stephen Jay Gould (1990), as well as by conservative Catholic lay theologians like Jacques Maritain (1968). The most striking common feature of these high-level attacks is their rapid and peremptory execution. They could even pass for intelligent philosophy, science, or theology, and are sometimes quoted as if they were exactly this (e.g. Berry, 2005). Yet as John Haught perceptively observes, something more than plain scientific disagreement is at stake in such engagements. What they fundamentally represent is a clash of worldviews, with totalizing naturalistic discourses confronting with incomprehension the idea that the natural world could be open to the transcendent and be developing according to a teleological process (Haught, 2000: 83).

The aims on which this chapter is converging are to understand the structural character of these oppositions and to establish the continued relevance of natural theology for both theologians and evolutionary theorists. Yet any attempt to situate natural theology 'after' Darwin needs to begin by examining Darwin's own account of evolution in order to establish which aspects of natural theology it called into question, which it confirmed, and which it left open. I shall focus on *The Origin of Species* since this collection marks the sesquicentenary of its publication, although in so doing I shall cast appropriate forward glances to *The Descent of Man*. This perspective will enable me to examine the specific context of the *Origin* and some common assumptions about the book. I will then consider theological issues raised by the text before moving on to reflect on wider questions surrounding the relation between scientific and religious discourses. These will be addressed via an examination of engagements by two major theologians, Henri de Lubac and Donald MacKinnon, with the work of the French Jesuit theologian and paleontologist Pierre Teilhard de Chardin.

1. After Darwin, or Back to Darwin?

What does it mean to speak of natural theology 'after' Darwin? *The Origin of Species* is a more ambiguous text than many of its critics and enthusiasts have allowed – a fact illustrated by its three epigraphs. The first, from William Whewell's *Bridgewater Treatise*, asserts that 'events are brought about not by insulated interpositions of Divine power, exerted in each particular case, but by the establishment of general laws'. Whewell thus presented God as the cause of order in the material world, operating through the laws he had established when creating that world. The second epigraph, from Joseph Butler's *Analogy of Revealed Religion* (added to the *Origin* in its 1860 second edition), states that 'what is natural as much requires and presupposes an intelligent agent to render it so ... as what is supernatural or miraculous does to effect it for once'. In other words, Butler sought to defend divine authorship not only of nature, as did deists, but of scripture too. The final epigraph, taken from Francis Bacon's *Advancement of Learning*, urges an 'endless progress or proficience' in both the 'book of God's word' (scripture) and the 'book of God's works' (nature, studied by science). Bacon thus presented a similar picture to Butler's of the nature-scripture relation as mutually confirming.

In 1859, when the *Origin* was first published, Darwin situated his work in the tradition of William Paley that pictured God designing the world and causally ordering natural events within it, as discussed by David Fergusson earlier in this collection. Indeed, Darwin affirmed in his autobiography that, at the time of writing, he believed in a personal God. Referring to the 'impossibility of conceiving this immense and wonderful universe . . . as the result of blind chance or necessity', he explained: 'When thus reflecting I feel compelled to look to a First Cause having an intelligent mind in some degree analogous to that of man; and I deserve to be called a Theist' (1969: 93). Moreover, the trio of epigraphs remained at the head of the *Origin* through to its sixth and final edition of 1872.

The previous year, however, Darwin's *Descent of Man, and Selection in Relation to Sex* had appeared, marking a key point in his drift towards agnosticism. In the *Descent*, Darwin dismissed the view that the idea of God was universal, attributing it instead to cultural formation (1993: 93–4). He attacked, more pointedly, the theory that belief in God was innate. Importantly, his reason for so doing was not hostility to religion, but that this theory suggested an absolute distinction between humans and other animals, which were considered not to possess innate ideas (612–13). More prominent in wider perception of the *Descent* among a fairly prurient public was its explicit attribution of human development not to high-minded spiritual ideals but to power, violence and, especially, sex. Humans were provocatively presented as subject to exactly the same base drives as animals.

Darwin's dismissal in the *Descent* of the innateness of the idea of God in the human mind, and his reduction of human motivation to animal sexual impulses, cannot necessarily be read back into the *Origin*. These two points will therefore be addressed later. The *Origin* did, however, call into question several interrelated assumptions widely seen as fundamental to Christian doctrine and as bearing implications for natural theology. Many theologians have rightly regarded natural theology as providing by itself an inadequate basis for Christian faith, being founded on a reading of the book of nature rather than of scripture. The claims of natural theologians have, however, usually existed in peaceable relation with those of scripture, as suggested by the Butler and Paley epigraphs. The aim of natural theology has not been to uncover new evidence on which to found a new religion but to demonstrate the reasonableness of Christian claims. Its room for manoeuvre is therefore restricted by the need to preserve congruence between its own theses and those of scripture.

The first challenge that evolutionary theory seemed to pose to classic natural theology was its inherent dynamism, which contradicted a firm conviction that the universe was static. William Paley had portrayed, in his famous *Natural Theology; or, Evidences for the Existence and Attributes of the Deity*, an unchanging ordered universe in which the design of each of its components was the result of the direct, originating action of a divine craftsman. Against this background, a theory that pictured natural organisms as products of developmental biological processes suggested that the universe was, on the contrary, disordered. Since God obviously preferred order to disorder, the implication of a lack of order was either that God did not exist, or that God existed but no longer cared about the world or the human life he had brought into being.

The second point of contention emerging from the *Origin*, voiced famously by Bishop Samuel Wilberforce and many others, concerned the distinctiveness of the human species resulting from its creation in the image and likeness of God. This distinctiveness seemed to be undermined by Darwin's implication that humans had evolved gradually from animals as a result of biological developmental processes. In his elliptical phrasing, by means of evolutionary theory 'light will be thrown on the origin of man and his history'. Moreover, in the *Origin*'s sixth edition of 1872, the opening of this phrase was altered to 'much light' (Darwin, 2006: 757). The preoccupation of Darwin's detractors with cosmological boundaries stands in a long structuralist tradition that sees rules ordering the natural world and governing human behaviour within it. So far as human–animal interactions in the Bible are concerned, for instance, Leviticus and Deuteronomy lay down an array of regulations about which animals may be eaten as meat and how these animals must be killed. Concerns in the nineteenth century about species boundaries thus echoed perennial issues in Judeo–Christian cosmology and in anthropology more widely.

The third and most theologically controversial aspect of the *Origin* was its apparent undermining of the notion that humans possessed a distinct spiritual identity or 'soul'. The classic doctrine of a spiritual soul as the feature distinguishing humans from all other earthly beings appeared irreconcilable with the view that humans' distant ancestors were animals, who did not possess souls. For this reason, various other contemporary theorists had defended varieties of human exceptionalism by positing some kind of supernatural intervention which implanted a soul or spirit into humankind at the point of the creation of human life (Bowler, 2007: 129–31). These even included Alfred Russel Wallace, Darwin's former sympathizer, who embraced spiritualism. For scientific figures like these, as well as for a long succession of theological critics, the distinctiveness of human nature and the human soul became the single breach in the Christian worldview to be defended at all costs.

But how had the idea of the human soul come to assume such importance in Christian theology? For Aristotle, the entire cosmos was ensouled in the sense that every being within it was endowed with identity and purpose. According to this view, however, even stones had souls. The hypothesis that humans possessed a distinct and spiritual soul implanted in them by God had developed to account for the identity of the human person through time, as well as beyond earthly temporal life (Reynolds, 1999). The mutability of matter was a common theme in scholastic theology, and Christian thinkers were unwilling to accept that humans made in the image of God possessed no intrinsic identity through time. Moreover, a life beyond earthly death seemed difficult to imagine if that life was equated with nothing more than physical matter. Theologians also amused themselves with more abstruse problems. If, for instance, food ingested by a woman led to her body gaining new matter, on what grounds could it be claimed that she was the same person as before? Moreover, what would happen at the resurrection to a man who had fallen into the sea and been drowned, and then had his body devoured by a shoal of tuna, before the tuna was eaten by a shark? The notion of an individual human soul giving identity and continuity to the human body provided a satisfactory response to such problems, bestowing on human bodies an ontologically privileged status above that of animal bodies in the context of an essential continuity of biological life between the two (Agamben, 2004: 17).

Through the 1860s and 1870s, Darwin found his religious belief intellectually challenged from two different directions. On the one hand, his vision of fixed laws of nature caused him to question the symbolic universe of the Old Testament, as well as the literal historical accuracy of the Gospel narratives and the miraculous basis on which key doctrines like the resurrection rested. More seriously from the perspective of natural theology, he considered that the theory of natural selection refuted Paley's argument from design, which had attributed order in the world to the productive activity of an intelligent being (Darwin, 1969: 85–7).

How concerned was Darwin to address the three theological issues just outlined – the uniqueness of the human species, divine ordering of the world, and the human soul?

With regard to the first, he accepted in the *Descent* his continuing captivation by Paley's profoundly influential natural theology (which had been required reading during his years at Cambridge) in his inability 'to annul the influence of my former belief, then almost universal, that each species had been purposely created' (Darwin, 2003: 61). Darwin remained committed to the idea of discrete species, accounting for their existence with the hypothesis that beings born with a slight variation making them better-fitted to their environment will be more likely to survive and reproduce, and thus, over time, to multiply their characteristics through a population. Groupings lacking such positive marginal variations will, in contrast, tend over time to extinction. Larger groups will, moreover, be successful in reproducing, tending to become yet larger and to diversify their characteristics. Different varieties will be produced in these single species, leading to the development of new species within a single genus. It would appear that Darwin did, in fact, move beyond his former belief in the purposeful creation of species, if such purpose is understood as an outcome of direct divine agency. His commitment to the distinct nature of species, including the human species, nevertheless remained firm.

A response to the second area of theological difficulty, the divine ordering of the world, was implicit in the first of the epigrams of the *Origin* from William Whewell, which asserted that 'events are brought about not by insulated interpositions of Divine power, exerted in each particular case, but by the establishment of general laws'. This vision, beloved of liberal theologians, of the universe governed by natural law, was thoroughly compatible with scholastic thought, which similarly posited a texture of causes at work in the world, both immanent and transcendent. Humans did not need to be special creations of God in order for their existence to be seen as the outcome of God's creative action. On the contrary, Darwin stated: 'To my mind it accords better with what we know of the laws impressed on matter by the Creator, that the production and extinction of the past and present inhabitants of the world should have been due to secondary causes, like those determining the birth and death of the individual' (2006: 757–8).

The third and most serious theological objection to Darwin's evolutionary theory arose from the challenge it presented to the idea that humans possessed spiritual souls. Darwin did not develop this implication explicitly, even though Robert Chambers had already prepared the ground in his 1844 *Vestiges of the Natural History of Creation* by interpreting the human soul as a function of the physical development of the brain by employing the fashionable 'science' of phrenology. Yet even from a theological perspective, the Christian concept of the soul in the popular imaginary was by no means unproblematic. Pauline teaching pointed clearly to a *bodily* resurrection (2 Cor. 5:1–4), as did the post-Resurrection appearances of Christ in the Gospels of Matthew, Luke, and John, and the Acts of the Apostles. The idea that an entity called the soul could be abstracted from the body and resurrected independently of it did not, therefore, go far enough in defending Christian doctrine. Paul spoke, indeed, not of the persistence of the soul beyond death, but of the gaining of a spiritual *body* after death (1 Cor. 15:35–57). The other function, arguably more important, that the doctrine of the soul performed, was, as previously shown, to establish the identity and continuity of the person over the term of their earthly life. I will continue discussing this complex and crucial point in the next section of this chapter.

It would be easy to overstate the degree of intrinsic tension between Christian theology and Darwin's theory of evolution as developed in the *Origin*. His measured tone and systematic exposition are in marked contrast to the bombastic preaching of neo-Darwinists like Richard Dawkins and Daniel Dennett who seek to claim him as their own. Part of the difficulty of relating strictly Darwinian evolution to Christian theology originates in restrictive definitions of what counts as 'orthodoxy' in theology. Hence Christian attempts to redeem Darwin have even extended to creating legends of his deathbed 'conversion' back to evangelical Christianity (Moore, 1994).

2. De Lubac, Teilhard and the Cosmic Vortex

In the year that Darwin's *Descent* was first published an English Catholic biologist, St George Jackson Mivart (1827–1900), published a tract broadly accepting evolutionary theory but denying its applicability to the human mind. In his study *On the Genesis of Species*, Mivart described a 'perfect harmony in the double nature of man, his rationality making use of and subsuming his animality; his soul arising from direct and immediate creation, and his body being formed at first (as now in each separate individual) by derivative or secondary creation, through natural laws' (1871: 287).

To a theologian immersed, like me, in modern French Catholic thought, it is strange to see Cartesian dualism thus defended and made a touchstone of orthodoxy. Nowadays, theologians far more commonly identify such mind-body dualism with secular modernism, which, so the argument goes, inaugurated a rupture between the spiritual realm, inhabited by God and through which God interacted with humankind, and the world of nature, which continued to exist and function independently of divine action. This 'parallel universes' view of God and nature characteristic of the scholastic tradition of which Mivart was part forms a notable strand of the 'science and religion' debate. In *Rocks of Ages*, for instance, the biologist Stephen Jay Gould presented a similar parallelism in his 'blessedly simple and entirely conventional resolution' of conflicts between science and religion, asserting that 'principled and respectful separation' between these two 'Non-Overlapping Magisteria' is preferable to attempted synthesis or unification (1999: 3–4). The parallel universes view of revelation and evolution is also evident, more covertly, in Christian accounts of evolution. One example is the work of the influential old-earth creationist Hugh Ross (2006), which unfolds a progressive creationism positing successive creative acts during the course of evolution, each as a result of divine intervention. Ross is also sympathetic to fine-tuning arguments, which attribute the universe's ability to support developed life forms not to some self-organizing capacity but to divine intervention.

This range of positions allowing for a 'God of the gaps' might appear a noble and humble concession by both scientists and theologians: scientists admit some aspects of the world for which they are unable to account, while theologians acknowledge the closely circumscribed limits of their competence. Yet in the hymn of Augustus Toplady, to the opening words of which the title of Gould's book refers, the 'double cure' for the ills of humanity is not science and religion existing in a state of peaceful mutual disengagement, but the water and blood flowing from the side of Christ following his death on the Cross – the water for salvation from wrath, and blood for purification. There are not two Rocks of Ages, but one: Christ himself, suffering to redeem and raise fallen humanity. A 'God of the gaps' placement of theology in light of evolutionary theory gives to the natural sciences at once both too little and too much: too little, because it posits dimensions of natural reality for which science is in principle unable to account, yet too much, because it permits the natural sciences to delimit the extent of its overarching explanatory discourse.

The theological refutation of this philosophy of separation is associated particularly with the work of Henri de Lubac (1896–1991), who critically describes the dualistic scheme as one in which the 'two series—pure nature and supernaturalized nature, or nature called to the supernatural— flowed along parallel channels in complete harmony' (1998: 41). In place of this scheme, he envisions nature as open directly to receive divine grace by virtue of being a free creation of God, and therefore the one gift that God might *not* have given. It is no surprise that, during the 1960s, de Lubac showed so much interest in defending the work of his former confrère Pierre Teilhard de Chardin (1881–1955), since a large part of Teilhard's importance lies in providing an alternative to the 'double nature' cosmology and anthropology just sketched. Teilhard had been banned from publishing any theology from the early 1920s until his death in 1955 partly because his views on evolution were regarded as controversial by the Roman Catholic hierarchy. Yet for de Lubac, the importance of Teilhard's evolutionary theology lay in the radical freedom that it assigned to humankind as supremely complex and hence supremely conscious. In humans, evolution becomes interiorized as they apply science and technology to life in order to influence the future direction of its development. Evolution thus comes to acquire a moral and even mystical dimension in which the goal presented to humankind as its true end is reflective organization. This is especially evident in the development of technologies which make possible increasingly rapid global communication (de Lubac, 1967: 109–10).

De Lubac's most important analysis and evaluation of Teilhard's evolutionary theology is contained in a report presented to the sixth International Thomist Congress with the support of Pope Paul VI. The first substantive topic he there addresses is the 'rise of the spirit'. Teilhard does not, de Lubac makes clear, see spirit as simply a product of matter. Instead, Teilhard describes spirit as a source of consistency and as performing the function of synthesizing matter. He frequently describes spirit as if it were a collective entity in order to draw a clear distinction with the idea of completely individuated and separated souls implanted in each human being. Nevertheless, spirit 'has nothing of an undifferentiated collective reality: it is composed of personal spirits'. What

Teilhard pictures as the process of spiritualization of the world is 'in fact, identically, a process of personalization' (de Lubac, 1996a: 512–15).

In Teilhard's theory of spirit, several key features are identifiable that scholastic theologians have classically attributed to the soul. Spirit exercises a governing and organizing capacity over matter. Spirit is ontologically distinct from matter. Its identity constitutes the individual human person but is dependent upon a larger reality to which it is related. For Teilhard, self-reflective spirit emerges in mental life once that life attains, by means of evolution, a sufficiently advanced degree of complexity. This 'subjectivity in nature' cannot reasonably be ignored by scientists, even if they choose not to investigate it (Haught, 2000: 178). But another obvious connection can be drawn between Teilhard's idea of spirit and the Holy Spirit. His cosmology certainly has suggestive parallels in the Orthodox vision of the divine energies, identifiable with the Holy Spirit, pervading the whole world in ways that can nonetheless not be observed or quantified by any empirical method. The idea of 'spirit' in his theology thus connects with concepts of both the human soul and the Holy Spirit, emphasizing the relatedness of human souls as well as the pervasiveness of the Holy Spirit through the whole created order. So far as evolution is concerned, by arguing that it is significantly motivated by spirit Teilhard refuses the reduction of human motivation to sexual impulses shared with animals that Darwin presented in the *Descent*.

Despite these continuities between Teilhard's concept of spirit and the scholastic idea of the soul, his imagery differs in presenting spirit as exercising a unifying function over the whole cosmos. Its overarching cosmic activity is certainly continued in part through the activity of individual souls, yet is not denominated completely by those individual activities. Teilhard employs the Baroque imagery of a 'cosmic vortex, in the midst of which the material of the world, by a preferential utilization of chance, twists and winds more and more closely around itself in ever more complex and centred combinations' (de Lubac, 1996a: 514–15; Teilhard, 1978: 290). This convergent reality is effected by a process of segregation in which humanity, being the species in which spirit has become reflective, will co-operate with God in shaping the future evolution of the world by acting as co-creators with God (de Lubac, 1996a: 534–38).

What does all this mean for the traditional 'proofs' of God's existence? Teilhard founds his natural theology on the proposition that the immanent convergence of the universe presupposes a transcendent centre governing the convergence. This point of encounter he names Omega. Three distinct proofs of God's existence can be identified in Teilhard's thought, de Lubac argues: a proof by human action, a proof by efficient and governing causality, and a proof based on the aspirations of the human soul (de Lubac, 1996a: 517–18). All three rest on a common proposition, however:

that divine action is implicated in fundamental phenomena in the world, which is transcendentally disposed to this action. The proofs thus all point towards the same reality: God's unifying action on the evolution of the cosmos, which is inseparably both biological and spiritual.

In his important untranslated essay on Anselm of Canterbury, de Lubac (1979) makes clear that the function of natural theology is not to construct unassailable rational arguments for God's existence. Such a claim to total comprehension and the elimination of doubt necessarily mistakes the object of the quest of natural theology, reducing transcendence and excess to neat logical formulations. The greatness and immensity of God can never be grasped: in closeness to God, the believer is aware of absence, and in vision he senses obscurity. Echoing these themes, de Lubac states of Teilhard:

> He knows, in fact, that the reality of Christ can in no manner be *deduced* from the World, but he also knows that revelation consolidates, extends, achieves the work sketched by reason. He discovers with joy a 'remarkable similarity' between the dogmatic perspectives and the conclusions or the ultimate hypotheses to which the study of the phenomenon of man leads him, a similarity that he attributes with good reason to the 'influence' and the 'radiation' of Christian revelation. Between reason and faith, as between nature and grace, if there is discontinuity, distinction and hierarchy, there is also just as much harmony (de Lubac, 1996a: 523).

Thus is presented a symphony of reason and revelation similar to that implied by in the second and third epigrams of the *Origin* from Butler and Bacon. Science and religion perform distinct yet complementary and interrelated tasks in illuminating human understanding of evolution. Cosmology needs both methodologies, and they may be pursued as part of a single scholarly enterprise.

A point not often made in assessments of Teilhard concerns the wider intellectual context of the development of his work, in which the 'growth of a Catholic scientific structure had important consequences for Catholic thought'. Through the opening decades of the twentieth century, the scientific community in France included within it a significant number of clergy, especially Jesuits. In consequence, 'Catholic bio-philosophical positions were increasingly based on scientific work done by Catholic scientists' (Paul, 1979: 102). A Christian scientific community such as this does not surrender the possibility of objective enquiry into the sources of life and the mechanisms of its continuation, but makes its metaphysical commitments and final purpose clear and transparent to all.

Intrinsic to this vision of evolutionary science and evolutionary theology as mutually informing is, for de Lubac, a notion of the idea of God as naturally existing in the human mind, due to the 'presence of the soul present to itself, in which it may learn, as in a mirror, the presence of God to the soul' (1996b: 12–13). Contra Darwin in the *Descent*, the idea of God is innate because the mind, created by God, is oriented to acknowledge its likeness in its creator. This, for both de Lubac and Teilhard, is the fundamental significance of creation: an order given its existence by God, and as such, primordially related to God and ordained to acknowledge the source of its existence as subsisting beyond it.

One of the criticisms that can be levelled at Teilhard is that the view of evolution he presents is excessively optimistic, neglecting the problematic nature of the large-scale competition, suffering, and extinction intrinsic to evolutionary process (Southgate, 2008; Moltmann, 1990). This is a difficulty with which any theologian accepting Darwin's theory of evolution has to grapple – see Messer's contribution in this collection. First, it needs to be said that, in his portrayal of historical development, Teilhard identifies both regressive currents of history and progressive or constructive currents, stating: 'If you tell me that humankind is getting "better" or "worse", I hardly know or care what the words mean' (1978: 380). Under the influence of Catholic eucharistic and Passion imagery, he certainly sees natural evolution, and specifically human evolution, as including much suffering and sacrifice (de Lubac, 1996a: 529–34). He is not, however, insensitive to the painful reality that is their embrace, realizing that although they cannot be overcome in any straightforward sense, they can be transfigured by the work of Christ. When contemplating the life of his sister, Marguerite-Marie, Teilhard sees how, through suffering, egoism can be overcome, greater sensitivity and attentiveness to the world gained, and thus a transformative sharing in Christ's Passion endured (Teilhard, 1978: 247–9; Grumett, 2005: 73–102).

Teilhard's conception of evolutionary progress is ultimately Christological, drawing primarily not on Genesis but on the Pauline imagery of the cosmic Christ acting on the world and dwelling in the world (e.g., Col. 1:15–20; Lambert, 2002), transforming and unifying the whole cosmos through a developmental process at once both material and spiritual that is still to be completed (Grumett, 2007). This Pauline cosmic Christology is closely bound up with what John Haught has described as Teilhard's 'theological metaphysics of the future' (2000: 81–104). This Pauline background throws into relief the paradoxical privileging by young-earth creationists of the ancient myths contained in the opening chapters of Genesis, long predating the coming of Christ into the world, above the distinctively Christian scriptures. Yet as identified at the opening of this chapter, the entry of Christ into the world establishes a 'redemptive line' contrasting with previous static and cyclical conceptions of time. In recognizing this, Teilhard is one of very few Christian thinkers who attempted to grasp the significance of the work of Christ for confirming, correcting, redeeming and completing the evolutionary process.

3. MacKinnon and Teilhard: Theology as Contemplative Realism

Teilhard has been marginalized in much current academic discourse over the past thirty years. Why this decline in interest? The postmodern compartmentalization that has governed the construction and organization of knowledge in the academy and within theology has found little space for his sometimes broad and diffuse speculations. Within the subdisciplines of systematic and philosophical theology, moreover, it has become fashionable to see the most appropriate mode of engagement with other disciplines as one of 'overcoming' or 'outnarrating'. Teilhard by no means subordinates theology to other intellectual disciplines, as I have demonstrated in this chapter, and his evolutionary theology fits somewhat better with oppositional models of engagement than is typically supposed. Nevertheless, his method is based on attentive discernment, dialogue, and meditation, in the context of what John Haught has called 'layered explanation' or 'explanatory pluralism' (2003: 163). He is not motivated by a thirst for victory over debating opponents.

These currents are related to a deeper structural decline in mainstream intellectual disciplines in understanding the quest for knowledge as a synthetic enterprise. The theological and philosophical urgency of this enterprise is suggested by the interest shown in Teilhard by a theologian of the stature of Donald MacKinnon, Norris-Hulse Professor of Divinity at Cambridge from 1960 to 1976. MacKinnon saw Teilhard as embracing a 'contemplative realism' that sought to develop a theological explanation of the fundamental metaphysical truths about the way the world is (MacKinnon, 1962: 196). Teilhard believed passionately in the importance of metaphysics and the role of theology to the metaphysical quest. He also believed in the inalienable place of metaphysics within theology—understood as both an intellectual quest, and a spiritual or experiential quest—in which claims about Christ and his work are, MacKinnon states, 'not analytic, but synthetic: not, that is, merely explicative but ampliative'. Expressed more simply, Teilhard rekindles in his readers a 'sense of their natural environment as something which, even as its boundaries and frontiers are pushed further and further back, may yet furnish them, if they learn to read its import aright, new lessons from Him who before He left his own, warned them that He had still much to say to them which they could not yet bear' (MacKinnon, 1962: 197). In Teilhard's own words, 'God is arrived at not in a negation, but in an extension, of the world' (Teilhard, 1933: 106).

Statements of belief in Christ need to emerge from similarly comprehensive experience of the world, in which its reality is embraced and proclaimed, in faith, to the fullest degree possible. MacKinnon thus saw Teilhard's greatest achievement as lying in the field of spirituality rather than science. In consequence, MacKinnon believed his key work to be not *The Human Phenomenon*, to which enthusiasts and critics usually point, but *The Divine Milieu*. This 'interrogative meditation' denied to metaphysics the autonomy, rationality and unconditionality that modern thought had bestowed on it, seeing the whole of the created order as formed, preserved, pervaded and illuminated by divine power. Teilhard's vision of the universe thus echoes Ignatius Loyola, who urges: 'See God living in His creatures: in matter, giving it existence; in plants, giving them life; in animals, giving them consciousness; in humans, giving them intelligence' (1987: 230–7).

What philosophy and the natural sciences lose in such refusals of their explanatory autonomy in the realm of metaphysics, MacKinnon makes clear, theology gains: 'The insertion of such highly self-conscious reflection concerning the universe around us into religious meditation bestows upon the latter a quality of intellectual rigor and seriousness that it very easily loses, that it has indeed lost, and is continually in threat of losing' (1965: 62). By means of this methodology, Teilhard overturns the 'hardly curable anthropocentrism' of modern religious attitudes and also answers MacKinnon's 'realist disquiet' at the profoundly *un*realistic precision and certainty of the constructs of analytical philosophers.

Looking back almost twenty years later, MacKinnon acknowledged that, in *The Divine Milieu*, Teilhard 'returns again and again to the place of human existence in a universe whose dimensions, both spatial and temporal, defy the reach of imagination'. The natural universe is not, MacKinnon contended, merely a stage on which the drama of redemption is played out, but *itself provides the possibility of that redemption*, 'sustained by its creator, pervaded by his continuing presence, in its minutest detail the object of his concern and the place of his possible self-disclosure to men and women' (1983: 50). The concern for suffering and passivity expressed in *The Divine Milieu* provides an important antidote, moreover, to the evolutionary and technological optimism present in some of Teilhard's later works. MacKinnon also recognizes, significantly, the regulative character of Teilhard's oeuvre: in Kantian terms, it is concerned with Ideas, whose validity is merely provisional – or, in current terminology, performative – rather than with Categories, which are constitutive of human experience of the world. Teilhard, argues MacKinnon, is

> inviting the reader to follow him in an exercise of imagination and spiritual perception, through which he may so enlarge his sense of the mission of the Crucified that it encompasses the world which is still very much coming to be, and at the same time brings that world within the terms of that historical episode, as if there to find its foundation and its secret' (1983: 52).

4. Description and Evolution

In the third, 1861 edition of the *Origin*, Darwin inserted a digression in which he candidly acknowledged that natural selection was a 'metaphorical expression', stating in mitigation that such expressions are 'almost necessary for brevity' and a consequence of the fact that it is 'difficult to avoid personifying the word Nature' (2006: 165). In our current genetic age, it is a truism that Darwin's theory of natural selection failed to explain precisely *how* evolution occurred. The new genetic paradigm demonstrates the truth of Robert Young's claim that the *Origin* 'was really more effective in eliciting faith in the philosophical principle of the uniformity of nature than in providing an acceptable mechanism for evolutionary change' (1985: 79–125; also Swinburne, 1997: 185). Yet even in genetic science, metaphor abounds. The popular image of the 'selfish' gene, for instance, designed to explain why genes spread themselves through populations, is highly figurative, since selfishness is a human trait implying consciousness and a moral universe, two anthropological fundamentals that neo-Darwinians wish, ironically, to eliminate at all costs.

Well-founded evolutionary natural theology has the potential to correct the abstract and privatized character of much current spiritual and theological reflection, which lacks meaningful references in the material world. Notions of soul and spirit have largely been abstracted from a universal metaphysical context and any distinctively theological understanding of them thereby precluded. Teilhard's conception of evolutionary spiritual progression is quite different from this current postmodern conception of spirituality, grounding individual testimony in participation in a *collective* material and spiritual movement that both precedes individual persons and persists beyond them.

The redoubtable Thomas Huxley, known as 'Darwin's bulldog', had sought to destroy natural theology by promoting a purely naturalistic evolutionary theory. His grandson, Julian Huxley, famously wrote the preface to Teilhard's major study of evolution *The Phenomenon of Man*, in which he expressed sympathy for Teilhard's progressivist view of evolution as motivated by the rise of consciousness (1959). But is such reversion to evolutionary theology encouraged by current scientific research? Simon Conway Morris, Professor of Evolutionary Palaeobiology at Cambridge, is presently assembling evidence of common selection outcomes in unconnected branches of descent in support of the hypothesis that a mechanism of convergence is at work in evolution (2006). At the same time, radical transhumanists such as Raymond Kurzweil are developing pictures of a future in which human immortality will be guaranteed by the uploading of consciousness onto computers and other natural systems (2006). Teilhard's evolutionary theology appears mundane when set alongside Kurzweil's wacky ideology. Yet such an alternative suggests that what he affirms is, in the present day, more important than ever: that, as a result of creation, humans have been given a unique and inalienable spiritual function in the material, cultural and spiritual evolution of the world, which they are called to continue to exercise.

11

Hope for Creation After Darwin: The Redemption of 'All Things'

Denis Edwards

The great scientific break-through of the nineteenth century, Darwin's discovery of evolution by means of natural selection was followed by the equally dramatic discovery of twentieth-century science that our universe is not static but expanding dynamically. The universe itself is evolving. We now know that the observable universe began from an unthinkably small, hot and dense state 13.7 billion years ago, that life began on Earth about 3.8 billion years ago and that all the wonderfully diverse forms of life of our planet have evolved from this beginning.

In this chapter I will explore a Christian theology of final fulfilment after Darwin and after Einstein and Hubble. The question I will take up is centred not on the human but on the rest of creation: what does final fulfilment mean for nonhuman creatures? The focus will be on the way in which the wider creation can be thought to share in final redemption. I will start from the assumption of Christian faith in the bodily and personal resurrection of humans and will ask how the rest of creation might be thought of as participating with humans in resurrection life.

The guiding thought in this exploration is what I take to be the fundamental Christian conviction that in the incarnation God has embraced not just humanity, and not just the whole world of flesh, but the whole universe and all its dynamic history, and that this embrace constitutes an unbreakable promise. As Walter Kasper has put it: 'God has accepted the whole world finally in Jesus Christ, and God is faithful, so the world and history will not simply vanish into nothingness, rather God will be its "all in all" in the end (1 Cor. 15:28)' (Kasper, 1986: 378).

I will begin with what I take to be fundamental in this kind of discussion, an acknowledgment of what we do not know of God's future. Then, with this in place, I will take up the promise of hope for creation found in the New Testament, particularly in Paul's Letter to the Romans, and in patristic theology, exemplified in Maximus the Confessor. This will lead to an exploration of insights from Karl Rahner's theology of hope for the material universe. Then, in the final section, I will take up and explore hope for the animals, arguing that they too share in their own way in the final transformation and deification of all things.

1. We Hope for What We Do Not See: God as Absolute Future

At the end of the section from Romans which I will discuss below, Paul writes: 'For in hope we were saved. Now hope that is seen is not hope. For who hopes for what is seen? But if we hope for what we do not see, we wait for it in patience' (Romans 8:24–5). What Christians hope for, the resurrection of the body and a renewed creation, is not something we can see or imagine, because what we see is the empirical reality that surrounds us and what we can imagine is based upon what we already experience. According to Paul, God's transforming act in resurrection involves a radical change in bodily existence. What is sown in the grave as perishable, dishonoured, weak and physical will be raised as 'imperishable', 'in glory', 'in power' and as a 'spiritual body' (1 Cor. 15:44). As a risen body is beyond the grasp of our minds, so a universe transfigured in Christ is beyond imagining. We hope for what we do not see.

A Christian theologian is called to be critically aware of the limits of theological concepts and words about the future. She is called to an abiding awareness of what we do not know, and to a careful respect for the limits of language in speaking about what is ultimately unspeakable. There are serious theological reasons for this. They were articulated by Karl Rahner in a well-known article in the mid-twentieth century (Rahner, 1966: 323–46). Two fundamental principles can be distilled from Rahner's work that can guide the interpretation of eschatological statements. The first is that *the future of our world in God remains radically hidden to us*. The future has been announced and promised in Christ and his resurrection, but it is announced and promised precisely as hidden mystery. The Scriptures insist that God has not revealed the day when the end will come (Mark 13:32), and it is not simply the timing of the end that is hidden. The future is nothing else than the coming towards us of the incomprehensible God. Rahner insists that it is God who is our Absolute Future. The revelation of God's promise in Christ does not mean that what was unknown is now made known, clear and manageable. It is rather 'the dawn and the approach of mystery as such' (Rahner, 1966: 330). Because the future is the coming of God, it always escapes our comprehension. It is always a mistake, then, to interpret biblical images in literal terms as something like an 'eyewitness' account of what is to come.

The second principle is that *the future will be the fulfilment of the salvation in Christ that is already given to us.* It will be the fulfilment of what we experience in God's self-communication in Christ and in the grace of the Holy Spirit. Our knowledge of God's future is based upon what can be derived from what we experience in Christ and from what we can see as its fulfilment. We do not have supplementary knowledge of the eschatological future over and above what we have in the theology of Christ and of grace, but we can transpose these to their fulfilment. This means that all genuine theological knowledge of the future is an inner moment of the eschatological present.

For the Christian, who views the future as God's self-bestowal, the future is truly unknown and uncontrollable, and this is something that leaves a great deal of room for freedom, for hope and for trust. Of course, we are inescapably tied to our imaginations and images have their proper place in expressing religious ideas. But it is fundamental not to mistake the image for the reality. The image might be the great wedding feast, or Paul's angelic trumpet or Matthew's sheep and goats. But the reality that the images point to is based upon the experience we have of the grace of Christ already at work in us and drawing us into a future in God.

For Rahner, the absolute future is nothing else than God's self-bestowal. This is the consummation of the divine action of creation and redemption, a fulfilment promised and initiated in the life, death and resurrection of Jesus. Christianity proclaims that the becoming of the universe will end, not in emptiness, but in the divine self-bestowal. Moreover, this absolute future is already at work within history. It is already the divine creative power at work in all things, through the Creator Spirit who is immanent in every aspect of creation, bringing the universe to its fulfilment. The absolute future, this divine self-bestowal, has found its explicit and irreversible expression in Jesus. His resurrection is both the promise and the beginning of the absolute future, the transformation of human beings and the whole of the universe in Christ. For Rahner absolute future is another name for God. This absolute future not only comes towards us as the future of our world, but is also 'the sustaining ground of the dynamism towards the future' (Rahner, 1969: 62). It is the absolute incomprehensible mystery of love from which creation comes and to which it is directed.

2. Hope for the Whole Creation in the New Testament: Romans 8:18–25

For some Christians, the concept of salvation is centred on the individual human person, and sometimes simply on the individual human soul. The biblical account, by contrast, is of resurrection of the body, the coming of the Reign of God, communion with others in the life of God, and the transformation of the whole creation. In the Bible, human beings are understood in relationship with each other and in relation to the wider creation. The biblical narrative begins with God creating all the diverse creatures of our universe and declaring them to be good. After the terrible destruction caused by human sin, God makes a solemn covenant not only with Noah and his family, but with every living creature and declares that the sign of this covenant with every creature of flesh will be the rainbow (Gen. 9:16). The Bible concludes with a vision of a new heaven and new earth, a transformed world, a place where God dwells with God's people, a place of healing and life, where the leaves of the tree of life, growing alongside the river of life, are for 'the healing of nations' (Rev. 22:2).

Biblical hope is for a forgiven and renewed humanity within a transformed creation. It finds expression in the famous image of the peaceable animals, where the wolf lives with the lamb, the lion eats straw like an ox, and children play safely near snakes and God proclaims: 'They will not hurt or destroy on all my holy mountain; for the earth will be full of the knowledge of the Lord as the waters cover the sea' (Isaiah 11:6–9). This promise occurs in a series of prophetic texts (Isaiah 43:19–21; 55:12–13, Ezek. 34:25–31, Hos. 2:18; Zech. 8:12; Mic. 4:4) and in the divine commitment to create 'new heavens and a new earth' (Isaiah 65:17; 66:22).

The New Testament sees the resurrection of Jesus as involving the whole creation. Jesus risen from the dead, is the Wisdom and Word of God, the one in whom all things are created and sustained (1 Cor. 8:6; Heb. 1:2–3; John 1:1–14). He is the one in whom all things are to be redeemed, recapitulated and reconciled (Rom. 8:18–25; Col. 1:15–20; Eph. 1:9–10, 20–23). The risen Christ is the beginning of the new creation, the promised new heavens and new earth (2 Pet. 3:13; Rev. 21:1–5; 22:13). In this new creation, every creature of earth, sky and sea will sing praise to the Lamb who has redeemed the whole creation (Rev. 5:13–14). Each of these texts contributes to an overall understanding of the divine promise in relation to the whole creation. I will take up just one of them, Paul's reflection on suffering and the promise of God in Romans:

> I consider that the sufferings of this present time are not worth comparing with the glory about to be revealed to us. For the creation waits with eager longing for the revealing of the children of God; for the creation was subjected

to futility, not of its own will but by the will of the one who subjected it, in hope that the creation itself will be set free from its bondage to decay and will obtain the freedom of the glory of the children of God. We know that the whole creation has been groaning in labor pains until now; and not only the creation, but we ourselves, who have the first fruits of the Spirit, groan inwardly while we wait for our adoption, the redemption of our bodies. For in hope we were saved. Now hope that is seen is not hope. For who hopes for what is seen? But if we hope for what we do not see, we wait for it with patience (Rom 8:18–23).

In exploring this text, I will gather up insights from three specialist New Testament scholars. The Pauline authority, Joseph Fitzmyer, points out that in this text Paul is clearly thinking of redemption (*apolytrōsis*) in Christ as applying not only to human beings, but also to the whole creation:

> It is no longer considered from an anthropological point of view; it is now recast in cosmic terms. Human bodies that are said to await such redemption (8:23) are merely part of the entire material creation, which is itself groaning in travail until such redemption occurs. For the Christ-event is expected to affect not only human beings, but all material or physical creation as well (Fitzmyer, 1993: 507).

Creation is held in bondage to sin, decay and death and in this it shares the lot of humanity, but it also shares with humanity the hope of redemption. The word Paul uses for decay (*phthora*), Fitzmyer tells us, 'denotes not only perishability and putrefaction, but also powerlessness, lack of beauty, vitality and strength that characterizes creation's present condition' (Fitzmyer, 1993: 509). The freedom of creation from this bondage will occur in and with the glorification of the sons and daughters of God. Fitzmyer points out that Paul is here talking about the fulfilment of the biblical promise of 'new heavens and a new earth' found in Isaiah 65:17 and 66:22 (Fitzmyer, 1993: 505).

Australian Pauline scholar Brendan Byrne sees this passage from Romans as one of 'the most singular and evocative' texts in the whole of Paul's work (Byrne, 1996: 255). What is distinctive, he says, is the way in which it includes the whole of non-human creation within the sweep of salvation alongside human beings. Byrne carefully analyses the meaning of the word creation (*ktisis*) as Paul uses it here. He establishes that 'it refers to the entire non-human world which the biblical creation stories present as the essential context for human life' (Byrne, 1996: 255). Byrne goes on to show that Paul presupposes a Jewish tradition that sees non-human creation as intimately bound up with the fate of human beings. This tradition goes back to the creation story (Gen. 3:17–19). Creation and humanity are understood as sharing a 'common fate' in the prophetic literature of the Bible, particularly in the texts I have mentioned above (Byrne, 1996: 255–7). Paul builds on this 'common fate' tradition, proclaiming that non-human creation will share with human beings in the final restoration of all things in Christ, which will involve a cosmic renewal. According to Byrne, Paul's point is that the sufferings of the present are a small price to pay for the glory coming. Paul does not minimize the suffering of the present, but sets in a wider framework, one that looks beyond the present to 'the full realization of God's design for human beings and their world' (Byrne, 1996: 257).

N. T. Wright, the Bishop of Durham, says of this same text: 'The greatest Pauline picture of the future world is Romans 8:19–25' (Wright, 2006: 75). He has no doubt that transformation of the whole creation in Christ is fundamental to Paul's vision. He writes:

> Creation as we know it bears witness to God's power and glory (Romans 1:19–20), but also to the present state of futility to which it has become enslaved. But this slavery, like all slaveries in the Bible, is then given its Exodus, its moment of release, when God does for the whole cosmos what he did for Jesus at Easter. This is the vision that is so big, so dazzling, that many even devout readers of Paul have blinked, rubbed their eyes, and ignored it, hurrying on to the more 'personal' application in the following paragraph (Wright, 2006: 75).

But, Wright insists, this is where Paul's whole argument of the justice of God comes to one of its great climaxes. Wright sees Romans 8 as the deepest New Testament answer to the 'problem of evil', to the question of God's justice. Paul is declaring that 'the renewal of creation, the birth of the new world from the labouring womb of the old, will demonstrate that God is in the right' (Wright, 2006: 75). In a recent work on biblical hope, Wright has said of Paul and the other first Christians that 'they believed that God was going to do for the whole cosmos what He has done for Jesus at Easter' (Wright, 2007: 104).

Paul's image of creation groaning in giving birth to new creation can find new meaning in a new context, as is evidenced in Christopher Southgate's recent important theological work on the suffering of creation (Southgate, 2008). It may be that the context of Paul's thought was the apocalyptic expectation of cosmic turmoil that would precede the final victory of God (Byrne, 1996: 256). But Paul's reflection also seems shaped by what he saw in the natural world around him. His image functions anew in the context of an understanding of the world shaped by evolutionary biology, a world of fertility, generativity and wonderful creativity, but also of struggle and suffering and death. The metaphor of birthing is at the origin of the word 'nature'. In the world of nature as understood in evolutionary terms, suffering and death seem to be the shadow side of prolific creativity (Rolston, 1999: 30–7).

The Earth has given birth to bacteria, trilobites, dinosaurs, mammals and human persons with their immensely complex brains. It has been a labour that has brought forth staggeringly diverse and complex forms of life, but in a process that has been very costly. In the Pauline vision, it has not yet reached its completion and fulfilment. It will not be fulfilled until it shares with human beings in God's final redemption and transformation of all things. Creation groans still as something even more radically new is being born. With the information we have today, I imagine that Paul would see God at work in this whole process of the evolution of our universe over the last 13.7 billion years and the evolution of life on Earth over the last 3.8 billion years, and that he would see God in Christ as promising a future not just for human beings but for the whole labouring creation, when God will bring it all to redemption and fulfilment.

3. Hope for the Universe in Patristic Tradition: Maximus the Confessor

In the Eastern patristic tradition, creation and redemption are held together. For Irenaeus they form one story of what God has done for us through the Word and in the Spirit. The whole history of history is taken up and recapitulated in Christ. The visible universe is destined to be restored and to share in glorification with the human community saved by Christ. Athanasius could speak of *creation* being deified in the Spirit through the Word of God. He writes of the Holy Spirit: 'In him, then, the Logos glorifies creation, and deifying it and adopting it brings it to the Father' (Athanasius, 2004: 175). Athanasius sees nonhuman creation participates in some way with human beings in glory, deification and adoption. This theology has been the common heritage of the Eastern Christian tradition, and much of the Western, although it has seldom received sustained theological attention.

This tradition finds influential expression in the thought of Maximus the Confessor (580–662). For Maximus, the incarnate Word of God restores the unity of the whole creation and brings it to God. Originally, God had called humans to be the bond of union in all the divisions and the different aspects of cosmic reality. The human was meant to be a 'microcosm' (a little universe), mediating and uniting the extremes of the cosmos, drawing the created order into harmony within itself and into union with God (Louth, 1996: 73). Because of the fall, human beings have failed in this function, but in the incarnation, God unites and recapitulates all things in the Word made flesh.

Maximus sees God as creating the universe of creatures with the Incarnation in mind. The Incarnation is 'the end for whose sake all things exist' (Daley, 2004: 170). All things are created in the eternal

Word. Maximus plays on the relationship in Greek between the *Logos*, the eternal Word of God, and the *logoi*. The *logoi* are the fundamental meanings of individual creatures in their diversity. The *logoi* represent the distinct ways that different created entities participate in the *Logos* of God. Maximus sees all as brought into unity and right relationship in Christ, the *Logos* made flesh:

> By his own initiative, he joins together the natural ruptures in all of the natural universe, and brings to fulfilment the universal meanings (*logoi*) of individual things, by which the unification of the divided is realized. He reveals and carries out the great will of God his Father, 'summing up all things in himself, things in heaven and things on earth' (Eph. 1:10), since all were created in him. (Translation from Daley, 2004: 171).

Jesus Christ, the *Logos* of God, unites in himself the *logoi*, the fundamental meanings of each created being, and brings all to unity and healing. In the Word made flesh all the ancient polarizations of creation are overcome. Christ unites human beings with himself, so that we bear his image, and share his role with regard to the rest of creation: 'With us and through us he encompasses the whole creation through its intermediaries and the extremities through their own parts' (Maximus, 1996: 160). The transfiguration of Christ is an important symbol of the transformation of creation in Christ. In this event, not only Jesus, but his garments, are transfigured, and these garments become for Maximus a symbol of the whole creation that shares in Christ's transfiguration. Human beings renewed in Christ, participate in his transfiguration, and participate in the transformation and healing of the whole cosmos.

These themes of the transformation and deification of creation appear at least briefly in the work of contemporary Orthodox theologians. Dumitru Staniloae, for example, says that the material universe, like humankind, 'is destined for transfiguration, through the power of the risen body of Christ' (Staniloae, 1970: 211). Paul Evdokimov writes that the second coming of Christ, the *Parousia*, 'coincides with the transformation of nature and it will be visible not within history but beyond it' (Evdokimov, 2001: 26). Vladimir Lossky says that 'Divine love always pursues the same end: the deification of men, and by them, of the whole universe' (Lossky, 1978: 110). Boris Bobrinskoy speaks of the importance of 'a deification that is both personal and cosmic' (Bobrinskoy, 1999: 5). Hope for the universe is not foreign to the Western tradition and is enshrined in the teaching of the Second Vatican Council and in the *Catechism of the Catholic Church* (paras. 1046–50). The Council affirms the final consummation and transformation of the universe, and points out how little we know of them: 'We know neither the moment of the consummation of the earth and of humanity, nor the way in which the universe will be transformed.' But in this new creation, we will find again the fruits of our being, our action and our history, 'cleansed this time from sin, illuminated and transfigured, when Christ presents to his Father an eternal and universal kingdom' (Flannery, 1996: 204–5).

4. The Deification of the Universe (Karl Rahner)

Cosmologists tell us that the observable universe is made up of something like a hundred billion galaxies. It is expanding and evolving. We can trace its history back to the first second of its existence, about 13.7 billion years ago, when it was extremely small, dense and hot. As the galaxies move away from one another, the rate of expansion seems to be increasing.

There are two scientific scenarios for the future of the universe. Either it will stop expanding at some point in the future, then begin to collapse back into an extremely small, dense and hot state, or it will continue to expand and cool forever. The present view of many cosmologists is that the universe is destined to expand forever, becoming less energetic and incapable of supporting life. Clearly, all carbon-based life is destined for extinction. In about five billion years our Sun will become a red giant, engulfing the orbit of Earth and Mars, and eventually it will become a white dwarf star. In 40 to 50 billion years star formation will have ended in our galaxy and in others (Russell, 2008: 300–1).

This is a bleak scenario of the future. Where does it leave Christian hope? How can the predictions that science makes about the future be reconciled with the promise of new creation? Karl Rahner sees the resurrection of the crucified as the beginning of the deification of the world itself. This is not to be confused to any form of pantheism, but an appeal to the ancient Greek and Latin Patristic idea that we are called to participate by God's grace in Trinitarian life. This transforming, deifying participation in God will be the real fulfilment of our humanity. Rahner, in line with much of the biblical and Christian tradition, sees our human fulfilment, our deification, as linked to that of the rest of creation.

This transforming process of the whole of reality has begun with the resurrection of the crucified Jesus. Rahner insists that what has occurred in the resurrection of Jesus, as part of the physical, biological and human world, is *ontologically* 'the embryonically final beginning of the glorification and divinization of the *whole* reality' (Rahner, 1966: 128). In the following sections, I will explore Rahner's idea of the deification of the material universe against the background of the scientific picture of endless dissipation. This will involve a consideration of the mysterious nature of matter itself, its radical transformation in new creation and the real continuity between the universe that we are part of today and God's new creation.

What does it mean to speak of the deification of matter?

In the biblical and patristic traditions, the material universe was seen as God's good creation and as destined to share with human beings in God's final fulfilment when Christ comes again. Often the focus was on the human. But the human being was seen as necessarily bodily and as interconnected with a non-human world. Final fulfilment of human beings was understood as involving a new relationship with the triune God, with the human community and with the wider creation. In my view this tradition is a precious resource for contemporary theology. In the light of more recent understanding of the history of the universe and of life on our planet, and confronted by twenty-first century ecological issues, the theological meaning of non-human creation and its future in God needs to be raised today in a less anthropocentric way.

In exploring this issue, it is worth noting that while science has discovered a great deal about matter, there is much that remains beyond us. Common sense suggests that the world of matter is more or less straight forward, compared for example to our minds or spirits. But in this case common sense misleads us. Matter itself is mysterious. The more we know about quantum mechanics, general relativity, the origins of matter in the early universe and the nucleosynthesis of elements in stars, the more counter-intuitive and mysterious matter becomes. And we are far from understanding the relationship between the ever-changing matter that makes up our bodies and our personal and interpersonal 'I'. The mysterious nature of matter, as well as all that we mean by spirit, suggests that we might well be open to a future for matter and spirit that exceeds anything we can imagine at present.

Karl Rahner insists that matter really does matter to God. God created a universe of creatures as an act of self-bestowing love, always intending to embrace the material world in the incarnation and to bring it to its fulfilment in Christ. Some Christians have seen the material world as a kind of stage for the drama of salvation, a stage that will have no further use in eternal life. Rahner insists, by contrast, that matter is not something to be cast aside as a transitory part of the journey of the spirit. It has been carried from the beginning by God's self-bestowing love. We know that our universe began from a tiny, dense, and extremely hot state and has been expanding every since, allowing galaxies to form, stars to ignite, and planets like Earth to form. This whole process, and every aspect of it, has been carried by the triune God, present, in love, to every part of it. Every emergent aspect of the universe is sustained by the Source of All, created in the Word and empowered by the Holy Spirit.

Rahner speaks of this self-bestowal in love as 'the most immanent element in every creature'. Therefore he can say: 'It is not mere pious lyricism when Dante regards even the sun and the other planets as being moved by that love which is God himself as he who bestows himself' (Rahner, 1973: 289). In terms of contemporary cosmology, we would say that the innermost principle of the movement of the galaxies and their stars, the innermost principle of the expanding and evolving universe, is God present in self-bestowing love.

Because of God's creation of a material universe in self-giving love, because of the incarnation, and because of the resurrection, God and matter go together. As Creator, God has been intimately engaged with the material universe at every point. God has become flesh, and become matter in the incarnation. In the risen Christ, part of the material universe is already taken into God as pledge and beginning of the fulfilment of material creation in God. By speaking of the deification of the material universe, what is being claimed is that the universe will reach its own proper fulfilment in being taken up in God's self-giving love. This is to be distinguished from the interpersonal fulfilment offered to human beings. It is the fulfilment of matter precisely as matter. While it is distinguished from the deifying interpersonal fulfilment of human beings, it is profoundly interconnected with it.

All of this means that Christians are, or perhaps ought to be, 'the most sublime of materialists'. We cannot think of our fulfillment without thinking of the fulfilment of the material universe and we cannot conceive of the risen Christ except as existing forever in the state of incarnation. This means that 'as materialists we are more crassly materialist than those who call themselves so' (Rahner, 1971: 183). We recognize that matter will last forever, and be glorified forever.

Radical transformation

Rahner couples his claim that matter has an eternal destiny with the insistence that matter will undergo a radical transformation, 'the depths of which we can only sense with fear and trembling in that process which we experience as our death' (Rahner, 1971: 183). If, as Rahner claims, the only way we can get a sense of the radical nature of the final transformation is by analogy with our own deaths, clearly this new creation is not simply an outcome of the ongoing evolution of the universe or of human progress. I find this an important insight. The Christian basis for understanding the radical nature of the transformation of the universe is the transformation that occurs in the resurrection of the crucified Jesus, just as the continuity between Jesus who was crucified and the risen Christ provides a basis for understanding the continuity between this universe and new creation.

New creation radically transcends and transfigures the old. As Orthodox theologian Paul Evdokimov points out, the day of the coming of Christ cannot be numbered with other days; 'The hand of God seizes the closed circle of empirical time and lifts it to a higher horizon, a different dimension. This 'day' closes historical time but does not itself belong to time. It cannot be found on our calendars and for this reason we cannot predict it' (Evdokimov, 2001: 25). Time, space and matter will reach their fulfilment and find their future in the boundless and mysterious life of God. We have no information from the Scriptures or any other source about the nature of this deification of our universe – only the promise given in Christ and his resurrection of a future in God.

Jürgen Moltmann has been strong in his insistence that only a radical act of God can bring healing and redemption to the whole creation. We will *not* be redeemed by evolutionary processes. Salvation can come only from a universal transformation of this present world, of the kind described in Revelation, where God says: 'See, I am making all things new' (21:5). This means that 'everything created, everything that was here, is here, and will be here' is to be made new. The new, eternal creation is to be the radically new creation and redemption of this world that we know (Moltmann, 2002: 261; 1996: 257–319). Richard Bauckham agrees with Moltmann, and vigorously criticizes the importing of Enlightenment optimism and views of historical and evolutionary progress into eschatology (Bauckham, 2001: 271–3). I think that Moltmann and Bauckham are right when they insist that final salvation cannot come from more of the same, but only from a radical act of God that transforms the whole creation from beginning to end by taking it eternally into the divine life of the Trinity.

New creation depends upon a transforming act of God, as radical as the act by which God raised Jesus from dead. I see this theological insight as able to shed some light on the problem I have described concerning the difference between biblical hope and the current scientific picture of the future of the universe as expanding endlessly, becoming cold and lifeless. The problem is based in part on an assumption that the universe can be thought of evolving seamlessly towards new creation. If the theological idea of God's final transformation of creation is presumed to *coincide* with the far distant future of the universe, there is obviously a problem reconciling theological eschatology and scientific predictions. But there is no need to make this assumption. Theologically, we have a promise that the universe will be transformed and find its culmination in God. Theology has no information about when or how this will be. The theological claim is not that the universe will evolve into a perfect state at the end and that this will then coincide with the divine act that makes all things new. If God's act is a radical one, if the best analogy for this kind of transformation is what happens in death, above all the death of Christ, then the divine act of making the whole universe new does not depend on the universe gradually evolving towards perfection.

It is fundamental to remember that the resurrection of the crucified was not dependant on any obvious movement towards completion or perfection in the life and ministry of Jesus. Jesus' mission was interrupted by what seemed totally catastrophic. The resurrection was the transformation of a brutal execution and a disastrous end to Jesus' ministry into unpredictable new life. The resurrection was a radical overturning of the rejection and savage violence and apparent failure of Jesus' mission. Yet, at a deeper level, Christians have come to see that God's act of raising Jesus up was also in fact in profound *continuity* with Jesus' life lived in love and with his death as the most radical expression of this love.

Real continuity

While I agreed above with Moltmann and Bauckham about the radical transformation involved in new creation, I want to affirm more strongly than they do the *continuity* between this creation we experience and God's new act. I find this continuity expressed in Rahner's notion of self-transcendence. He holds that God gives to creatures themselves the capacity for the new. Because of God's creative and redeeming presence *to creatures they can become something they were not.* When matter comes to life on Earth, when life becomes self-conscious and personal, this occurs through God enabling creation to transcend itself and become something new. Above all when one of us in the human and creaturely community, Jesus of Nazareth, is so radically open to God, so one with God, that we rightly see him as God-with-us, then we can say that in this person creation transcends itself into God. Jesus then is both God's self-communication to creation and creation's self-transcendence into God.

Rahner argues that something similar happens when the whole creation is finally taken up into God. All that constitutes our cosmic, social and personal history, the emergence of the universe, the evolution of life on Earth and our human history, will be taken up and find fulfilment in the life of God. On the one hand, the coming Reign of God will not simply be the outcome of the evolution of cosmic history and it will not be simply the result of the history that is planned and accomplished by humans. On the other hand, it will not simply come upon creation as an act of God from outside. It will be the deed of God, but this deed of God is to be understood as the self-transcendence of history, both cosmic and personal. It will go beyond (transcend) natural and human history in a real transformation by God. But it will be a transformation and a transcendence of and from what is already there – hence Rahner's language of *self*-transformation.

In cosmic terms this suggests that the coming of God will fulfil rather than overturn the laws and processes at work in the history of our universe and the evolution of life on Earth. Robert John Russell argues, rightly in my view, that the new creation is not to be seen as replacement of the old, or as a new creation *ex nihilo*, and goes on to propose that we need to think of God as creating the universe 'such that it is transformable' (Russell, 2008: 308). Russell sees God as creating a universe with precisely those characteristics that are needed as preconditions for God's act of new creation. These conditions and characteristics of the present creation are created in such a way that they can be transformed in new creation. It seems to me that what Russell is describing here is an important part of what Rahner means when he speaks of God's action occurring in and through the self-transcendence of our cosmic and evolutionary history.

This view of new creation as the self-transcendence of the old is a matter of great importance for our good human actions. It gives them ultimate importance. They will have a place in God's future. Rahner points out that there is a dialectical tension between two statements, both of which are true: On the one hand, human history will endure and, on the other hand, it will be radically transformed. The tension between them is fundamental, because it 'maintains in us an openness to the future while still according a radical importance to the present'. Our own history and our own acts contribute to God's future. History is not left behind but 'passes into the definitive consummation of God' (Rahner, 1973: 270).

Our own efforts, our ecological commitments, our struggles for justice, our work for peace, our acts of love, our failures, our own moments of quiet prayer, our sufferings, all have final meaning. Human history, and our own personal story, matter to God. The Word of God has entered into history for our salvation. History is embraced by God in the Christ-event. In the resurrection part of our history, the created humanity of Jesus, is already taken into God. We are assured that all of our history has eternal meaning in God. This means that our stories have final significance, as taken up into God and transformed in Christ.

5. Hope for the Animals

In chapter 5 of the book of Revelation, the angels, with the four living creatures who represent creation and with the elders, all sing a hymn of praise to the Lamb who has been slain. Then every creature, without exception joins in:

> Then I heard every creature in heaven,
> and on earth
> and under the earth
> and in the sea,
> and all that is in them, singing,
> 'To the one seated on the throne and to the Lamb
> Be blessing and honor and glory and might
> forever and ever!' (Rev. 5:13)

In this vision, the chorus of praise of the Lamb is joined by every creature of the natural world: 'the doxology has four terms, "heaven," "earth," "under the earth," "sea," indicating that all nature – heaven, hell (Heb. *sheol*), earth and the sea . . . joins in the praise' (Massyngberde Ford, 1975: 95). Every creature in all four realms of sky, ground, underground and sea, unite in a song of praise, celebrating redemption in the Lamb who was slaughtered, and all are imagined as participating in the joy of the new creation.

How are we to understand this text? While the post-biblical tradition has found ways to affirm that new creation in Christ involves hope not only for human beings but for the universe itself, it has not often dealt in an explicit way with hope for other animals. Implicitly, of course, Paul's words about suffering creation can be taken as involving the living, biological world. Can we make a more explicit claim? I propose that we can. As always, such a claim needs to be prefaced by acknowledging how little information we have about the nature of the life of the new creation. We know very little. What we can know is the nature of the God revealed to us in Jesus and the promise given to our world in his resurrection. This, I will propose, allows us to say some important things about hope for the other animals.

1. *Individual animals are known and loved by God.* In the Gospel of Matthew, we find Jesus calling his disciples to radical trust in God's providence, and pointing to God's care for each single sparrow: 'Yet not one of them will fall to the ground without your Father' (Matt. 10:29). The Wisdom of Solomon tells us that God creates each creature out of love. Animals, birds and insects exist because God loves them. They are called forth and held in existence only out of love (Wis. 11:24–26). The biblical God is a God of tenderness and compassion for all creatures. I think it is helpful to reflect on our own capacity as human beings to relate to other animals. We have the capacity for feeling with them, of feeling empathy with their pain, and joy in their well-being and vitality. This, surely, can give us a glimpse into the Creator's feeling for living things. We are right to think that our human experience of compassion for other creatures is but the palest reflection of the divine compassion for animals. The God of Jesus is a God of radical compassion, a compassion that has no boundaries. Such a God can be thought of as knowing each creature's experience, delighting in each, suffering with each and embracing each in love.

2. *The Creator Spirit is interiorly present to each creature enabling it to exist and to act.* It is the presence of God in the Spirit that confers existence on each animal. As theologians like Aquinas have taught, creation is a relationship by which God is interiorly present to each creature enabling it to exist and to act. Nothing is more interior to an

entity than its existence and this means for Aquinas that God's presence
and creative action is what is most interior to all things. In the language
of the Bible, the Spirit breathes life into all things of flesh. They have life
only because of the Breath of God: 'If he should take back his spirit to
himself, and gather to himself his breath, all flesh would perish together,
and all mortals return to dust' (Job 34:14–15). Psalm 104, the great
celebration of God's creation, sings of the heavens, the earth, the living
creatures of the land and sky, and the sea with all its life forms small
and great and sees them all as held in being by God's Spirit: 'When
you take away their breath, they die and return to their dust. When you
send forth your spirit, they are created; and you renew the face of the
ground' (Ps. 104:27–30). The Spirit is creatively present to every creature,
dwelling in each, surrounding it with love, holding it in a community of
creation and accompanying it in its life and in its death.

3. Animals participate in some way in redemption in Christ. When
Revelation envisions all living creatures, 'in heaven and on earth and
under the earth and in the sea', singing praise to the One sitting on the
throne and the Lamb who had been slain, it is clear that all these creatures
are thought of as sharing in some way in the redemption brought about
by the crucified and risen Christ. When Paul speaks of the groaning of
creation, and sees it as awaiting its participation in redemption, it seems
that the suffering creation he has in mind includes non-human biological
life. When Colossians and Ephesians insist that 'all things' in the cosmos
are recapitulated (Eph. 1:10) and reconciled (Col. 1:20) in Christ, it would
seem that 'all things' would include not only the material creation, the
cosmic powers and human beings, but also other animals.

While the Christian tradition has not often reflected carefully on the
redemption of animals, a theology of incarnation, such as is found in the
great patristic theologians like Athanasius, is a theology cast in the widest
possible terms, those of God and the whole creation. God embraces and
takes to God's self the whole creation in the incarnation. In a particular
way God embraces flesh, not just human flesh, but all the flesh that is
so intimately connected with it. In taking flesh in Jesus of Nazareth,
God becomes part of the history of biological evolution of life on Earth,
with the whole web of life and all that supports it. This can be taken as
suggestion, I believe, that God's redemptive act in the incarnation may
be seen as taking the whole world of flesh into the divine life, in the
new creation and the deification of all things in Christ. But the question
remains: What does it mean to speak of other animals participating with
us in the new creation?

4. Each animal abides forever in the living memory of God. In Luke's
version of the saying about the sparrow, Jesus states that not one

sparrow is 'forgotten before God' (Luke 12:6). It is held eternally in the divine memory. This concept of the divine memory provides a basis for an approach to the final redemption of other living creatures. In the liturgy of the church, we remember the wonderful things God has done in creation and redemption. When we celebrate the Eucharist in memory (*anamnēsis*) of Jesus, we are dealing with a remembrance that not only brings to mind the past, but acts powerfully in the present and anticipates an eschatological future. This experience of living memory may provide a pale analogy for God's redemptive memory. What is being suggested here is that God can be thought of not only as present with each creature in the Spirit, loving it and conferring on it existence and the capacity to act, but also as inscribing it eternally in the living memory and experience of divine Trinitarian life.

For the Bible, while our memory of God is a fundamental requirement, it is God's remembrance that is primary. God remembers God's covenant with us forever (Ps. 105:8). Human beings pray that God will hold them in the divine memory (Job 7:7; 10:9; 14:13; Ps. 78:39). Humans exist because God remembers them and holds them in provident care (Ps. 8: 4). Alexander Schmemann writes of this biblical concept of memory:

> Memory refers to the attentiveness of God to his creation, the power of divine providential love through which God 'holds' the world and *gives it life*, so that life itself can be termed abiding in the memory of God, and death the falling out of this memory. In other words, memory, like everything else in God, is *real*, it is that life that he grants, that God '*remembers*'; it *is* the eternal overcoming of the 'nothing' out of which God called us into 'his wonderful light' (Schmemann, 1988: 125).

In this view, it is the divine memory that enables creatures to be and to interact. It is powerfully and wonderfully creative. To be held in the divine memory it to be continually created '*ex nihilo*', to be enabled to exist, to find food and water and to reproduce. The divine memory creates. It makes things live. It enables a diverse world of creatures to evolve on our planet. In response to God's creative remembrance, humans are the creatures who are particularly called to remember God. This is the human gift and responsibility: the human person is one who 'comprehends the world as God's world, receives it from God and raises it up to God' (Schmemann, 1988: 125). In response to God who keeps the whole of creation in mind, and brings it to life, the human being is called to remember the Creator and thus enter more fully into the life bestowed on them. The human remembrance of God is 'the reception of this life-creating gift, the constant *acquisition* of and increase in life' (Schmemann, 1988: 126).

Based on the faithful love of God revealed in Christ, I think it can be said that God will not forget any creature that God loves and creates.

Each is inscribed eternally in the divine life. The sparrow that falls to the ground is not abandoned, but is gathered up and brought to redemptive new life in Christ, in whom 'creation itself will be set free from its bondage to decay' (Rom. 8: 21). The sparrow that falls to the ground is among the 'all things' that are reconciled (Col. 1: 20), recapitulated (Eph. 1:10) and made new (Rev. 21:5) in the risen Christ. The shared life of God can be thought of as involving the holding and treasuring of every creature of every time in the living present of the Trinity. In the Communion of Saints, we can be thought of as coming to share the divine delight in each creature. The Communion of Saints would, then, open up as the communion of all creation. The capacity we already have to treasure all that makes up the history of life offers a hint of what might be possible to God. Again, our memory, even our liturgical remembering, can only be a poor analogy for the divine capacity to hold all things and make them live in the eternal memory of the triune God.

In the incarnational theology being suggested here, each sparrow is known and loved by God, participates in redemption in Christ, and is eternally held and treasured in the life of the Trinity. The creatures that spring from the abundance of divine Communion find redemption in being taken up eternally into this Communion in a way that we cannot fully articulate. John Haught speaks of the whole of creation as being redeemed by being taken up into the enduring divine experience of the world. He says that everything in creation, 'all the suffering and tragedy as well as the emergence of new life and intense beauty' is being *saved* by 'being taken eternally into God's feeling for the world' (Haught, 2000: 43). Individual creatures abide permanently within the everlasting compassion of God.

In this proposal, individual creatures are taken up into the living experience of the Trinity, and are celebrated, respected and honoured in the divine Communion and in the Communion of Saints. I have already pointed out that we know very little about the *how* of our risen life in Christ, and we know less about that of other creatures. We hope for what is beyond our capacity to imagine because our hope is in the God who remains always incomprehensible mystery. We hope for what we do not see (Rom. 8:24) and cannot imagine, the transformation of the whole creation in Christ. What we know is the promise of God given in the resurrection of the Word made flesh. We can hope that, in our participation in the Communion of Saints, we will also participate in God's delight in other animals within the abundance of creation that reaches it fulfilment in God. In particular we may hope that the relationship we have with particular creatures, such as a beloved dog, does not end with death, but is taken into eternal life.

5. There is reason to hope that animals participate in resurrection life in Christ. I have been proposing that each animal is known and loved by

God, is the dwelling place of the Creator Spirit, participates in redemption in Christ, and abides forever in the living memory of God. Can more be said? I think it can. I think it can be said that animals will reach their redemptive fulfilment in Christ. They will not only be remembered and treasured, but remembered in such a way as to be called into new life. We do not have an imaginative picture of the new creation. Any imaginative picture we can form that is based on our present experience will quickly prove inadequate. But this is true, as well, for the resurrection of human beings. We can imagine the resuscitation of a corpse, but we cannot imagine the radical transformation of resurrection. The fact that resurrection life is beyond imagination does not mean that it is not real. Our imaginations are of limited use, and do not function well in dealing with God, who is the absolute future and the power of new life. Of course, they are also inadequate for dealing with quantum physics and with cosmology. What is real can be beyond our imaginations and our concepts.

The basis for hope is not our imagination but the God revealed in Jesus. As I pointed out earlier, we need to know the limits of our knowledge of our future in God. What we have is hope based on our experience of God with us in Jesus and in the Spirit. As Elizabeth Johnson has said, our hope is not based upon information about the future but on 'the character of God' revealed in the Christ-event (Johnson, 1998: 201). What I am proposing is that we can think that, based on the character of God revealed in the Christ-event, individual animals and birds will participate in some way in risen life. They will find their fulfilment in God. The God of resurrection life is a God who brings individual creatures in their own distinctiveness *in some way* into the eternal dynamic life of the divine Communion.

In Revelation the one sitting on the throne says: 'Behold I make all things new' (Rev. 21:5). I am proposing that this 'all things' includes other animals. It is clear that God will respect the particular nature that is specific to each creature. What is appropriate fulfilment for a human being may not be appropriate to a crab, a mosquito or a bacterium. It is important to remember that great theologians like Thomas Aquinas and Bonaventure saw the diversity of creatures as expressing the boundless abundance of the divine goodness. There is every reason to hope that the diverse range of creatures that spring from the abundance of this divine Communion will find redemption in being taken up eternally into this divine Communion in ways that are appropriate to each. Because God relates to each creature on its own terms, final fulfilment will fit the nature of each creature. With this in mind, I think it can be said that individual creatures will find their proper redemption in the divine Communion in a way that we cannot fully imagine or articulate.

Epilogue:

Darwin and the Theologians

Thomas Henry Huxley, Darwin's 'bulldog', notoriously wrote, 'Exhausted theologians lie about the cradle of every science as the strangled snakes beside that of Hercules; and history records that whereas science and orthodoxy have been fairly opposed, the latter has been forced to retire from the lists, bleeding and crushed if not annihilated; scotched if not slain' (Huxley, 1896: 52). Intriguingly, the same bruiser wrote later in life:

> It is the secret of the best theological teachers to the majority of their opponents that they substantially recognize the realities of things, however strange the forms in which they clothe their conceptions. The doctrines of predestination; of original sin; of the innate depravity of man and the evil fate of the greater part of the human race; of the primacy of Satan in this world, faulty as they are, appear to me to be vastly nearer the truth than the 'liberal' popular illusions that babes are all born good and that the example of a corrupt society is responsible for their failure to remain so; that it is given to everybody to reach the ethical ideal if he will only try . . . (Huxley, 1892).

Huxley's comments were – as always – robust, but he was not contradicting himself in these judgements. Though not obvious at the time, the *Origin* forced a re-aligning of faith and reason in ways unexpected by most, not least Darwin himself. We need to recognize the historical context of Darwin's time. Don Cupitt has described the situation at the beginning of the nineteenth century:

Mechanistic science was allowed to explain the structure and workings of physical nature without restriction. But who designed this beautiful world-machine and set it going in the first place? Only Scripture could answer that question. So science dealt with the everyday tick-tock of the cosmic framework and religion dealt with the ultimates: first beginnings and last ends, God and the soul . . . It was a happy compromise while it lasted. Science promoted the cause of religion by showing the beautiful workmanship of the world . . . This was the old Argument from Design, and if it seems quaint to us now, it once seemed cogent and did a good job by shifting people away from seeing God in the freakish and fearful to admiring his wisdom and workmanship in the ordinary course of things . . . But there was a fatal flaw in the synthesis. Religious ideas were being used to plug the gaps in scientific theory. Science could not yet explain how animals and plants had originated and had become so wonderfully adapted to their environment – so that was handed over to religion. People still made a sharp soul-body distinction and the soul fell beyond the scope of science – so everything to do with human inwardness and personal and social behaviour remained the province of the preacher and moralist (Cupitt, 1984: 58).

Into this situation came first the discoveries of deep time and deep space, and with them development of new tensions between faith and reason. Then came the *Origin*. It made sense of a vast amount of apparent disparate data on anatomy and physiology, animal and plant distribution, and ecological processes, which together have provided a basis for scientific advances as far-reaching as relativity theory or the Periodic Table. It also sounded the death knell of deism and the opening of new ways to explore the relationship of the Creator to the creation. Aubrey Moore saw Darwin as a saviour of good theology:

The breakup of the mediaeval system and thought had resulted in an atomism which, if it had been more perfectly consistent with itself, would have been fatal alike to knowledge and society . . . Its theory of knowledge was a crude empiricism. Its theology unrelieved deism. God was 'throned in magnificent inactivity in a remote corner of the universe' . . . His immanence in nature, the 'higher pantheism', which is a truth essential to true religion, as it is to true philosophy, fell into the background . . . [Then] Darwinism appeared and, under the disguise of a foe, did the work of a friend. It has conferred upon philosophy and religion an inestimable benefit, by showing that we must choose between two alternatives: either God is everywhere present in nature or He is nowhere . . . It seems as if, in the providence of God, the mission of modern science was to bring home to our unmetaphysical ways of thinking the great truth of the Divine immanence in creation, which is not less essential to the Christian idea of God than to a philosophical idea of nature. And it comes to us almost like a new truth, which we cannot at once fit in with the old (Moore, 1899: 99–100).

As Moore recognized, the advent of Darwinism made it possible to think of a world without God, a world ruled entirely by 'natural processes'. This is the choice which allowed Dawkins to proclaim that 'although atheism was logically tenable before Darwin, Darwin made it possible to be an intellectually fulfilled atheist'. If decision about the existence or not of God depended on natural theology – the old evidence of 'design' – the case for theism would be seriously weakened. But Christianity is based on the historical coming of the Christ and his resurrection from the dead. The Christian faith does not stand or fall on inferences from the natural world; evolution and Darwinism buttress faith, they neither prove nor banish it. This is the context in which we should site Darwin.

It would have been truly good if Darwin had managed to negotiate a true peace between theology and biology, between science and religion, but the message of virtually every chapter in this book shows that the war is not over. Indeed there are many dissidents who regard Darwin as an agent of the Devil, provoking disbelief, never mind racialism, Marxism, eugenics, and a host of other social and spiritual ills. We hope that the contributions herein will encourage positive debate and constructive thought on 'Darwinian issues'. Perhaps most of all, we hope that readers may be stimulated to go beyond the negative 'devotion to endless myths and genealogies' (which can be regarded as an obsession with evolutionary questions) condemned by Paul, which only 'give rise to mere speculation and do not further God's plan for us' (1 Tim. 1:4).

Christian debate about evolution is a diversion from building a firm doctrine of creation. We believe that this is the tragic legacy of Darwinism. Too often the Christian response to environmental issues are entirely pragmatic. In his history of Church of England evangelicals, Kenneth Hylson-Smith notes that the Victorian evangelicals achieved much, but lacked social policy. As a result the endeavours of the Clapham sect never became part of mainstream action (Hylson-Smith, 1988: 208). Peter Harris has identified the same doctrinal blindness in the modern-day Church:

> As I have puzzled over the causes for current evangelical indifference to creation, it has become uncomfortably clear that its roots lie in unbiblical belief. It is not that evangelicals shrink from paying a price in lost comfort for a change of lifestyle. There are many wonderful examples of how the Christian church worldwide live very sacrificially in the face of human need, and in many places it is a compelling stimulus for social change and redemption. The problem is that we do not extend that commitment and concern to the wider creation, nor are we persuaded that God cares about it (Harris, 2000: 133).

Harris sees the covenant made at the creation and repeatedly renewed in scripture as a central expression of God's relationship to the world (Murray, 1992). In it, we are given an intensely practical way of living faithfully and to a proper relationship to the wider world. The true value of other [*i.e.* non-human] life on earth is that it is created and cared for by a personal Creator. It is not merely raw material for economic growth or semi-divine emanations of some impersonal creative force, or, even worse, our enemy in the struggle for species dominance, to be subdued in our fight to survive. It is the confusion over what status to give to the rest of creation that has led to the incoherence of our relationships with our environment (Harris, 2005: 51).

Walter Brueggemann underlines this, pointing out that for the author of Deuteronomy, the Promised Land in which the Israelites will lack nothing (Deut. 8:7–10) is not primarily about the existence or prosperity of its inhabitants, but refers to an indissoluble partnership with Yahweh, 'never only with Yahweh as though to live only in intense obedience, never only with land as though simply to possess and manage' (Brueggemann, 1977: 52).

How can we move on from the kick-start of 1859 and develop a strong doctrine of creation? How can we rise above the utilitarianism of reacting to issues of climate change, population pressure, resource depletion, and the like? Lynn White stirred many with his criticism of unthinking human reliance on technology in his essay on the 'Historical roots of our ecologic crisis' (White, 1967), despite the legitimate criticisms of it by both historians and theologians (Sheldon, 1992; Northcott, 1996). Recent decades have seen a considerable rise in Christian concern for and action over the creation, but creation care still remains a minority passion for enthusiasts, rather than an integral part of Christian belief. Is it too simplistic to see this failure of understanding as at least in part a reaction against the evolution-creation struggles – a reaction against both the naiveties of Darwinian atheists on the one hand and the 'creationists' on the other?

Over the centuries this obfuscation has taken many guises. Irenaeus derived a theology of nature through an account of the cosmic significance of the incarnation, death and resurrection of Jesus Christ, contrary to the sub-Christian Gnosticism of his time. His starting-point was a God who brought the whole creation into being, with the incarnate Word as the ever-present life-giving principle who moves the whole creation towards a divinely intended goal. He interpreted the vocation of Jesus Christ as serving the whole creation, not merely fallen and redeemed humankind, until its divine fulfilment (*telos*) when he will deliver his rule to the Father (Santmire, 1985: 35–44). Irenaeus's clarity was then clouded by the Neoplatonism of Origen and Plotinus.

In Colossians, Paul speaks of God reconciling *all things* to himself through the death of Christ on the cross (Col. 1:20). Paul expands on this in Romans 8:19–22, speaking of the creation being 'made subject to frustration' and to 'groaning as if in the pangs of childbirth'. Derek

Kidner links it with the Fall story in Genesis 3: 'Leaderless, the choir of creation can only grind on in discord. It seems from Romans 8:19–23 and from what is known of the pre-human world that there was a state of travail from the first which man was empowered to "subdue" until he relapsed into disorder himself' (Kidner, 1967: 73).

For Tom Wright,

> Romans 8:18–28 is one of the most central statements in the New Testament about what God intends to do with the whole creation'. He grieves that it 'is regularly marginalized in mainstream Protestant interpretations of Romans. If you insist on reading Romans simply as a book about how human beings "get saved" in the sense of "going to heaven when they die", you will find that these verses function as a kind of odd apocalyptic appendix. That in consequence is how the tradition has often regarded them, both in the 'radical' scholarship of Lutherans like Bultmann and Käsemann and in the 'conservative' readings of much evangelical scholarship. In fact, the passage is the deliberate and carefully planned climax to the whole train of thought in Romans 5 – 8, and indeed Romans 1 – 8, as a whole (Wright, 1999a: 12).

He has extended the same argument elsewhere:

> The Christian inheritance is not one piece of geographical countryside. It is nothing less than the renewed, restored creation. Paul's spectacular picture of creation groaning in birth-pangs, longing to share the freedom of the glory of God's people (8: 16–27), owes a great deal on the one hand to the image of the 'Messianic woes', but on the other hand to the scriptural sense in which the fate of the land is bound up with the fate, and the covenant behavior of Israel [For the positive side, see, e.g. Is. 35; for the negative compare the suggestive Lev. 26:24, 43; 2 Chron. 36: 21]. When Christians are finally redeemed, Paul is saying, then the land – only now, in this case, the whole cosmos – will be redeemed (Wright, 1999b).

Charles Moule agrees: for him Romans 8:19–21 means that 'man is responsible before God for nature. As long as man refuses to play the part assigned him by God, so long the entire world of nature is frustrated and dislocated. It is only when man is truly fitting into his proper position as a son in relation to God his Father that the dislocation of nature will be reduced' (Moule, 1964: 12).

Science is an immensely potent tool. It connects us with the material world. It enables us to discover properties and ways to modify 'nature'. But it cannot give the answers to all questions that we can ask. The Nobel Laureate, Peter Medawar wrote a book on *The Limits of Science* to stress that 'science should not be expected to provide answers to such as the purpose of life or the existence of God, for which it was unfitted' (Medawar, 1990: 220). He described science 'as the most successful enterprise human beings have ever engaged upon'. He was happy to accept that there are no discernible limits to the power of science to answer those questions which it is capable of answering, mainly those where we can suggest and investigate the causes(s) of some phenomenon. But he unapologetically believed that there are some questions that science cannot answer. For him there was a class of 'ultimate questions', which are simply outside scientific logic, just as it is impossible to deduce 'from the axioms and postulates of Euclid a theorem having to do with how to bake a cake' (Medawar, 1984: 67). In this he followed Karl Popper, who had written, 'Science does not make assertions about ultimate questions – about the riddles of existence or about man's task in the world' (Popper, 1978: 342). Steve Jones made a very similar comment in his Reith Lectures:

> It is the essence of all scientific theories that they cannot resolve everything. Science cannot answer the questions that philosophers – or children – ask: why are we here, what is the point of being alive, how ought we to behave? Genetics has almost nothing to say about what makes us more than machines driven by biology, about what makes us human. These questions may be interesting, but scientists are no more qualified to comment on them than is anyone else. In its early days, human genetics suffered greatly from its high opinion of itself. It failed to understand its own limits (Jones, 1978: xi).

We can, of course, deny that God exists. There are vociferous proponents of such a belief. But for those who accept the God revealed in scripture, we must also acknowledge that we live in a world designed and made by Him, which belongs to Him, and which is entrusted to us as His caretakers (Berry, 2006; C. T. H. Wright, 2006: especially chapter 12). The implications of this are far, far greater than any debates about evolutionary mechanisms – and theologians must not ignore it.

Bibliography

Agamben, G. (2004). *The Open: Man and Animal*. Stanford, CA: Stanford University Press.

Alexander, D. (2008). *Creation or Evolution: Do We Have to Choose?* Oxford: Monarch Books.

Allen, C. and M. Bekoff (2005). 'Animal Play and the Evolution of Morality: An Ethological Approach', *Topoi*, 24, 125–135.

—— (2007). 'Animal Minds, Cognitive Ethology and Ethics', *The Journal of Ethics*, 11, 299–317.

Anonymous (1864). 'Mr. Kingsley's *Water-Babies*', Reviews, *The Times*, January 26, 6.

Artigas, M., T. F. Glick and R. A. Martinez (2006). *Negotiating Darwin: The Vatican Confronts Evolution, 1877–1902*. Baltimore, MD: Johns Hopkins University Press.

Athanasius (2004). 'First Letter to Serapion' in Norman Russell (2004) *The Doctrine of Deification in the Greek Patristic Tradition*. Oxford: Oxford University Press, 175.

Attfield, R. (2006). *Creation, Evolution and Meaning*. Aldershot: Ashgate.

Augustine (1955). *Confessions and Enchiridion*, translated by A.C. Outler. London: SCM Press.

—— (1982). *The Literal Meaning of Genesis*, translated by J. H. Taylor. New York Paulist Press.

—— (1998). *The City of God against the Pagans*, translated by R. W. Dyson. Cambridge: Cambridge University Press.

Axe, D. D. (2004). 'Estimating the Prevalence of Protein Sequences Adopting Functional Enzyme Folds'. *Journal of Molecular Biology*, 341:5, 1295–1315.

Ayala, Francisco J. (2006). *Darwin and Intelligent Design.* Minneapolis, MN: Fortress Press.

—— (2007). *Darwin's Gift to Science and Religion.* Washington, DC: Joseph Henry Press.

Barr, James (1992). *The Garden of Eden and the Hope of Immortality.* London: SCM Press.

—— (1993). *Biblical Faith and Natural Theology: The Gifford Lectures for 1991 delivered in the University of Edinburgh.* Oxford: Clarendon.

—— (1994). *Biblical faith and Natural Theology.* Oxford: Oxford University Press.

Barth, Karl (1956). *Church Dogmatics,* vol. IV/1, trans. G. W. Bromiley. Edinburgh: T & T Clark.

—— (1960). *Church Dogmatics,* vol. III/3, trans. G. W. Bromiley and R. J. Ehrlich. Edinburgh: T & T Clark.

—— (1961). *Church Dogmatics,* vol. III/4, trans. A. T. Mackay et al. Edinburgh: T & T Clark.

Bauckham, Richard (2001). 'The Future of Jesus Christ' in Markus Bockmuehl, *The Cambridge Companion to Jesus.* Cambridge: Cambridge University Press.

Bechtel, L. M. (1995). 'Genesis 2.4b-3.24: A Myth about Human Maturation', *Journal for the Study of the Old Testament,* 67, 3–26.

Behe, M. (2008). 'Can a Scientific Theory Ameliorate a Theological Difficulty?' *Theology and Science* 6, 147–152.

Berry, R. J. (2007). *Creation and Evolution, not Creation or Evolution.* Faraday Paper 12, The Faraday Institute.

Berry, R. J. (1982). *Neo-Darwinism.* London: Edward Arnold.

—— (1988). *God and Evolution.* London: Hodder & Stoughton.

—— (1989). 'Ecology: Where Genes and Geography Meet'. *Journal of Animal Ecology,* 58, 733–59.

—— (1999). 'This Cursed Earth: Is "the Fall" Credible?' *Science and Christian Belief,* 11:1, 29–49.

—— (2001). *God and Evolution.* Vancouver: Regent College Publishing.

—— (2005). 'The Lions Seek their Prey from God: A Commentary on the Boyle Lecture', *Science and Christian Belief,* 17, 41–56.

—— (ed.). (2006a). *Environmental Stewardship.* London: T & T Clark.

—— (2006b). 'Nothing in Biology Makes Sense Except in the Light of Evolution'. *Science & Christian Belief,* 18, 23–29.

Berry, R. J., T. J. S. Crawford & G. M. Hewitt (eds.) (1992). *Genes in Ecology.* Oxford: Blackwell Scientific.

Berry, Wendell (1983). *Standing by Words.* Washington, DC: Shoemaker & Hoard.

Bimson, J. J. (2006). 'Reconsidering a Cosmic Fall', *Science & Christian Belief,* 18:1, 63-81.

Blocher, H. (1984). *In the Beginning: The Opening Chapters of Genesis.* Leicester: InterVarsity Press.

—— (1997). *Original Sin.* Leicester: Apollos.

Bobrinskoy, Boris (1999). *The Mystery of the Trinity.* Crestwood, NY: St. Vladimir's Seminary Press.

Bowler, Peter J. (1986). *Theories of Human Evolution: a Century of Debates 1844–1944.* Oxford: Basil Blackwell.

—— (2001). *Reconciling Science and Religion.* Chicago: Chicago University Press.

—— (2007). *Monkey Trials and Gorilla Sermons: Evolution and Christianity from Darwin to Intelligent Design*. Cambridge, MA: Harvard University Press.

Boyle, Robert (1965). 'A Free Inquiry into the Vulgarly Received Notion of Nature', in M. B. Hall (ed.), *Robert Boyle on Natural Philosophy*. Bloomington IN: Indiana University Press, 150–53.

Britten, R. J. (2002). 'Divergence Between Samples of Chimpanzee and Human DNA Sequences is 5%, Counting Indels', *Proceedings of the National Academy of Sciences of the USA*, 99, 13633-35.

Broadie, Alexander (2001). *The Scottish Enlightenment*. Edinburgh: Birlinn.

Brooke, J. H. (2001). 'The Wilberforce-Huxley Debate: Why Did it Happen?' *Science & Christian Belief*, 13, 127–141.

Browne, J. (2002). *Charles Darwin. The Power of Place*. London: Jonathan Cape.

Brueggemann, Walter (1977). *The Land*. Minneapolis, MN: Fortress Press.

—— (1982). *Genesis*. Atlanta: John Knox Press.

Brunner, Emil, and Karl Barth (1946). *Natural Theology: Comprising 'Nature and Grace' by Professor Dr. Emil Brunner and the Reply 'No!' by Karl Barth*, trans. Peter Fraenkel. London: Geoffrey Bles.

Burge, T. (2005). *Science and the Bible: Evidence-based Christian Belief*. London: Templeton Foundation Press.

Butler, Samuel (1863). 'Darwin Among the Machines', Letter to *The Times*, signed Cellarius.

—— (1886). 'Letter to Mrs Taylor', *Memoir*, vol. II. London: Jonathan Cape.

—— (1887). *Luck, or Cunning as the Main Means of Organic Modification?* London: Jonathan Cape.

Byrne, Brendan (1996). *Romans*. Collegeville, MN: Liturgical Press.

Calvin, John. *Institutes of the Christian Religion* 1.16.2.

Catechism of the Catholic Church (1994*)*. Homebush, NSW: St Pauls.

Cela Conde, C. J. and F. J. Ayala (2007). *Human Evolution. Trails from the Past*. Oxford: Oxford University Press.

Chalmers, Thomas (1833). *The Bridgewater Treatises on the Power, Wisdom, and Goodness of God as Manifested in the Adaptation of External Nature to the Moral and Intellectual Constitution of Man, Treatise I*. London: Pickering.

Clarke, R. W. (1984). *The Survival of Charles Darwin*. London: Weidenfeld & Nicolson.

Clayton, Philip D. (1997). *God and Contemporary Science*. Edinburgh: Edinburgh University Press.

Clayton, P. and S. Knapp (1996). 'Rationality and Christian Self-Conceptions', in W.M. Richardson and W.J. Wildman (eds.), *Religion and Science: History, Method, Dialogue*. London and New York: Routledge.

Collins, Francis (2006). *The Language of God: A Scientist Presents Evidence for Belief*. New York and London: Free Press and Simon & Schuster.

Colwell, J. E. (1988). 'Fall', in S. B. Ferguson & D. F. Wright (eds.), *New Dictionary of Theology*. Leicester: InterVarsity Press, 249–51.

Conway Morris, Simon (2003). *Life's Solution: Inevitable Humans in a Lonely Universe*. Cambridge: Cambridge University Press.

Coyne, J. A. and A. H. Orr (2004). *Speciation*. Sunderland, MA: Sinauer.

Cullmann, Oscar (1962). *Christ and Time*. London: SCM Press.

Daley, Brian (2004). '"He himself is our Peace" (Ephesians 2:14): Early Christian Views of Redemption in Christ,' in Stephen T. Davis, Daniel Kendall and

Gerald O'Collins (eds.) *The Redemption: An Interdisciplinary Symposium on Christ as Redeemer*. Oxford: Oxford University Press.

Darwin, Charles (1859). *On the Origin of Species by Means of Natural Selection, or the Preservation of Favoured Races in the Struggle for Life.* London: John Murray.

—— (1867). *Die Entstehung der Arten im Thier- und Pflanzen-Reich durch natürliche Züchtung, oder Erhaltung der vervollkommneten Rassen im Kampfe um's Daseyn*, trans. H. G. Bronn and J. V. Carus, 3rd ed. Stuttgart: Schweizerbart.

—— (1867). *On the Origin of Species by Means of Natural Selection: or the Preservation of Favoured Races in the Struggle for Life*, Sixth Edition, London, John Murray.

—— (1871). *The Descent of Man and Selection in Relation to Sex*, London: Watts and Co.

—— (1905). *More Letters of Charles Darwin*, eds. Francis Darwin and A. C. Seward, vol. 1, New York: D. Appleton and Company.

—— (1969). *The Autobiography of Charles Darwin, 1809–1882*, ed. Nora Barlow. New York: Norton.

—— (1987). *Charles Darwin's Notebooks, 1836–1844* ed. Paul H. Barrett et. al. Ithaca: Cornell University Press.

—— (2003). *The Descent of Man and Selection in Relation to Sex*, 2nd ed. London: Gibson.

—— (2006). *The Origin of Species. A Variorum Text*, ed. Morse Peckham. Philadelphia: University of Pennsylvania Press.

Darwin, Francis (ed.) (1887). *The Life and Letters of Charles Darwin, including an Autobiographical Chapter*, 3 volumes. London: John Murray, online at http://darwin-online.org.uk/content/frameset?itemID=F1452.2&viewtype=text&pageseq=1 (accessed 29 February 2008).

Davis, Ellen F. (2009). *Scripture, Culture, Agriculture: An Agrarian Reading of the Bible*. Cambridge and New York: Cambridge University Press.

Dawkins, Richard (1986). *The Blind Watchmaker*. London: Longman.

—— (1996). *Climbing Mount Improbable*. London: Viking.

—— (2003). *A Devil's Chaplain: Reflections on Hope, Lies, Science, and Love*. London: Weidenfeld & Nicolson.

—— (2004). *The Ancestor's Tale*. London: Weidenfeld & Nicolson.

Day, A. J. (1988). 'Adam, Anthropology and the Genesis Record – Taking Genesis Seriously in the Light of Contemporary Science', *Science & Christian Belief*, 10:2, 115–143.

Deason, Gary B. (1986). 'Reformation Theology and the Mechanistic Conception of Nature', in D.C. Lindberg & R.L. Numbers (eds), *God and Nature*. Berkeley, CA: University of California Press. 167–191.

Dembski, W. A. (1998). *The Design Inference: Eliminating Chance Through Small Probabilities*. Cambridge, Cambridge University Press.

—— (1999a). *Intelligent Design – the Bridge Between Science and Theology*, Downers Grove, Illinois: IVP Academic.

—— (1999b). 'Signs of Intelligence: a Primer on the Discernment of Intelligent Design'. *Touchstone*, p. 84.

—— (2004). *The Design Revolution*, Downers Grove, IL: InterVarsity Press.

—— (2008). 'Ayala's Potemkin Village', *Theology and Science* 6, 159–163.

Dennett, Daniel (1995). *Darwin's Dangerous Idea*. New York: Touchstone.

Desmond, A. and J. R. Moore (2009). *Darwin's Sacred Cause: Race, Slavery and the Quest for Human Origins*. London: Allen Lane.

Desmond, Adrian, and James Moore (1991). *Darwin*, London: Michael Joseph.

—— (1992), *Darwin*, London: Penguin.

Desmond, A. (1989). *The Politics of Evolution*. Chicago: Chicago University Press.

Desmond, A. and J. R. Moore (1991). *Darwin*. London: Michael Joseph.

De Waal, F. (1996). *Good Natured. The Origin of Right and Wrong in Humans and Other Animals*. Cambridge, MA: Harvard University Press.

Diamond, J. (1991). *The Rise and Fall of the Third Chimpanzee*. London: Radius.

Dickey, James (2002), 'The Heaven of Animals', in Neil Astley (ed.), *Staying Alive: Real Poems for Unreal Times*. Tarset: Bloodaxe. 221–2.

Dobzhansky, T. (1937). *Genetics and the Origin of Species*. New York: Columbia University Press.

Dostoevsky, Fyodor (1912), *The Brothers Karamazov*, trans. Constance Garnett. London: Heinemann.

Draper, W. (1875). *History of the Conflict between Religion and Science*. London: Henry King.

Dugatkin, Lee Alan (2006). *The Altruism Equation: Seven Scientists Search for the Origins of Goodness*. Princeton: Princeton University Press.

Dunbar, R. (1996). *Grooming, Gossip and the Evolution of Language*. London: Faber & Faber.

Dunn, J. D. G. (1988). *Romans 1-8*. Dallas, TX: Word Books.

Duns, John. (c.1866). *Science and Christian Thought*. London: The Religious Tract Society.

Durant, J. (ed.) (1985). *Darwinism and Divinity*. Oxford: Basil Blackwell.

Ecklund, E. H. and C. P. Scheitle (2007). *Social Problems*, 54:2, 289–307

Ellegård, A. (1958). 'Darwin and the general reader'. *Acta Universitatis Gothoburgensis*, 64, 1–394.

Emerton, N. (1989). 'The Argument From Design in Early Modern Natural Theology'. *Science and Christian Belief* 1, 129–147.

Evdokimov, Paul (2001). *In the World, Of the Church: A Paul Evdokimov Reader*. Crestwood, NY: St. Vladimir's Seminary Press.

Finlayson, C. (2005). 'Biogeography and Evolution of the Genus *Homo*'. *Trends in Ecology and Evolution, 20*, 457–63.

Fisher, R. A. (1918). 'The Correlation Between Relatives on the Supposition of Mendelian Inheritance'. *Transactions of the Royal Society of Edinburgh, 52*, 399–433.

—— (1922). 'On the Dominance Ratio'. *Proceedings of the Royal Society of Edinburgh*, 42, 321–41.

—— (1930). *The Genetical Theory of Natural Selection*. Oxford: Clarendon Press.

—— (1954). 'Retrospect of the Criticisms of the Theory of Natural Selection', in J. Huxley, A. C. Hardy, and E. B. Ford (eds), *Evolution as a Process*. London: Allen & Unwin. 84–98.

Fitzmyer, Joseph A. (1993). *Romans: A New Translation with Introduction and Commentary*. New York: Doubleday.

Flannery, Austin (ed.) (1996). *Vatican Council II: The Basic Sixteen Documents*. Northport, NY: Costello.

Ford, E. B. (1931). *Mendelism and Evolution*. London: Methuen.

Fretheim, T. E. (1969). *Creation, Fall and Flood: Studies in Genesis 1–11*, Minneapolis, MN: Augsburg.

—— (2005), *God and World in the OT: A Relational Theology of Creation*. Nashville, TN: Abingdon.

Friedman, Richard Elliott (2001). *Commentary on the Torah*. New York: HarperCollins.

Galton, Francis (1871).'Gregariousness in Cattle and in Men,' *Macmillan's Magazine*, 23:136, 353–357.

Gamble, G. (2007). *Origins and Revolutions: Human Identity in Earliest Prehistory*. Cambridge: Cambridge University Press.

Giberson, K. W. (2008). *Saving Darwin*. New York: HarperOne.

Gillispie, C. C. (1951). *Genesis and Geology*. Cambridge, MA: Harvard University Press.

Girard, R. (1987). *Things Hidden Since the Foundation of the World*. Stanford: Stanford University Press.

Godfrey, L. R. (ed.) (1983). *Scientists Confront Creationism*. New York: Norton.

Goldingay, J. (2003). *Old Testament Theology. Volume 1: Israel's Gospel*. Downers Grove, IL: InterVarsity Press.

Gould J. L. and C. G. Gould (1999). *The Animal Mind*. 2nd ed. New York: Scientific American Library.

Gould, Stephen Jay. (1990). *Hen's Teeth and Horse's Toes*. London: Penguin.

—— (1995). 'Ladders and Cones: Constraining Evolution by Canonical Icons', in Robert Silvers, *Hidden Histories of Science*. New York: New York Review of Books.

—— (1999). *Rocks of Ages*. New York: Ballantine.

Grant, P. R. and B. R. Grant (2008). *How and Why Species Multiply. The Radiation of Darwin's Finches*. Princeton: Princeton University Press.

Greenslade, S. L. (ed.) (1963). *The Cambridge History of the Bible: The West from the Reformation to the Present Day*. Cambridge: Cambridge University Press.

Gregersen, Niels Henrik (2006). 'Emergence: What is at Stake for Religious Reflection', in Philip Clayton and Paul Davies (eds.), *The Re-emergence of Emergence: The Emergentist Hypothesis from Science to Religion*. Oxford: Oxford University Press. 279–302.

Gregory of Nyssa (1988). 'On the Making of Man', in *Nicene and Post-Nicene Fathers of the Christian Church*, series II, vol. 5. Grand Rapids, MI: Eerdmans.

Griffen, Donald R. (1978). 'Prospects for a Cognitive Ethology'. *The Behavioral and Brain Sciences*, 1:4, 527–38.

Grumett, David (2007). 'Teilhard de Chardin's Evolutionary Natural Theology'. *Zygon*, 42, 519–34.

Grumett, David (2005). *Teilhard de Chardin: Theology, Humanity and Cosmos*. Leuven: Peeters.

Gunton, Colin (1998). *The Triune Creator: A Historical and Systematic Study*. Edinburgh: Edinburgh University Press/Grand Rapids, MI: Eerdmans.

——(2002). *Act and Being: Towards a Theology of the Divine Attributes*. London: SCM Press.

Habel, N. (1965), *The Form and Meaning of the Fall Narrative*. St Louis: Concordia Seminary Print Shop.

Haeckel, Ernst (1992). *The Riddle of the Universe*. Buffalo, NY: Prometheus Books.

Haldane, J. B. S. (1932). *The Causes of Evolution*. London: Longmans.

Hall, Amy Laura (2007). *Conceiving Parenthood: American Protestantism and the Spirit of Reproduction*. Grand Rapids, MI: Eerdmans.

Hamilton, W. D. (1964). 'The Genetical Evolution of Social Behaviour'. *Journal of Theoretical Biology*, 7, 1–52.

Harris, P. (2000). 'A New Look at Old Passages', in R. J. Berry (ed.), *The Care of Creation*. Leicester: InterVarsity Press, 132–9.

—— (2005). 'God's Covenant with the Earth', in S. Tillett (ed.), *Caring for Creation*. Oxford: Bible Reading Fellowship. 48–52.

Hart, David Bentley (2005), *The Doors of the Sea: Where Was God in the Tsunami?* Grand Rapids, MI: Eerdmans.

Haught, John F. (2000). *God After Darwin: A Theology of Evolution*. Boulder, CO: Westview.

—— (2003). *Deeper than Darwin: The Prospect for Religion in the Age of Evolution*. Boulder, CO: Westview.

Hauser, A. J. (1980), 'Linguistic and Thematic Links Between Genesis 4:1–16 and Genesis 2-3', *JETS*, 23, 297–305.

Hawkins, Mike (1997). *Social Darwinism in European and American Thought. 1860 – 1945*, Cambridge: Cambridge University Press.

Hedley Brooke, John (1992). 'Natural Law in the Natural Sciences: the Origins of Modern Atheism?' *Science and Christian Belief*, 4:2, 83–103.

Hennig, W. (1950). *Grundzüge einer Theorie derphylogenetischen Systematik*. Berlin: Deutscher Zentralverlag.

Hick, John (1966). *Evil and the God of Love*. London: Macmillan.

Hill, J. (2003). *The History of Christian Thought*. Oxford: Lion.

Hobhouse, L. T. (1906). *Morals in Evolution: A Study in Comparative Ethics*. London: Chapman and Hall.

Hodge, Charles (1874), *What Is Darwinism?* New York: Scribner, Armstrong.

—— (1994). *What is Darwinism? And other Writings on Science & Religion*, eds. Mark N. Noll and David Livingstone. Grand Rapids, MI: Baker Books. First published in London by Nelson in 1874.

Hofstadter, Richard (1992). *Social Darwinism in American Thought*. Boston: Beacon Press.

Holmes, R. (2008). *The Age of Wonder*. London: HarperCollins.

Hooker, Richard (1888). *Of the Laws of Ecclesiastical Polity*. London: Routledge.

Hume, David (1991). *Dialogues Concerning Natural Religion*, ed. Stanley Tweyman. London: Routledge.

Hull, D. L. (1973). *Darwin and His Critics*. Chicago: Chicago University Press.

Huxley, J. S. (1942). *Evolution: the Modern Synthesis*. London: Allen & Unwin.

—— (1947). 'Evolutionary Ethics: The Romanes Lecture, 1943', in T. H. Huxley and Julian Huxley, *Evolution and Ethics: 1893–1943*. London: Pilot Press. 103–51.

—— (1959). 'Introduction', in Pierre Teilhard de Chardin, *The Human Phenomenon*. London: Collins. 11–28.

Huxley, Leonard (1900). *Life and Letters of Thomas Henry Huxley*, vol. II. London: Macmillan and Co.

Huxley, T. H. (1863). *Evidence as to Man's Place in Nature*. London: Williams & Norgate.

—— (1888). 'The Struggle for Existence: A Programme'. *Nineteenth Century*, 23, 163–5.

—— (1894a). *Evolution and Ethics*. London: Macmillan and Co.

—— (1894b). 'The Struggle for Existence in Human Society', in *Collected Essays*, vol. IX. London: Macmillan and Co. 195–236.

Hylson-Smith, K. (1988). *Evangelicals in the Church of England, 1734–1984*. Edinburgh: T & T Clark.

Inge, William Ralph (1926). *Outspoken Essays* (second series). London: Longman, Green and Co.

InterAcademy Panel (2006). *Statement on the Teaching of Evolution*. Accessed at www.interacademies.net

Iverach, James (1894). *Evolution and Christianity*. London: Hodder & Stoughton.

Jackson, Wes (2000). 'The Changing Relationship Between the Tree of Knowledge and the Tree of Life', *The Land Report*, 68, 12–17.

Johnson, Elizabeth A. (1998). *Friends of God and Prophets: A Feminist Theological Reading of the Communion of Saints*. London: SCM Press.

Johnson, P. E. and D. O. Lamoureux (eds.) (1997). *Testing Darwinism*. Leicester: InterVarsity Press.

—— (1999). *Darwinism Defeated? The Johnson-Lamoureux Debate on Biological Origins*. Vancouver: Regent College Publishing.

Jones, J. E. (2005). http://en.wikisource.org/wiki/Kitzmiller_v._Dover_Area_School_District/1:Introduction [accessed 24 August 2008]. See also Elsberry, W. R. and Matzke, N. 'The Collapse of Intelligent Design' in Robert B. Stewart (ed.) *Intelligent Design*, Minneapolis, MN: Fortress Press, 2007. 72–89.

Jones, J. S. (1993). *The Language of the Genes*. London: HarperCollins.

—— (1999). *Almost Like a Whale. The Origin of Species Updated*. London & New York: Doubleday.

Kaiser, C. B. (1991). *Creation and the History of Science*. London: Marshall Pickering.

Kaplan, Amy (1998). 'Manifest Domesticity', in Cathy N. Davidson and Jessamyn Hatcher (eds.), *No More Separate Spheres!* Durham: Duke University Press, 581–606.

Kasper, Walter (1986). 'Hope in the Final Coming of Jesus Christ in Glory'. *Communio: An International Catholic Review*, 12, 368–84.

Kaye, Howard L. (1986). *The Social Meaning of Biology*. New Haven: Yale University Press.

Keller, C. (1986). *From a Broken Web: Separation, Sexism, and Self*. Boston: Beacon.

Kellogg, V. L. (1907). *Darwinism Today*. London: George Bell & Sons.

Kidner, D. (1967). *Genesis*. London: Tyndale.

Kingsley, Charles (1864). *The Water-Babies*. Boston: Burnham.

—— (1871). 'The Natural Theology of the Future'. *Macmillan's Magazine*, 23:137, 369–78.

—— (1887). *At Last: A Christmas in the West Indies*. New York: Macmillan and Co.

Kitcher, P. (1982). *Abusing Science*. Cambridge, MA: MIT Press.

—— (2007). *Living with Darwin*. New York: Oxford University Press.

Kittler, R., M. Kayser and M. Stoneking (2003), 'Molecular Evolution of *Pediculus humanus* and the Origin of Clothing'. *Current Biology*, 13:16, 1414–17.

Knight, G. A. F. (1981). *Theology in Pictures: A Commentary on Genesis 1–11*. Edinburgh: Handsel Press.

Koenig, Kevin (2007). 'Ecuador's Oil Change: An Exporter's Historic Proposal'. *Multinational Monitor*, 28:4, 10–14.

Kohn, D. (ed.) (1985). *The Darwinian Heritage*. Princeton: Princeton University Press.

Kropotkin, Peter (1902). *Mutual Aid: A Factor of Evolution*. New York: McClure Philips and Co.

Kurzweil, Raymond (2005). *The Singularity is Near: When Humans Transcend Biology*. New York: Viking.

Lambert, Dominique (2002). 'Teilhard et la Bible', in Françoise Mies, *Bible et sciences: déchiffrer l'univers*. Namur: Presses universitaires de Namur. 125–56.

Larson, Edward J. (1992). *Evolution's Workshop: God and Science on the Galapagos Islands*. London: Allen Lane.

Larson, E. J. and L. Witham (1997). 'Scientists are Still Keeping the Faith'. *Nature*, 386, 435–6.

Leopold, Aldo (1966). *A Sand County Almanac*. New York: Oxford University Press.

Lewis, C. L. E. and S. J. Knell (eds.) (2001). *The Age of the Earth: from 4004 BC to AD 2002*. London: Geological Society Special Publication No. 190.

Lewis, C. S. (1940). *The Problem of Pain*. London: Geoffrey Bles.

—— (1943). *Voyage to Venus (Perelandra)*. London: John Lane.

Linzey, A. (2000). 'Good News for the World?' *Third Way* 23:6, 24.

Livingston, James C. (2006). *Religious Thought in the Victorian Age*. London: T & T Clark International.

Livingstone, David N. (1987). *Darwin's Forgotten Defenders: The Encounter between Evangelical Theology and Evolutionary Thought*. Grand Rapids, MI: Eerdmans.

—— (2004). 'Public Spectacle and Scientific Theory: William Robertson Smith and the reading of evolution in Victorian Scotland'. *Studies in History and Philosophy of Biological and Biomedical Sciences*, 35, 1–29.

Lloyd, Michael (1998a). 'Are Animals Fallen?', in Andrew Linzey and Dorothy Yamamoto (eds.), *Animals on the Agenda: Questions about Animals for Theology and Ethics*. London: SCM Press. 147–60.

—— (1998b). 'The Humanity of Fallenness', in Timothy Bradshaw (ed.), *Grace and Truth for a Secular Age*. Grand Rapids, MI: Eerdmans. 66–82.

Lossky, Vladimir (1978). *Orthodox Theology: An Introduction*. Crestwood, NY: St. Vladimir's Seminary Press.

Lopez, Barry (2001). 'The Naturalist'. *Orion Magazine*, 20:4, 38–43.

Louth, Andrew (1996). *Maximus the Confessor*. London and New York: Routledge.

Lovejoy, Arthur (1936). *The Great Chain of Being*, Cambridge, MA: Harvard University Press.

de Lubac, Henri (1967). *The Religion of Teilhard de Chardin*. London: Collins.

—— (1979). *Recherches dans la foi: trois études sur Origène, saint Anselme et la philosophie chrétienne*. Paris: Beauchesne.

—— (1996a). 'Tradition and Innovation in the Position of the Problem of God in Father Teilhard de Chardin', in Henri de Lubac, *Theology in History*. San Francisco: Ignatius. 505–40.

—— (1996b). *The Discovery of God*. New York and London: T & T Clark.

—— (1998). *The Mystery of the Supernatural*. New York: Crossroad.

Lynch, J. M. (ed.) (2002). *Creationism and Scriptural Geology, 1814–1857*. Bristol: Thoemmes Press.

MacArthur, J. (2001). *The Battle for the Beginning: The Bible on the Creation and the Fall of Adam*. Nashville, TN: W Publishing Group.

McConville, J. G. (1980). 'Interpreting Genesis 1–11', in N.M. de S. Cameron (ed.), *In the Beginning . . . A Symposium on the Bible and Creation*. Biblical Creation Society. 5–17.

McFadyen, A. (2000). *Bound to Sin: Abuse, Holocaust and the Christian Doctrine of Sin*. Cambridge: Cambridge University Press.

McGrath, A. (2005). *Dawkins' God*. Oxford: Blackwell.

Macintyre, Alasdair (1999). *Dependent Rational Animals*. London: Duckworth.

MacKinnon, Donald (1962). 'Teilhard de Chardin: A Comment on his Context and Significance'. *The Modern Churchman*, 5, 195–99.

—— (1965). 'Teilhard's Achievement', in Neville Braybrooke (ed.), *Teilhard de Chardin: Pilgrim of the Future*. London: Darton, Longman and Todd. 60–66.

—— (1983). 'Re-Review: Pierre Teilhard de Chardin's *Le Milieu divin*.' *The Modern Churchman*, 25, 49–53.

Malthus, Thomas Robert (1798). *An Essay on the Principle of Population*. London: J. Johnson.

Manning, Richard (2004). *Against the Grain: How Agriculture Has Hijacked Civilization*. New York: North Point Press.

Mather, K. (1973). *Genetical Structure of Populations*. London: Chapman & Hall.

Maritain, Jacques (1968). *The Peasant of the Garonne: An Old Layman Questions Himself about the Present Time*. London: Chapman.

Marshall, I. H. (2004). *Beyond the Bible. Moving from scripture to theology*. Milton Keynes: Paternoster.

Massyngberde Ford, J. (1975). *The Anchor Bible: Revelation: Introduction, Translation and Commentary*. Garden City, NY: Doubleday.

Maximus the Confessor (1996). *Ambigua*, in *Maximus the Confessor*, trans. Andrew Louth. London and New York: Routledge.

Mayr, E. (1991). *One Long Argument*. Cambridge, MA: Harvard University Press.

Mayr, E. & W. B. Provine (eds.) (1980). *The Evolutionary Synthesis*. Cambridge, MA: Harvard University Press.

Medawar, J. (1990). *A Very Decided Preference*. Oxford: Oxford University Press.

Medawar, Peter (1984). *The Limits of Science*. New York: Harper & Row.

—— (1996). *The Strange Case of the Spotted Mice; and other Classic Essays on Science*. Oxford: Oxford University Press.

Messer, Neil (2007). *Selfish Genes and Christian Ethics: Theological and Ethical Reflections on Evolutionary Biology*. London: SCM Press.

Middleton, J. R. (2005). *The Liberating Image: The* imago Dei *in Genesis 1*. Grand Rapids, MI: Brazos Press.

Midgley, M. (1985). *Evolution as a Religion*. London: Methuen.

Millennium Ecosystem Assessment (2005). *Ecosystems and Human Well-Being*, vol. 1, *Current States and Trends*. Washington, DC: Island Press.

Miller, K. B. (ed.) (2003). *Perspectives on an Evolving Creation*. Grand Rapids, MI: Eerdmans.

Miller, Kenneth R. (1999). *Finding Darwin's God: A Scientist's Search for Common Ground between God and Evolution*. New York: HarperCollins.

Miller, Patrick (2007). *The Way of the Lord: Essays in Old Testament Theology*, Grand Rapids, MI: Eerdmans.

Mithen, S. (1998). *The Prehistory of the Mind: A Search for the Origins of Art, Religion and Science*. London: Thames & Hudson.

Mivart, St George Jackson (1871). *On the Genesis of Species*. London: Macmillan.

Moltmann, Jürgen (1990). *The Way of Jesus Christ: Christology in Messianic Dimensions*. London: SCM Press.

—— (1996). *The Coming of God: Christian Eschatology*. London: SCM Press.

—— (2002). "Cosmos and Theosis: Eschatological Perspectives on the Future of the Universe," in George F. R. Ellis, *The Far Future Universe: Eschatology from a Cosmic Perspective*. Philadelphia and London: Templeton Foundation Press.

Monod, J. (1971). *Chance and Necessity*. London: Collins.

Moore, Aubrey (1889a). *Science and the Faith*. London: Kegan Paul.

—— (1889b). 'The Christian Doctrine of God', in C. Gore (ed.), *Lux Mundi*. London: John Murray. 57–109.

Moore, J. R. (1979). *The Post-Darwinian Controversies*. Cambridge: Cambridge University Press.

—— (1991). 'Deconstructing Darwinism: The Politics of Evolution in the 1860s'. *Journal of the History of Biology*, 24:3, 353–408.

—— (1994). *The Darwin Legend*. Grand Rapids, MI: Baker.

—— (1986). 'Geologists and Interpreters of Genesis in the Nineteenth Century', in D. C. Lindberg and R. L. Numbers (eds), *God and Nature*. Berkeley, CA: University of California Press. 322–50.

Moule, C. F. D. (1964). *Man and Nature in the New Testament*. London: Athlone,

Murray, R. (1992). *The Cosmic Covenant*. London: Sheed & Ward.

Murray, Michael (2008). *Nature Red in Tooth and Claw: Theism and the Problem of Animal Suffering*. Oxford: Oxford University Press.

National Academy of Sciences (1998). *Teaching About Evolution and the Nature of Science*. Washington, DC: National Academy Press.

—— (1999). *Science and Creationism*, 2nd edition Washington, DC: National Academy Press.

Nilsson, D-E. and S. Pelger (1994). 'A Pessimistic Estimate of the Time Required for an Eye to Evolve'. *Proceedings of the Royal Society of London*, B, 256, 53–58.

Noll, M. A. and D. Livingstone (2003). 'Charles Hodge and B. B. Warfield on science, the Bible, evolution and Darwinism', in K. B. Miller (ed.), *Perspectives on an Evolving Creation*. Grand Rapids, MI: Eerdmans. 61–71.

Northcott, Michael S. (1996). *The Environment and Christian Ethics*. Cambridge: Cambridge University Press.

Northcott, Michael S. (2003). 'Do Dolphins Carry the Cross? Biological Moral Realism and Theological Ethics'. *New Blackfriars*, 84, 540–553.

Numbers, R. L. (1992). *The Creationists*. New York: Alfred Knopf.

—— (1998). *Darwinism Comes to America*. Cambridge, MA: Harvard University Press.

Numbers, R. L. and J. Stenhouse (eds.) (1999). *Disseminating Darwin*. Cambridge: Cambridge University Press.

Oliver, Simon (2008). 'What, if Anything, can Theology Offer to Religious Studies?', in Maya Warrier and Simon Oliver (eds.), *Theology and Religious Studies: An Exploration of Disciplinary Boundaries*. London: T & T Clark, 2008. 15–29.

Paul, Diane B. (2003). 'Darwinism, Social Darwinism and Eugenics', in Jonathan Hodge and Gregory Radick (eds), *Cambridge Companion to Darwin*. Cambridge: Cambridge University Press. 214–39.

Paul, Harry W. (1979). *The Edge of Contingency: French Catholic Reaction to Scientific Change from Darwin to Duhem.* Gainesville: University Presses of Florida.

Pauly, Philip J. (1982). 'Samuel Butler and his Darwinian critics'. *Victorian Studies,* 25, 161–80.

Peacocke, Arthur (1990). *Theology for a Scientific Age.* Oxford: Blackwell.

—— (2001a), 'The Cost of New Life', in John Polkinghorne (ed.), *The Work of Love: Creation as Kenosis.* Grand Rapids: Eerdmans/London: SPCK. 21–42.

—— (2001b). *Paths from Science towards God: The End of all our Exploring.* Oxford: Oneworld.

Pearce, E. K. V. (1969). *Who Was Adam?* Exeter: Paternoster.

Pennock, R. T. (ed.) (2001). *Intelligent Design Creationism and Its Critics.* Cambridge, MA: MIT Press.

Peters, Ted and Martinez Hewlett (2003). *Evolution from Creation to New Creation: Conflict, Conversation and Convergence.* Nashville, TN: Abingdon.

Phillips, D. Z. (2005). *The Problem of Evil and the Problem of God.* London: SCM Press.

Pius IX (1864). *Syllabus Errorum.* www.papalencyclicals.net/Pius09/p9syll.htm.

Plutarch (1936). *Plutarch's Moralia,* Volume V *(Loeb Classical Library),* trans. by F.C. Babbitt. London: William Heinemann.

Polkinghorne, John (1989). *Science and Providence.* London: SPCK.

—— (1991). *Reason & Reality,* London: SPCK.

—— (1996). *Scientists as Theologians,* London: SPCK.

—— (ed.) (2001). *The Work of Love: Creation as Kenosis.* Cambridge: SPCK.

—— (2001). 'Kenotic Creation and Divine Action', in John Polkinghorne (ed.), *The Work of Love: Creation as Kenosis.* London: SPCK. 90–106.

—— (2005). *Exploring Reality: The Intertwining of Science and Religion.* London, SCM Press.

Popper, K. R. (1978). 'Natural Selection and the Emergence of Mind'. *Dialectica,* 32, 339–55.

Provine, W. B. (1971). *The Origin of Theoretical Population Genetics.* Chicago: Chicago University Press.

Rachels, James (1990). *Created from Animals: The Moral Implications of Darwinism.* London: Oxford University Press.

Rahner, Karl (1966a). 'The Hermeneutics of Eschatological Assertions', in Karl Rahner, *Theological Investigations* 4. New York: Seabury Press.

—— (1966b). 'Dogmatic Questions on Easter', in Karl Rahner, *Theological Investigations* 4. New York: Seabury Press.

—— (1969). 'Marxist Utopia and the Christian Future of Man', in Karl Rahner, *Theological Investigations* 6. London: Darton, Longman & Todd.

—— (1971). 'The Festival of the Future of the World', in Karl Rahner, *Theological Investigations* 7, London: Darton, Longman & Todd. 183.

—— (1973a). 'Immanent and Transcendent Consummation of the World', in Karl Rahner, *Theological Investigations* 10. London: Darton, Longman & Todd.

—— (1973b). 'The Theological Problems Entailed in the Idea of the "New Earth"', in Karl Rahner, *Theological Investigations* 10. London: Darton, Longman & Todd.

Rainy, Robert (1874). *Evolution and Theology.* Edinburgh: Maclaren and Macniven.

Reardon, Jenny (2004). *Race to the Finish: Identity and Governance in an Age of Genomics*. Princeton, NJ: Princeton University Press.

Reed, D. L., V. S. Smith, S. L. Hammond, A. R. Rogers, and D. H. Clayton (2004). 'Genetic Analysis of Lice Supports Direct Contact Between Modern and Archaic Humans'. *PLoS Biology*, 2/11, e340.

Renfrew, C. (2007). *Prehistory: The Making of the Human Mind*. London: Weidenfeld & Nicolson.

Reynolds, Philip Lyndon (1999). *Food and the Body: Some Peculiar Questions in High Medieval Theology*. Leiden: Brill.

Ricoeur, P. (1969). *The Symbolism of Evil*. Boston: Beacon Press.

Ridley, Matthew (1997). *The Origins of Virtue*. London: Penguin.

Roberts A. and J. Donaldson (eds) (1956). *The Ante-Nicene Fathers, Volume 1: The Apostolic Fathers with Justin Martyr and Irenaeus*. Grand Rapids, MI: Eerdmans.

—— (1956), *The Ante-Nicene Fathers, Volume 2: The Fathers of the Second Century: Hermas, Tatian, Athenagoras, Theophilus and Clement of Alexandria*. Grand Rapids, Eerdmans.

Roberts, M. B. (1997). 'Darwin's Doubts About Design – the Darwin-Gray Correspondence of 1860', *Science & Christian Belief*, 9, 113–127.

—— (1998). 'Genesis and Geology Unearthed'. *The Churchman*, 112, 225–55.

Rogerson, J. (1991), *Genesis 1-11*. Sheffield: JSOT Press.

Rolston III, Holmes (1994). 'Does Nature Need to be Redeemed?' *Zygon*, 29:2, 205–29.

—— (1999). *Genes, Genesis and God: Values and their Origins in Natural and Human History*. Cambridge: Cambridge University Press.

—— (2001). 'Kenosis and Nature', in John Polkinghorne (ed.), *The Work of Love: Creation as Kenosis*. Cambridge: SPCK. 43–65.

—— (2003). 'Naturalizing and Systematizing Evil', in Willem B. Drees (ed.), *Is Nature Ever Evil? Religion, Science and Value*. London and New York: Routledge. 67–86.

Ross, Hugh. (2006). *Creation as Science: A Testable Model Approach to End the Creation-Science Wars*. Colorado Springs: NavPress.

Ruse, Michael (1999). 'Evolutionary Ethics: What Can We Learn From the Past?' *Zygon*, 34, 437.

—— (2005). *The Evolution-Creation Struggle*. Cambridge, MA: Harvard University Press.

Russell, Robert John (2008). *Cosmology: From Alpha to Omega: The creative mutual interaction of science and theology*. Minneapolis, MN: Fortress Press.

Russell, R. J., W. R. Stoeger, and F. J. Ayala (eds.) (1998). *Evolutionary and Molecular Biology*. Vatican City: Vatican Observatory Publications.

Santmire, P. (1985). *The Travail of Nature*. Philadelphia: Fortress Press.

Schmemann, Alexander (1988). *The Eucharist: Sacrament of the Kingdom*. Crestwood, NY: St. Vladimir's Seminary Press.

Schwager, R. (2006). *Banished from Eden: Original Sin and Evolutionary Theory in the Drama of Salvation*. Leominster: Gracewing.

Secord, J. A. (2000). *Victorian Sensation*. Chicago: University of Chicago Press.

Shanks, N. (2004). *God, the Devil and Darwin*. New York: Oxford University Press.

Shaw, George Bernard (1921). *Back to Methuselah: A Metabiological Pentateuch.* London: Constable.

Sheldon, J. K. (1989). 'Twenty-One Years After "the Historical Roots of Our Ecologic Crisis": How has the Church Responded?' *Perspectives on Science and Christian Faith*, 41, 152–8.

Shermer, M. (2006). *Why Darwin Matters.* New York: Henry Holt.

Shepard, Paul and Daniel McKinley (eds) (1969). *The Subversive Science: Essays toward an Ecology of Man.* Boston: Houghton Mifflin.

Singer, Peter (1984). *How Are We To Live? Ethics in an Age of Self-Interest.* London: Mandarin.

Southgate, Christopher (2002). 'God and Evolutionary Evil: Theodicy in the Light of Darwinism'. *Zygon*, 37:4, 803–24.

—— (2008). *The Groaning of Creation: God, Evolution and the Problem of Evil.* Louisville: Westminster John Knox Press.

Spencer, Herbert (1873). *The Study of Sociology.* London: Kegan Paul.

—— (1891). *Education: Intellectual, Moral, and Physical.* New York: Appleton and Company.

—— (1898). *The Principles of Biology II.* New York: Appleton. and Company.

—— (1969). *The Principles of Sociology* abridged. ed. S. Andreski. London: Macmillan.

Speth, James Gustave (2008). *The Bridge at the Edge of the World: Capitalism, the Environment, and Crossing from Crisis to Sustainability.* New Haven: Yale University Press.

Srivastava, M. et al (2008). 'The *Trichoplax* Genome and the Nature of Placozoans'. *Nature*, 454, 955–60.

Staniloae, Dumitru (1970). *Theology and the Church.* Crestwood, NY: St. Vladimir's Seminary Press.

Stott, John R. W. (1972). *Understanding the Bible.* London: Scripture Union.

Straley, Jessica (2007). 'Of Beasts and Boys: Kingsley, Spencer, and the Theory of Recapitulation,' *Victorian Studies*, Vol. 49, Issue 4, 583–609.

Stringer, C. (2002). 'Modern Human Origins – Progress and Prospects'. *Philosophical Transactions of the Royal Society of London*, B, 357, 563–79.

Swinburne, Richard (1997). *The Evolution of the Soul.* Rev. edn. Oxford: Oxford University Press.

Tattershall, I. (2002). *The Monkey in the Mirror.* New York: Harcourt.

—— (2006). 'How We Came to Be Human', *Scientific American* 16:2 *(Special Edition. Becoming Human: Evolution and the Rise of Intelligence)*, 66–73.

Taylor, J. H. (ed.) (1982). *St. Augustine, The Literal Meaning of Genesis.* Mahwah NJ: Paulist Press.

Teilhard de Chardin, Pierre (1972). *The Phenomenon of Man.* London: Collins.

—— (1978). *Activation of Energy.* San Diego: Harvest.

—— (2005). *The Divine Milieu.* Brighton: Sussex Academic Press.

Temple, F. (1884). *The Relations between Religion and Science: Eight Lectures Preached before the University of Oxford in the Year 1884.* London: Macmillan, online at http://anglicanhistory.org/england/ftemple/bampton/04.html (accessed 29 February 2008).

—— (1885). *The Relations Between Religion and Science.* London: Macmillan.

Tennant, F. R. (1903). *The Sources of the Doctrines of the Fall and Original Sin.* Cambridge: Cambridge University Press.

Thomson, J. Arthur and Patrick Geddes (1912). *Evolution*. London: Williams & Norgate.

Thompson, Paul (1999). 'Evolutionary Ethics: Its Origins and Contemporary Face'. *Zygon*, 34, 471.

Thorpe, W. H. (1978). *Purpose in a World of Chance*. Oxford: Oxford University Press.

Tillich, P. (1957). *Systematic Theology*, vol. 2. London: Nisbet & Co.

Tindal, Matthew (1730). *Christianity as Old as the Creation*. London.

Torrance, Thomas F. (1981). *Divine and Contingent Order*. Oxford: Oxford University Press.

Tracy, Thomas F. (1998). 'Evolution, Divine Action, and the Problem of Evil', in Robert John Russell, William R. Stoeger and Francisco J. Ayala (eds.), *Evolutionary and Molecular Biology: Scientific Perspectives on Divine Action*. Vatican City: Vatican Observatory/Berkeley: Center for Theology and the Natural Sciences. 511–30.

Trewavas, Colin (2003). 'Aspects of Plant Intelligence'. *Annals of Botany*, 92:1, 1–20.

Uffelman, Larry (1979). *Charles Kingsley*. Boston: Twayne Publishers.

van Huyssteen, Wentzel (2006). *Alone in the World? Human Uniqueness in Science and Theology*. Grand Rapids, MI: Eerdmans.

van Til, Howard (1998/9). 'The Creation: Intelligently Designed or Optimally Equipped?' *Theology Today*, 55, 344–64.

Vitek, Bill and Wes Jackson (2008). *The Virtues of Ignorance: Complexity, Sustainability, and the Limits of Knowledge*. Lexington: University Press of Kentucky.

de Waal, Frans (1996). *Good Natured: The Origins of Right and Wrong in Humans and Other Animals*. Cambridge, MA: Harvard University Press.

Walton, J. H. (2007). *Ancient Near Eastern Thought and the Old Testament*. Nottingham: Apollos.

Ward, K. (1998). *God, Faith and the New Millennium: Christian Belief in an Age of Science*. Oxford: Oneworld.

Ward, P. D. and D. Brownlee (2000). *Rare Earth: Why Complex Life is Uncommon in the Universe*. New York: Copernicus.

Weinreich, D. M. et al. (2006). 'Darwinian Evolution Can Follow Only Very Few Mutational Paths to Fitter Proteins'. *Science*, 312:5770, 111–14.

Wenham, G. J. (1986). 'Sanctuary Symbolism in the Garden of Eden Story'. *Proceedings of the 9th World Congress of Jewish Studies*. Jerusalem: Institute of Contemporary Jewry, Hebrew University of Jerusalem .19-25.

—— (1987). *Genesis 1-15*. Waco TX: Word Books.

—— (1990). 'Original Sin in Genesis 1-11'. *Churchman*, 104, 319–20.

Westermann, C. (1984). *Genesis 1-11*. London: SPCK.

White, A. D. (1886). *A History of the Warfare of Science with Theology*. New York: Appleton.

White, L. (1967). 'The Historical Roots of Our Ecologic Crisis'. *Science*, 155, 1203–7.

Whitehead, Alfred North (1929). *Process and Reality: An Essay in Cosmology*. Cambridge: Cambridge University Press.

Wildman, Wesley J. (2007). 'Incongruous Goodness, Perilous Beauty, Disconcerting Truth: Ultimate Reality and Suffering in Nature', in Nancey Murphy, Robert J. Russell and William Stoeger (eds.), *Physics and Cosmology: Scientific Perspectives on the Problem of Evil in Nature*. Berkeley: Center for Theology and the Natural Sciences/Vatican City: Vatican Observatory. 267–94.

Willey, Basil (1960). *Darwin and Butler: Two Versions of Evolution*. London: Chatto and Windus.

Williams, P. A. (2001). *Doing Without Adam and Eve: Sociobiology and Original Sin*. Minneapolis, MN: Fortress Press.

Williams, Rowan (2000). 'On Being Creatures', in Rowan Williams, *On Christian Theology*. Oxford: Blackwell. 63–78.

Wilson, D. S. (2002). *Darwin's Cathedral: Evolution, Religion and the Nature of Society*. Chicago: Chicago University Press.

Wilson, Edward O. (1975). *Sociobiology: The New Synthesis*. Cambridge, MA: Harvard University Press.

—— (1978). *On Human Nature*. Cambridge, MA: Harvard University Press.

—— (1998). *Consilience*. New York: Knopf.

Wolff, H. W. (1974). *Anthropology of the Old Testament*. London: SCM Press.

Wright, C. T. H. (2006). *The Mission of God*. Leicester: InterVarsity Press.

Wright, N. T. (1999a). *New Heavens, New Earth*. Cambridge: Grove Biblical Series B11.

—— (1999b). 'New Exodus, New Inheritance: The Narrative Substructure of Romans 3-8', in S. K. Soderlund and N. T. Wright (eds), *Romans and the People of God*. Grand Rapids, MI: Eerdmans. 26–35.

—— (2004). *Paul for Everyone: Romans Part 1, Chapters 1–8*. London: SPCK.

—— (2006). *Evil and the Justice of God*. London: SPCK.

—— (2007). *Surprised by Hope*. London: SPCK.

Wright, S. (1932). 'Evolution in Mendelian populations'. *Genetics*, 16, 97–159.

Young, D. A. (1995). *The Biblical Flood: A Case Study of the Church's Response to Extrabiblical Evidence*. Carlisle: Paternoster Press.

Young, Robert M. (1985). *Darwin's Metaphor: Nature's Place in Victorian Culture*. Cambridge: Cambridge University Press.

Index

Debating Darwin

Two Debates: Is Darwinism True and Does it Matter?

Graeme Finlay, Stephen Lloyd, Stephen Pattemore and David Swift

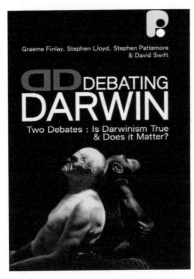

Christians continue to disagree about whether Darwinism should be baptised into our theology or rejected as anti-Christian. This book is aimed at Christians on both sides of the debate and hopes to further discussion by giving space for an open airing of the case both ways. Two distinct questions are under the microscope.

1. Is Darwinism compatible with orthodox Christian faith?
2. Does the scientific evidence support Darwinism?

The book begins with a simple explanation of the neo-Darwinian theory of evolution. Stephen Lloyd then opens the first debate by making a theological and biblical case against Darwinism. He is met in 'battle' by Graeme Finlay and Stephen Patterson who argue that Christian Scripture and theology are compatible with Darwinism. Each set of authors then has a chance to respond to their opponents.

In the second debate David Swift argues that whilst the science does support micro-evolution by natural selection it does not support macro-evolution. In fact, he says, the science *undermines* neo-Darwinian claims. 'Not so!' says Graeme Finlay, who argues that the latest work in genetics demonstrates the truth of neo-Darwinism beyond reasonable doubt. Swift and Finlay then interact with each other. This book will not tell readers what to think but it will inform the more intelligent debate.

978-1-932805-619-8

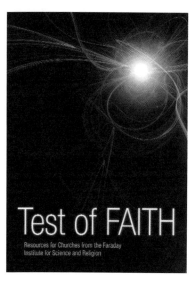

Test of FAITH

A Course for Thinking Afresh About Science and Christian Faith

There is a popular myth at large in both modern society and in many churches. According to this myth science and Christianity have been engaged in a long battle over the centuries. For many secularists this means that we must embrace science and reject religion, whilst for some Christians it means the exact opposite. But are science and Christian faith really in conflict? Test of FAITH is an innovative new resource designed for use by small groups wishing to explore major issues raised by science for both religion and ethics. It introduces a wide range of hot topics including:

- Are science and Christianity in conflict?
- Is evolution compatible with religious faith?
- Are humans no more than biological machines?
- Is cloning ethical?
- Has the Big Bang pushed God out of the universe?

Test of FAITH is designed to enable non-specialists to join the discussion. Test of FAITH resources include the following:

- **DVD** (TOFDVD)
- **Study Guide** (978-1-84227-664-8)
- **Leader's Guide** (978-1-84227-663-1)
- **Book of scientist's testimonies** (978-1-84227-661-7)

Visit www.testoffaith.com

Think God, Think Science

Conversations on Life, the Universe and Faith

Michael Pfundner in discussion with Ernest Lucas

Has science killed God? How, if at all, are we to 'think God' in the scientific twenty-first century? That question is at the heart of this introductory yet intelligent book in which Michael Pfundner talks to biblical scholar and biochemist, Ernest Lucas. The conversation engages three broad areas:

- *The Sky*: as our scientific understanding of the universe – its vastness, its age, and its origins – has increased, have the stars stopped declaring the glory of God?
- *The Cell*: What place is there for a good creator amidst the random genetic mutations and brutal processes of neo-Darwinian evolution? How can mere 'naked apes' think of themselves as being made in the image of God? Did Genesis get it wrong?
- *The Faith*: Has the recent work of historians and archaeologists undermined traditional Christian belief in the historical reliability of the gospels and in Jesus' resurrection?

Ernest Lucas argues that modern science is fully compatible with Christian theology and Scripture.

This is a wonderfully inspiring book! An immensely valuable – and readable – contribution to the field.' – **John Bryant**, Professor of Genetics, Exeter University

Ernest Lucas is Vice-Principal and Tutor in Biblical Studies, Bristol Baptist College; Michael Pfunder is Bible & Church Development Officer, Bible Society, UK.

978-1-84227-609-9